Messenger Gods of Battle

RADIO, RADAR, SONAR:
THE STORY OF ELECTRONICS IN WAR

Also available from Brassey's

CHANT
Air Defence and Weapons Systems

FIGGURES
Surveillance and Target Acquisition Systems

GARDEN
The Technology Trap

HARTCUP
The War of Invention
Science in the Great War, 1914–18

KIELY
Naval Electronic Warfare

RICE AND SAMMES
Communications and Information Systems
for Battlefield Command and Control

The Radar Whose Warning Was Ignored The SCR270 early warning radar was the American equivalent of Britain's Chain Home and Germany's Freya (see Chapter 7). It became the centre of the greatest controversy in radar history. On the morning of 7 December 1941 an SCR270 on Hawaii picked up what proved to be an incoming Japanese torpedo bomber attack on Pearl Harbor. It did so at the extreme range of 137 miles, and more than fifty minutes before the first bombs exploded. The attack, launched before declaration of war, crippled America's Pacific fleet. But the radar's warning was not heeded, a failure all the more difficult to understand because penetration of encrypted Japanese communications had already alerted America to the imminence of hostile action. The SCR270 worked on 106 megahertz and was well designed for long range coverage over water. (*Photo: By courtesy of Westinghouse*)

Messenger Gods of Battle

RADIO, RADAR, SONAR: THE STORY OF ELECTRONICS IN WAR

Tony Devereux

BRASSEY'S (UK)

Member of Maxwell Macmillan Pergamon Publishing Corporation

LONDON • OXFORD • WASHINGTON • NEW YORK • BEIJING
FRANKFURT • SÃO PAULO • SYDNEY • TOKYO • TORONTO

UK (Editorial)	Brassey's (UK) Ltd., 50 Fetter Lane, London EC1A 4AA, England
(Orders, all except North America)	Brassey's (UK) Ltd., Headington Hill Hall, Oxford OX3 0BW, England
USA (Editorial)	Brassey's (US) Inc., 8000 Westpark Drive, Fourth Floor, McLean, Virginia 22102, USA
(Orders, North America)	Brassey's (US) Inc., Front and Brown Streets, Riverside, New Jersey 08075, USA Tel (toll free): 800 257 5755
PEOPLE'S REPUBLIC OF CHINA	Pergamon Press, Room 4037, Qianmen Hotel, Beijing, People's Republic of China
FEDERAL REPUBLIC OF GERMANY	Pergamon Press GmbH, Hammerweg 6, D-6242 Kronberg, Federal Republic of Germany
BRAZIL	Pergamon Editora Ltda, Rua Eça de Queiros, 346, CEP 04011, Paraiso, São Paulo, Brazil
AUSTRALIA	Brassey's Australia Pty Ltd., PO Box 544, Potts Point, NSW 2011, Australia
JAPAN	Pergamon Press, 5th Floor, Matsuoka Central Building, 1-7-1 Nishishinjuku, Shinjuku-ku, Tokyo 160, Japan
CANADA	Pergamon Press Canada Ltd., Suite No. 271, 253 College Street, Toronto, Ontario, Canada M5T 1R5

First edition 1991

Library of Congress Cataloging in Publication Data

Devereux, Tony
Messenger gods of battle: radio, radar, sonar, the story of electronics in war / Tony Devereux. – 1st ed.
p. cm.
Includes bibliographical references
1. Electronics in military engineering – History. I. Title.
UG485.D48 1990 623'.043'09 – dc20 90-2090

British Library Cataloguing in Publication Data

Devereux, Tony
Messenger gods of battle.
1. Military communications equipment, history.
I. Title
623.73

ISBN 0-08-035829-2

Printed in Great Britain by BPCC Wheatons Ltd., Exeter

In memory

H. E. F. Pope

Contents

List of Plates, Maps, Figures and Tables

PLATES

MAPS

FIGURES

TABLES

Acknowledgements

THIS book largely owes its existence to Bruce Neale, who as Chief Engineer of Marconi Radar at Chelmsford, Essex, UK, gave me all possible assistance with it and pointed me in all the right directions.

When the book reached draft stage, Bruce asked two of his Marconi colleagues, Gerry Taylor and Harry Cole (himself the distinguished author of *Understanding Radar*), to read the draft through and provide me with their comments. This they did with the most generous expenditure of time and trouble.

Needless to say the book has benefited immensely from their interest. It incorporates much additional information and many suggestions and corrections.

For faults which remain, I as author am responsible.

In some respects my friends at Marconi found the book highly controversial and disagreed with the conclusions presented.

I have not sought to remove controversial opinions, believing that in the history of electronic warfare, particularly radar, there is ample scope for them. It is the reader's privilege to make up his mind on these matters.

My thanks are also owed to the Marconi Company in general, and others of its staff, particularly Roy Rodwell and Dr Brian Wardrop for assistance and facilities freely given. I should make it clear that the book is completely impartial as between the various companies it mentions, Marconi amongst others; I trust this will be apparent to the reader.

Other people whom I gratefully acknowledge for their assistance and most helpful replies to correspondence are: Professor R. V. Jones; Professor Sir Harry Hinsley; Professor J. F. Coales (especially regarding British naval radar); Sir Robert Cockburn; David Pritchard (especially regarding German radar); L. A. Thomas (especially regarding the history of British radar); William Cox. They cannot, however, in any way be held to account for views I have expressed.

I should like to thank Roger Dence for much initial help.

My special thanks are due to Sir Edward Fennessy for replying patiently and at length to my enquiries about the early days of British Chain Home radar, and for allowing me to reproduce material from his letters in an appendix to the book.

Finally, I must record my posthumous debt to H. E. F. Pope, to whom the book is dedicated, for initiating my interest in the subject and fuelling it over a period of many years.

Author's postscript: It remains to me to regret the death of Bruce Neale shortly before *Messenger Gods of Battle* went to press.

Introduction

ELECTRONIC warfare must not be left to specialists. It is too important. This book is intended for the widest readership. It breaks with tradition in many ways.

The first break is its approach. Many people know that the use of radio, radar, computers and other electronic means is vital in modern war, whether hot or cold, regional, guerrilla or terrorist. They realise that this use conceals much that is exciting and mysterious, including intelligence gathering. But they consider the subject can only be interesting if it can be understood, and this, they believe, cannot be expected of non-experts.

This attitude must be rejected. The subject should take its place and be enjoyed like any other aspect of war history. Indeed it must take its place if its tactical and strategic lessons are to be learned. This does not require immersion in electronic technicalities. On the contrary, technicalities prevent the historical pattern from being seen.

The second break is its interpretation of the term 'electronic warfare'. The term is frankly confusing. Chapter 1 begins by asking what it should mean and suggests that it is often usefully replaced by electronics in war (sometimes used in this introduction).

Another break is its expansion of the historical timescale. Electronic warfare is often seen as beginning with the Second World War, and this is plausible in that the word 'electronics' was not in widespread use before that war. But as the opening chapters seek to show, although the word was not in use, the typical methods of electronics were having their effect on war a century earlier.

The book aims to be impartial. This is another break with tradition, because so much of what has been written about electronic warfare is not impartial. Not deliberately so; unconsciously it is influenced by the Anglo-American ethics of the Second World War.

This was the conflict which inspired most writing about electronic warfare. At the time it was all but impossible to disentangle the ethics from the technology. This is no reproach; we are all human, and those who wrote about that war were mainly those who had won it. They tended to explain everything that happened in terms of the triumph of their own ideals, even in areas where, objectively considered, moral ideals should be irrelevant.

Lest anyone doubt this assertion, let them consider a passage from Winston Churchill's *The Second World War*, in reference to the German technique of using radio beams to guide bombers to their targets at night: 'The German pilots followed the beam as the German people followed the Führer. They had nothing else to follow.'[1]

This sounds well; it exactly reflects British sentiment at the time; but militarily it is a red herring. The retort might be made that at the same time as the German pilots were following the beams, British pilots had nothing at all to follow, which was absolutely true so far as night navigation was concerned.

Why was this the case? The attempt to answer the question proves very instructive. It leads back to the radio-navigated Zeppelin bombing of the First World War. It highlights the strength which Germany built up in radio technology from the beginning of the 20th century.

The aim is not to detract in any way from the stature of Winston Churchill. It is simply to recognise that time has moved on. The achievement of every country must be fairly assessed. Patriotism, or even morality, must not come in the way of setting out the facts of the historical story as impartially as possible.

This is true not just of electronic warfare. The whole history of the First and Second World Wars – which are, surely, two phases of the same historic convulsion – needs to be refocused. It needs to be seen against a broader, more impartial background. Directly after the Second World War such a mature perspective would have been impossible to hope for. The war was too bitter. Forty-five years later it is time to begin trying. Electronics is a good place to make a new start.

Philosophy

The philosophy on which the book is based is as follows:

Electronics in war began as a simple but new way of doing some militarily useful things. Its ability to do these things advanced by leaps and bounds as one simple step followed another.

As an example consider a piece of insulated wire. Everyone understands it. It has a metal core, usually copper, surrounded by a non-metallic covering, often nowadays plastic. We call the core the conductor and the covering the insulation.

We well realise the purpose of both and why neither would work without the other. Nothing could be simpler – but it is as fundamental to electronics as the wheel to transport. In fact it is the way of transporting electrons. Fortunately history records the emergence of insulated electric wire more clearly than that of the wheel. It deserves its place in the history of electronic warfare because it swiftly drew military interest. It could detonate a remote explosive charge or carry messages. It offered better alternatives to the fuze and the semaphore.

Electric wire was but one of many such simple steps. It is one of the many components out of which electronics is built. It is appropriate to notice some of these, because of their special significance, but not all.

These steps continued while fundamental ideas remained little changed. Indeed all the fundamental ideas used in electronic warfare had been grasped by the end of the 19th century.

The important thing, militarily, became the 'rolling snowball' effect which increasingly thrust electronic warfare into tactical, strategic and political considerations. This process was seen at work in the Second World War. It is seen at work today.

In other words, electronics in war transforms itself from a record of simple scientific discoveries with straightforward military applications to a study of the way in which the accumulation of electronics begins to affect the whole character of war, begins to influence its conduct and sway political calculations of military possibility.

The latter is a highly sensitive development. One has only to remember how the military possibilities of another technique of war, *blitzkrieg*, influenced politics. Holding out the seeming promise of swift and final political 'solutions', *blitzkrieg* became a formative factor in 20th-century history.

Electronics is sometimes seen as the latest candidate for a role rather like *blitzkrieg*. This is the 'ace in the hole' theory of electronic warfare. Or electronics is seen in yet another special role: that implied for it in the Strategic Defence Initiative, or 'Star Wars'.

It is in this ever-increasing military and political significance that the ultimate interest of electronics in war lies. It is the main theme of this book.

For this reason the book does not attempt to catalogue radio and radar equipments. Where necessary it focuses on whatever example of a type has most vividly demonstrated the combat importance of that breed in general. The principle is not the first in chronological order but the first in practical military significance. From the military standpoint, what counts is not first invention but first military effectiveness.

A classic example is the Soviet Guideline missile with its associated radar and radio guidance. It was neither the first nor probably the best of the surface-to-air missiles which appeared in the inventories of many countries during the 1950s. But by being coupled with the shootdown of the U-2 and a new era of air warfare in Vietnam, it wrote itself into history as no other such missile did.

Backgrounds

Every application of electronics in war needs to be seen in its strategic setting. Only then can one appreciate its contribution to the outcome, and how significant that contribution was. In this book a brief political and military background forms part of the approach to every electronic warfare conflict.

Here the Korean War is an appropriate example. Superficially it might seem that the contribution of electronics was rather moderate. But this was a three-year war for two years of which the land position was static and deadlocked. The only fluid battle was in the air, and it was through the air that pressure was maintained during the two years of on-off negotiations which at last reached a settlement.

The air battle got tougher all the time. A sure sign is that even before the war was half-way through, American bombing of North Korea had been forced on to a night offensive. Sufficient daytime air superiority to guarantee the safety of bombers no longer existed. Air operations at night are far more dependent on electronics than those by day. From the time bombing switched to the cover of darkness, the air battle, on which hung the outcome of negotiations, was keyed to electronics.

Electronic warfare therefore claims its share in the political outcome. It played a more decisive role than it played through the bombing of Germany in the Second World War. Despite the massive investment in electronic systems which supported the bombing, strategic bombing did not prove to be the decisive factor in the European theatre. The advance of land armies did.

From this point of view, the Korean War was a strategic inversion of the Second World War. As an example, it shows the steady historical tendency for the importance of electronics in war to increase, in underlying practical terms if not in obviousness. Electronics in the Second World War became very obvious, but it was still far from being mature. Perhaps this may seem controversial; readers will doubtless make up their minds after considering the facts. But there are other controversies to face.

One is the role of radar in the Second World War. Numerous myths have come down: that radar was, for example, 'the war's decisive weapon'. This myth obstructs historical truth in various ways, one of them by obscuring the role that radio played. Radio was less glamorous but more omnipresent. It was often vital when radar was not. It was the handmaiden of *blitzkrieg*, without which the war would hardly have started.

The radar myth ignores the Eastern Front between Germany and Russia. Here Germany had unquestioned radar superiority, and gave her radar mobility by rail-mounting it. Here, however, she began to lose as early as December 1941 before Moscow, and finally lost catastrophically at Stalingrad. On this front, the main land front of the war, radar played only a small operational role by comparison with radio and the telegraph and telephone.

Of course there were other fronts on which radar played a conspicuous role. We return to these matters later. For the moment they show that the first question is always, what role did electronics as a whole play, and only in second place comes the question what roles did radio and radar play individually. It generally turns out that their roles were mutually supporting. The whole was greater than the sum of the parts.

Radar Priority

Another myth is British priority with radar. This, as is now increasingly realised, does injustice to American and German claims. But it is worth examining closely, for the myth has lessons to teach. It begins to reveal both where Britain undoubtedly did lead other countries, and where she lagged.

She led in political appreciation of the strategic importance of radar – and lagged in technology. This, in turn, led to the quixotic position where she put a high stake on her own radar capabilities, which in truth she was over-rating, whilst being blind to the existence of Germany's, which at the time were more advanced.

Britain's appreciation of radar's importance was well shown in 1938 before the Munich conference. She saw herself as threatened by an instant German airborne strike if the need should develop, during the conference, to resist German demands. Five early radar stations were specially activated on the British coast and linked into the British Fighter Command Headquarters, to give warning of incoming air attack.

Regardless of the outcome of Munich, which is a separate historical issue, the precaution shows remarkable awareness of radar as a card in the political hand.

Compare this with the events leading up to Japan's airborne attack on America's main Pacific base, Pearl Harbor, on 7 December 1941. Objectively, electronic warfare should have been a stronger card for America in 1941 than it was for Britain in 1938. America had advantages which Britain had not possessed: she was decrypting Japanese codes and she had a later generation of early warning radar. But she did not have the same political and military alertness to their significance, even though her negotiations with Japan were no less crucial than Britain's had been with Germany.

Strategically, by interception of communications, electronic warfare revealed the Japanese plans in advance. Tactically, by radar, it identified the incoming attack. More could not have been asked. Yet because of failure to appreciate the importance of the information that electronic warfare might provide, and failure to combine its inputs, Pearl Harbor became America's disaster.

These instances are introduced purely for the historical lesson they provide. At the political level, Britain was ahead of both Germany and America, understanding the need for investment in radar and the value of coupling it into her political and military functioning. But she failed in intelligence, in not appreciating the extent of Germany's progress. When the war began she was totally unaware both of German radar and German target-finding radio beam systems.

For this she paid a high price. Britain did not realise that German radar was the cause of grievous aircraft losses which were puzzling to explain. She was led to underestimate the defence which Germany could offer to the strategic bombing offensive which Britain decided to prepare, allotting massive resources in the hope that it would win the war.

This in turn was a misjudgement which is almost the central issue in Britain's strategic conduct of the Second World War. It is the subject of questioning studies such as Max Hastings' *Bomber Command.* It is important to realise that what led to it was the initial misjudgement of British electronic capabilities, particularly radar, in relation to German.

The British radar myth is not alone, for there is something of an American myth as well, part true part false. Germany has been unlucky to not to have a myth, for her achievements merit it.

Greatest Influence

This by no means exhausts the supply of radar controversies. Centimetric radar is a fertile field. Nothing can diminish the importance of this development which Britain started by inventing the cavity magnetron and turned into military reality (powerfully assisted by the United States) with equipments such as H_2S and airborne anti-surface vessel radar.

The latter was electronic warfare's greatest influence on the course of the Second World War. It was the best dividend that Britain received from her continuing investment in electronic warfare. But once centimetric radar arrived on the offensive, a corresponding German defensive sought to parry it with 'anti-centimetric' technology. It would be wrong to ignore the impressive results which this defensive achieved.

Naturally these themes cannot be pursued exhaustively in the introduction. They are simply instances of the subject's many controversial aspects.

Examples and information in this book are drawn more from Anglo-American sources than from others, for varied reasons including their greater number and accessibility. The book's accounts of particular events by themselves may create an impression in favour of one or other of the sides, whichever best emerged from the event in question. This is inevitable. It is necessary to take a view of particular events, otherwise nothing is learnt.

Electronics in war is, more than any other military branch, the story of countries and their peoples, their scientific culture and their executive efficiency, all considered as a whole. It is not the story of Napoleonic individuals. Therefore personalities have been treated with reserve or mentioned in 'Notes and Sources', except where directly relevant.

The same observation applies to anecdotes. It is possible to write a highly anecdotal account of electronic warfare, but its value as history is as questionable as accounts based on personalities.

Editorial Conventions and Synopsis

As a matter of policy, armed forces are referred to as German air force, British navy, US air force, British air force, German navy and so forth, rather than Luftwaffe, Royal Navy, US Army Air Forces, Royal Air Force, Kriegsmarine. This may lose some distinctions and some historical colour, but is a standardisation of terms in the interests of clarity and impartiality.

Many words need to be used with a clear meaning in mind. Some usages are best mentioned here. The word 'military' is always used in the completely general sense, not, that is to say, as comparable with 'naval' or 'air force'. 'Army' is used as the equivalent to 'naval' or 'air force'. 'Military' embraces 'army', 'naval', and 'air force'.

The words 'defence' and 'defensive' are used as the opposite of 'offensive', not as euphemisms for all military preparations. The euphemisms are understandable, but realistically, military preparations generally include both defensive and offensive capabilities, and the distinction must not be lost.

A characteristic of electronic warfare is that it generates a profusion of initials, or acronyms, such as ECCM standing for electronic counter counter measures, or RHAW, radar homing and warning. Once these are allowed to enter the text in any number their meanings cease to be easily recalled. They have accordingly been banished to the Glossary.

Only one exception has been allowed. This is the designation of frequency bands such as medium frequency, high frequency, very high frequency, by the accepted contractions MF, HF, VHF and so on. The use of these contractions helps to remind that the frequency bands are precisely determined by international convention. Their specific properties are important and change from band to band, the bands merging gradually into each other.

HF, for example, always means the range of frequencies between 3 and 30 megahertz. It is never a vague label for high frequencies generally. The unique properties of HF, as compared with every other frequency band, are a dramatic part of the story of electronic warfare.

The definition of electronic warfare is a topic of Chapter 1. This chapter also starts upon the early, 19th-century history of electronics in war, which is continued in Chapters 2, 3 and 4. Another function of these chapters is to look at some further fundamental discoveries – comparable to but more exciting than electric wire! – and to preview, in very broad outline, the developments they set in progress. Chapter 4 bridges the 19th century and the 20th.The narrative of electronics in war in the 20th century begins in Chapter 5. It may suit the interests of some readers to go to it directly. Chapters 6 to 11, about half the book, cover the Second World War. This reflects the Second World War's domination of the subject in terms of battle experience.

The remaining chapters relate to the post-Second World War period. 1945 marked a sharp division in the history of electronic warfare; up to that year the subject had been dominated by the rivalry of Germany and Britain, afterwards it was dominated by the United States and the Soviet Union. This is, of course, a generalisation, and is not intended to belittle the contributions of other countries.

The Germany-versus-Britain phase, which began with the First World War, was one of deadly conflict. The United States-versus-Soviet Union phase has been chiefly one of shadow boxing, during which the actual conflicts have been temporary sideshows staged by proxies. Despite the avoidance of major conflict between the principals, it is during this period that electronic warfare has completed its transformation into a technology of over-riding importance in preserving the global strategic balance. This is the note on which the book ends, pointing to the need for electronic warfare to take its place along with nuclear weaponry in international disarmament treaties.

1

Historical Questions

Is THERE a subject such as 'electronics in war'? Is it the same as 'electronic warfare'? Is it truly a part of history?

Yes, there is such a subject. It is not only part of military history over the last two centuries, but fundamental to it. Apart from nuclear weapons, hardly anything has changed the aspect of war so much as electronics.

War has always been part of history. This is a regrettable fact, but one which only emphasises the necessity of studying it. War comes when basic forces of evolution have set the scene for collision. We know we can never escape from these forces, but we nowadays hope to find less destructive ways of submitting to them. If war is to be studied for this reason, electronics in war is part of the study.

As compared with 'electronic warfare', 'electronics in war' is valuable as an all-embracing definition. Perhaps it embraces too much. It cannot help embracing trivial, militarily non-essential use, such as a celebrated coded radio message of the Second World War to send on the commander's silk pyjamas.

In other words, it embraces much military electronics which has no purpose differing from civilian electronics, or from other forms of communication adequate to non-combat applications. On the other hand, the dividing line cannot be sharply drawn between electronics as a weapon and electronics as a general lubricant of military communications, improving the fighting efficiency of armed forces in all kinds of incidental ways.

'Electronic warfare' attempts to be a more specific concept than electronics in war. This would be all to the good, if only there were a settled view as to what this specific concept should be. It is most often taken to be the use of electronics to thwart or exploit the other side's use of electronics; in other words, electronic countermeasures.

But this is not a satisfactory definition. It is not consistent with general military use. We do not speak of tank warfare, meaning only warfare in which tanks counter other tanks. We mean all the possibilities that open up with the use of tanks. Logically, electronic warfare should mean all the possibilities that open with electronics.

Tanks may well be opposed in many ways without the countervailing use of other tanks at all. What is chiefly important is the style of warfare which results from one side, or the other, or both, using tanks. In the same way electronics may be opposed without the countervailing use of other electronics, for example by the bombing of radar stations. Bombing radar stations is undoubtedly electronic warfare. Here again, what is chiefly important is the style of warfare which results from one or other side or both using electronics.

The aim of the tank commander may often be to achieve surprise in such a way that he avoids being countered by other tanks. The principle of surprise applies equally in electronic warfare.

Yet another concept of electronic warfare holds it to be warfare hinging on the electromagnetic spectrum, the spectrum of radiation from radio waves to infra-red and light.

This concept has weighty support. It is enshrined not only in the official United States services definition, but in the famous words 'the next war will be won by whichever side controls the electromagnetic spectrum', attributed to Admiral Gorshkov of the Soviet Navy.

Despite this impressive double sponsorship, the concept suffers from the unfortunate defect that a great deal of electronic warfare goes on without the use of the electromagnetic spectrum at all, for example under the oceans.

Consequently these oft-quoted concepts really do nothing much to help. Better service is given by the simple definition of electronic warfare suggested above, namely that type of warfare which is made possible by electronics or results from electronics.

This is often interchangeable with the general term 'electronics in war'. It is more specific, but it still avoids the excessively cramped perspective of the traditional interpretation.

An Alternative Definition

Of course, it is possible to ask for a different type of definition, clarifying just what it is that electronics contributes to military operations. This turns out to be much the same as electronics contributes to civilian life – such things as rapid exchange of information by radio and telecommunications, observation by radar, particularly of aircraft and ships, management of data by computers, presentation of data, navigation, range-finding, surveillance and security. The practical differences are that the urgencies are greater, the penalties of failure are greater, and everything has to be done under hostile conditions including deliberate electronic disruption.

This is a useful definition for many purposes, but it does not highlight the fact that electronics actually changes the nature of conflict, and this change is the chief reason for studying the subject.

It is surprising that electronic warfare is not more clearly seen for the tactical, strategic, political thing that it is, because that is the way that one of the greatest of military practitioners and writers saw it, Winston Churchill. Churchill was not an expert on electronics, but he understood its importance as part of the war effort he directed. He managed electronics strategically, in the sense that an expert chess player strategically manages the game that he is playing.

Churchill as a player was not fault-free. Moreover, he was obliged to take over a position that was compromised and inferior to that of his opponents. But he understood that it was a new kind of war and he understood that it had to be fought as such. In this he was a long way ahead of most of those around him. He also had the greatest gift of all – of picking the right people. All things considered, he made brilliant use of the resources available to him.

Having done this, he wrote about it. He explained himself. It might well seem that any future approach could do no better than follow in his footsteps.[1]

This cannot be denied, but there is today a much vaster area to be covered. Churchill was concerned only with the Second World War. It is necessary to go back before that period as far as possible, and to come forward from it. There is a challenge to see the whole of military history projected from the standpoint of electronics.

There is, of course, a chronological limitation, for electronics is a young science. But much has happened in the time during which it has played a military role, enough to support a division of military history into the pre-electronic and electronic ages.

To take, at random, some comparative examples, it is possible to see military history projected from the standpoint of firearms, or armour, or mobility. None of these categories is complete in itself, but each reveals some things that might not be evident from a broader standpoint.

It is the same with electronics. Electronics has become so pervasive that there is no area of warfare that it does not contribute to, from land to sea and air, from under water to outer space. As a standpoint, it may be specialised, but it is revealing.

Electronics – Early Applications

If there is a problem in approaching electronics in war, it is in the term electronics itself. The word is much younger than similar words such as 'electricity' and 'electrify'.

Electron is the Greek word for amber. Nearly four centuries ago it was borrowed from Greek to form such words as 'electric' and 'electrify', to describe what happened when amber was rubbed.[2] Rubbing caused amber to attract some kinds of objects, such as straws. It was known that materials other than amber, such as glass and jet, could respond in the same way. They were said to be 'electrified'. Electricity was the notional fluid responsible, elusive but sometimes to be perceived in sparks.

This was a technology for war, because sparks could detonate explosives. Ways had been found of conducting electricity, first using damp hemp cord, later wires. By 1800 the electric battery was known, and by 1812, at the height of the Napoleonic Wars, experiments had begun in detonating mines.

This was possible only with the use of metallic wires insulated to prevent the charge leaking away. In damp earth or under water, very effective insulation was needed. The Russian Baron Schilling succeeded in providing it with his 'subaqueous galvanic conducting cord'. The conductor was copper wire, insulated with rubber and varnished. In addition to making the conductor, Schilling had to devise a means of detonating the gunpowder with an ingenious arrangement of charcoal 'points'.

As the first to try to use electricity for military purposes,[3] Schilling deserves credit as the pioneer of electronic warfare. His first recorded explosions used cables laid across the River Neva at St Petersburg (Leningrad) in 1812, and the River Seine at Paris in 1814. 1812 was the year of the Napoleonic invasion of Russia; by 1814 the tables were turned and troops under Tsar Alexander I entered Paris.

His invention does not seem to have played any operational role at the time, but undoubtedly entered Russian military practice. When the Russians abandoned Sevastopol to the besieging Anglo-French forces in 1855 during the Crimean War, the fortifications were found to have been mined and wired.

Schilling had grasped the essential advantages of electronic devices in war: instantaneous effect, communication over a considerable distance. The decision to explode a mine could, in theory, be communicated by a length of fuze (though hardly underwater), but not with an instant result.

The facility of causing instantaneous remote destruction fascinated the military mind ever afterwards. Schilling's pioneer 'electric

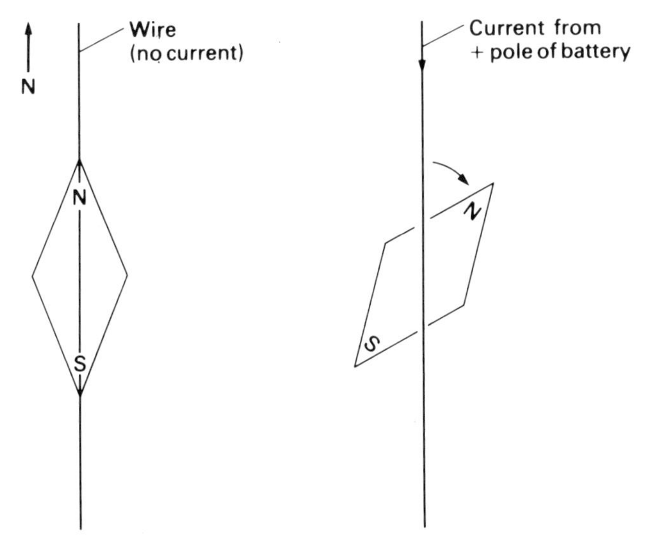

FIG. 1.1 **Oersted's Discovery** In 1820 the Danish scientist Oersted discovered that an electric current in a wire would deflect a magnetic (compass) needle. This opened the way to telegraphy by wire, the military value of which was rapidly realised. The wire telegraph played a significant role in the Crimean War (1853–56), the American Civil War (1861–65), and the Franco–Prussian War (1870–71), amongst others.

exploder' has had many later echoes, including the 'death rays' which helped to trigger the development of radar in Britain, and today's so-called 'Star Wars'.

Electricity generated by rubbing amber was not the only natural mystery of its kind. Another was magnetism. Magnetism went back further than electricity, back to the ancient Chinese. In Western Europe, the use of the lodestone, a natural magnet, as a compass to assist navigation was known for many centuries.

At first there was nothing to connect electricity and magnetism. Two things changed this. The first was the discovery of the chemical battery, by the Italian Volta, in 1800. The battery caused a steady flow of electricity instead of a build-up of electrostatic charge as with amber. The battery sent a continuous current through a wire connecting its terminals, in contrast to a brief spark discharge.

The second was the discovery, by the Dane Oersted, that a steady electric current in a wire, produced in this way, turned a magnetic needle placed directly under or over the wire. The magnetic needle was just a magnetised needle balanced on a point like a compass needle.

When electric current passed in the wire, it swung round. This discovery came in 1820. For the first time it linked electricity and magnetism.

The Electric Telegraph

It was a wonderful discovery. Amongst other things, it opened the way to the electric telegraph. Telegraphy already existed, but using other means, for example semaphore signals – mechanical arms on a post, moving like a man waving flags.

Telegraphy even existed after a fashion using electricity – by exploiting electrostatic charge. Attempts to make telegraphs using electrostatic charge had been going on for the best part of a century. It was not easy, but the prize was great and the inventors persistent.

In 1816 Sir Francis Ronalds offered an electrostatic telegraph to the British Admiralty.[4] This was rejected with the comment '. . . telegraphs of any kind are now wholly unnecessary . . . no other than the one in use will be adopted . . .'. Presumably the latter reference was to the mechanical semaphore.

It was thanks to these earlier efforts that the conducting properties of copper wire and the need for insulation had been realised. With this and the chemical battery, the turning, or deflection, of a magnetic needle by current in a wire was the last idea needed to make the electric telegraph work.

There were many ways the effect could be used. The battery could be alternately connected and disconnected in order to flick the needle. But if, instead, it was alternately connected one way then the other, the needle made a bigger movement. In other words the polarity of the electrical connection was reversed and the needle reversed its swing.

This idea was used by Baron Schilling, who is indeed far better known as a pioneer of the electric telegraph than as the father of electronic warfare. He made an instrument coupling the deflection of the magnetic needle to a suspended circular disc, which swung from 'edge on' to show one or other of its faces, one black the other white. This gave unmistakable visual indication.

It was an example of a 'bi-signal' telegraph, and Schilling invented a code for it that preceded Morse but is remarkably reminiscent. While in 'off' condition the disc was edge-on, a single show of the black face meant E, a single show of the white T. Black followed by white was A, S was two whites, I was two blacks, and N was white then black. And so forth. Sometimes the instrument was constructed with faces showing horizontal and vertical lines instead of black and white discs.

Schilling was not the only one to see the jump from Oersted's discovery to a practical electric telegraph. It had no shortage of inventors and he was simply the first of them. In the United States, Samuel Morse is regarded as the father of the telegraph.

But the most famous patent was the one secured by the British scientists Wheatstone and Cooke in 1837. Their telegraph was for railway use, but by 1844 the British Admiralty, which had spurned Ronalds' offer in 1816, contracted with them for a telegraph between London and the Commander-in-Chief's residence in Portsmouth.

The invention of the electric telegraph flew rapidly around the world, as rapidly as a comparable invention might do today, if not more so. It supplied a need for communications on land, but its potential to cross stretches of water, by the use of submarine cables, was quickly realised.

The Telegraph in War

A submarine telegraph was laid across New York harbour in 1842. The problems of obtaining watertight insulation were not, however, successfully solved until the introduction of the rubber-like substance gutta percha later in the 1840s. The English Channel was crossed by submarine cable in 1850. Water was an ancient communications barrier which the electric telegraph at last began to lift.[5]

In the circumstances it should not be surprising that the first major military application of the telegraph came at sea rather than on land. It is a paradox, however, because the telegraph undoubtedly promised more to armies than to navies. The history of the second half of the 19th century confirms this. But at the beginning it happened the other way about. This was in the Crimean War, 1854–56.

The Crimean War was a conflict on a much larger scale than the name suggests. It was between Tsarist Russia on one side and the Allied Forces of Britain and France supporting Turkey on the other. Military operations were conducted on both the western and eastern sides of the Black Sea – the Balkans and the Caucasus – as well as on the Crimean peninsula itself.

There were also operations by Britain and France in the Baltic and White Seas and halfway round the world, at Kamchatka and Sakhalin. Historically, the Crimean War prefigured the strategy of the Cold War between the Soviet Union and the Western powers which has dominated much of the second half of the 20th century.

Despite the war's far-flung character, the Black Sea was the crucial arena. Here the Allied landing on the Crimea, at a range of 300 miles from the Balkan base of the Allied armies, was a daring amphibious operation. There was a problem of communications.

It brought forth an imaginative answer: a 300-mile submarine telegraph cable laid between Varna, on the western shore of the Black Sea, and the Allied landing area near Balaclava in the Crimea. This is known as the 'Black Sea Cable'. Apparently it functioned well, which was highly creditable in view of the difficulties experienced only a few years earlier in laying a reliable telegraph cable between Britain and the continent of Europe, a much shorter distance.

Stalemate eventually overtook the Crimean fighting and the warring sides, convinced of the futility of continuing, made peace. The Black Sea cable did not, therefore, contribute to any dramatic outcome. But there can be no doubt that it greatly speeded the flow of information between the Allied capitals in Western Europe and the distant front.

The question can be asked, 'What would have been the military

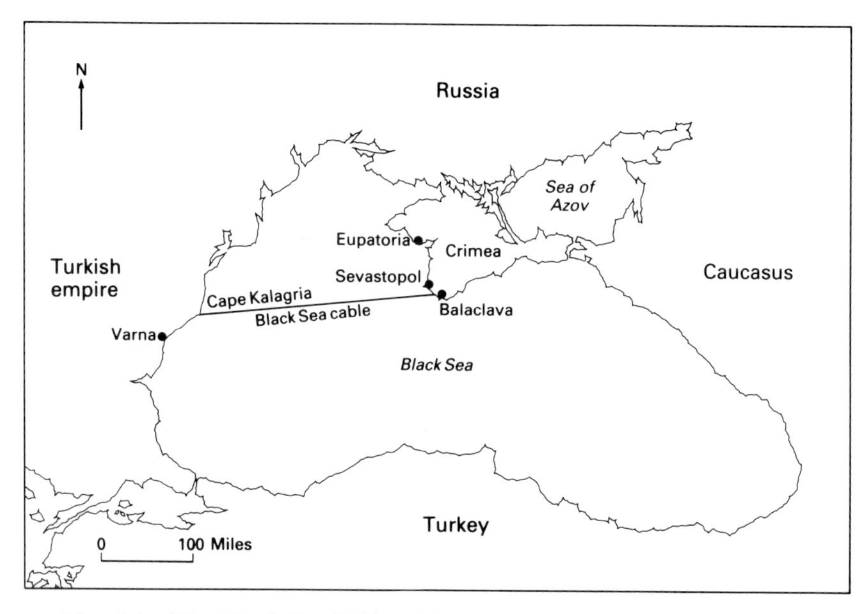

MAP 1.1 **The Black Sea Cable (Crimean War)** The war was a bid by Britain and France to check Russian expansion by supporting the Turkish (Osman) Empire, which was struggling to maintain its Balkan conquests. The main theatre of war was the Black Sea. From a base at Varna (then in the Turkish Empire, now in Bulgaria), British and French forces made a landing at Eupatoria in the Crimea (1854), and advanced southwards towards the Russian naval base Sevastopol. Another landing was made at Balaclava on the other side of Sevastopol. In April 1855 a submarine cable was laid from Cape Kalagria, about 30 miles north of Varna, to Balaclava, where it came ashore at St George's monastery. This established direct telegraphic contact between the Crimean front and London, and quickened the flow of despatches in both ways. Hitherto, about 30 hours were needed for the British commander Lord Raglan to pass a communication to the government in London. Its value was shown following his unexpected death (not in action) a few months later.

value to the Russians of cutting it, supposing they had been technically capable of such a feat?' This would have needed to be done in advance of a surprise stroke, such as the despatch of fresh Russian forces. The war never took such a turn; the Crimean position remained basically defensive for the Russians.

Significant as it was, the submarine cable was accompanied by the use of land telegraphs by both sides in the Crimean War. The land telegraph was more important to the Russians. It was even immortalised in the name of one crucial Russian strongpoint, 'Telegraph Hill'. Their cable to St Petersburg was laid by Siemens.

Yet the 300-mile link across the sea remains the memorable strategic concept. Had events taken a different course it could have played a dramatic part. It showed an amazing early grasp of the military potential of rapid long-distance electronic communications. It was all the more amazing because of the later occasions when this understanding failed.

Land Wars

Not long after the Crimean War came the American Civil War of 1861–65. This was in a country where the development of the telegraph had been especially vigorous. Given huge overland distances, there was inevitably a premium on telegraphic communications. The American east–west transcontinental telegraph was completed in 1861.

In this war the use of the telegraph became an integral part of military operations. The necessity for mobile equipment was realised, so that the telegraph could follow the armies. The war brought the use of balloons for military observation, and the telegraph sometimes provided a communications link between the balloon-borne observer and the ground.

In 1870–71 two countries representing Europe's cultural heartland and biggest concentration of industrial and technical strength became locked in battle. These were France and Germany in the Franco–Prussian War. In this ominous struggle the electric telegraph, a symbol of technical and industrial advance, played a key role. It became the focus of communications warfare.

Germany was not yet a state but still a patchwork of principalities when the war broke out. During it she was formally united under Prussian leadership. The war served notice that Germany's united industry and technology would prevail over any other single European nation, particularly in military applications. This fact is central to European history up to 1945, and to the development of electronic warfare.

While Paris was the centre of Europe's most important commercial telegraph network, Prussian interest had long been concentrated on the telegraph's military potential. Prussia had used it in the war of 1866 against Austria. Now methodical German organisation ensured efficient telegraphic communications to the German armies on the French frontier. It underpinned German ability firstly to contain France's attack, and then win a frontier victory.

The strategic penalty for the French of starting a war on the frontier and losing it was that the road was thereby thrown open to their capital. The German armies advanced to besiege Paris.

Suddenly the telegraph meant everything. The German military telegraph network was extended into France. But the French telegraph network based on Paris was, to use the modern term, decapitated, and with it the whole national system of communications, a military disaster.

Paris, the cultural capital of the world, was cut off. Rare ingenuity was manifested in ideas to overcome its isolation, often hinging on such novel ideas as 'laying' telegraph wires through the air at great height, but to no avail.

A celebrated feature of the siege became the launch of balloons from Paris with the aim of crossing over the German lines and landing in French territory beyond. But the balloon did not prove capable of restoring the communications lost in the telegraph.

On the other hand, the potential of the telegraph for quick reaction was demonstrated by the Germans, who used it, following balloon launches, to alert military units in whatever direction was appropriate, so increasing the chances of intercepting them when they came down.

France's defeat was accompanied by the birth of Germany's Second Reich, under which German science and technology advanced to be second to none in the world. This was recognised both by Germany's neighbours and Germany herself. It ultimately became a factor in Europe's increasing tension. It set the scene for the future role Germany would play in electronic warfare.

Electronic warfare has proved sensitively related to the level of scientific culture, more so than any other branch of warfare. Nevertheless, it was not possible then – any more than it is now – for any single nation to occupy the forward frontier on every single facet of science and technology.

Countermeasures

The telegraph's military role continued to the end of the 19th century, becoming ever more clearly apparent. The countermeasure of cutting telegraph wires equally became standard military practice. This was evident in the Spanish–American War, 1898, in which both landlines and submarine cables were cut.

At the end of the century there was a long conflict between the Boers and the British in South Africa. It was often guerrilla war, with raiding parties. The distances and the type of terrain made the telegraph as essential as it was vulnerable. It came to the forefront as a military factor. A good indication of the telegraph's importance was that the British burnt Boer farms as a reprisal for cutting the wires.

In 1896 the British mounted the clandestine Jameson Raid. This proved abortive. One of the reasons for its failure was that communications to the Boer leadership in the Transvaal had to be cut off at the outset, but the troops detailed to perform this vital mission clipped the wrong wires and left Cape Town in the dark instead.

A New Strategic Factor

One side of military affairs goes hand-in-hand with politics; this is generally the strategic aspect. The telegraph began its involvement in conflict chiefly as a tactical communications carrier. But as the 19th century went on, major national and international telegraph networks began to form, setting the scene for a strategic and political role.

European countries built up networks reflecting their commercial and political requirements, influenced as in the case of Britain by existing patterns of imperial, colonial, or transoceanic communications. The linking of Europe and the United States by submarine telegraph in 1866 was particularly important. It put Britain, where the cable came ashore, in an advantageous position amongst the countries of Europe, astride the main lines of telegraphic communication between the New World and the Old. She did not miss the implications.

The world-wide cable network was laid peacefully enough. The military significance was for the future. But while it was being laid, another development was impending. Oersted's discovery in 1820 was only the first link between electricity and magnetism. Another, still more fruitful link remained to be discovered before the 19th century was out.

2

Battleground

THE MYSTERIOUS phenomena of electricity and magnetism always challenged human understanding. How could action at a distance be possible, the attraction or repulsion which seemingly leapt across empty space? To design or operate a telegraph, understanding was not necessary. It was enough to work with these forces at the short ranges involved in telegraph apparatus, measured in centimetres or fractions thereof.

For practical purposes it was accepted that somehow, in the space around a wire carrying electric current, there existed a magnetic field, as shown by the response of a compass needle. This was a field created by the electricity in motion in the wire. Equally obviously there was some other kind of field around a piece of charged amber – an electrostatic field, the field created by static electricity.

The idea arose that these forces were not separate and not limited to the short ranges over which the simple effects seemed to operate. The British scientist Maxwell produced a theory which suggested that they could, in combination, travel great distances, and this in turn inspired the German scientist Hertz.

Hertz experimented with electric sparks. In 1888 he found that a spark, made to jump between two small metallic globes connected by a wire loop, would cause another spark to jump between two other globes connected by a wire loop, even though they might be many metres away.[1]

This was something new and bore out Maxwell's theory, according to which the electric spark was acting on space like a stone dropping on to the surface of a pond. It sent out ripples, or waves. Just as water waves made objects floating on the surface bob, even at considerable distance, so the spark induced other sparks to jump. Hertz had demonstrated the existence of electromagnetic or radio waves.

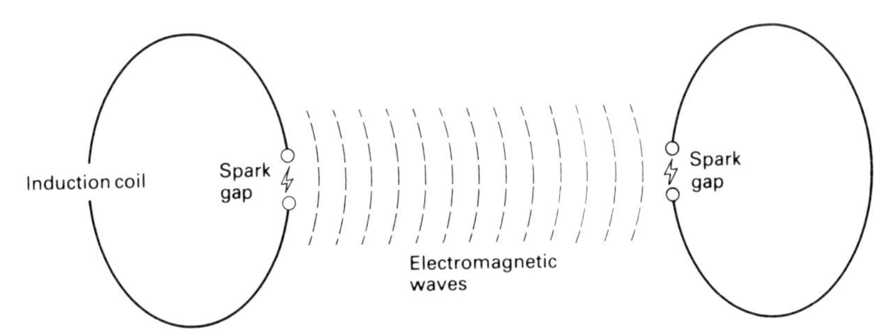

FIG 2.1 **Hertz's Discovery of Electromagnetic Waves** In 1888 the German scientist Hertz found that a spark jumping between two metal spheres in a loop of wire would cause another spark to jump between two other metal spheres in a similar loop, even though they might be several metres away. He recognised that the effect was caused by electromagnetic waves. The spark remained the primary means of generating electromagnetic waves until the First World War. It gave birth to wireless telegraphy (W/T), the most suitable communications technique for the majority of military purposes, thanks to cryptography. The spark transmitter was well developed at the time of the Battle of Tsushima in 1905.

The implications were tremendous. It was realised that here was a possible alternative to telegraph that would work without wires. This was the beginning of wireless, or radio, in the 1890s.

Initially radio was a long way from challenging telegraphy as a means of communication. Its range was that of the laboratory, not of the open countryside. Much more needed to be discovered. Fortunately Hertz had given researchers the electric spark as a powerful means of generating radio waves and this was the key to progress. While further discoveries followed and ranges increased amazingly, the spark transmitter retained its unique position for almost thirty years.

Early radio apparatus shaped itself around two metal spheres, separated by a gap, forming the transmitter. The gap might be as long as 30 centimetres. It might not always be in air; the spheres might be immersed in oil.

Many emblems and badges, of radio institutions or military radio units, to this day retain the symbolism of the spark, even though the spark has been banished. Sparking apparatus is now more likely to be associated with something going wrong, with the lack of suppression.

What was so special about an electric spark? It was not just electricity leaping through the air in one direction from one metal sphere to another. The electric current leapt *to and fro*, along the conducting path of incandescent air which was the visual spark. The spark current was an oscillating current, and the oscillation was essential to its effect of generating electromagnetic waves.

Plate 2.1 **The Heart of an Early Transmitter** This photograph shows the spark gap of a ship's wireless transmitter, circa 1900. The scale is shown by the foot rule against the terminals at the top of the stout wooden box. The front panel has been swung down to reveal the device but would be closed in operation for protection against noise and ozone. The electrical oscillations inherent in sparks were conveyed to the antenna through a transformer. The hemispheres were energised from an induction coil. The development of this basic technology was driven equally by naval and civil maritime needs, but its culmination came in the First World War for the transmission of wireless telegraphy.

With oscillation, the fields in space oscillated – both the electrostatic field from the charge on the spheres, and the magnetic field from the flow of current. They built up, fell to zero, built up in the opposite direction, fell to zero again, and continuously repeated this cycle.

The Ether

Maxwell's theory said that these oscillating electric and magnetic fields, intangible though they were, reacted upon each other in the emptiness of space. They sustained themselves in outward motion away from the spark, just as waves on water sustain themselves in outward motion away from the disturbance which causes them. The name electromagnetic implies the existence of the two components.

All this was far from easy to understand. Maxwell had been proved correct, but did there not need to be some medium in space for these waves to propagate in – analogous to the water? It was a severe challenge to 19th-century imagination, and a vexatious problem for 19th-century science. Science christened the medium ether and strove to find it, but did not succeed.

To be frank, both to scientists and to the public at large, radio waves posed a credibility crisis. The traces have not vanished even to this day. Not surprisingly at the time many people expressed scepticism.

But the radio experimenters were not among the sceptics. Whether they understood electromagnetic waves or not, they took them for granted as one of nature's most mysterious and exciting phenomena, and worked with them. They did this in the same way as earlier researchers had taken simple electric and magnetic effects and developed the electric telegraph.

For most people, the effort to understand radio waves has been replaced by practical acceptance. For scientific purposes, the idea of the ether has been abandoned, yet it remains a convenient figure of speech.

At the practical level, radio had problems enough. One was the need to understand the many-sided importance of 'frequency'. Frequency meant nothing other than the frequency of electrical oscillation: how many times the current surged back and forth in each second.

The importance was that the frequency of the electrical oscillations in a spark was the frequency of the electromagnetic waves the spark generated. It became clear that the waves had variable properties based on their frequency.

In other words, frequency was the basic difference between electromagnetic waves, and therefore was the main way of classifying them. This took some time to be appreciated, even though Maxwell had explained frequency, and Hertz had designed his experiments to generate particular frequencies.

Maxwell's theory brought in not only frequency but speed. It showed how to calculate the speed at which electromagnetic waves would travel. This turned out to be 300,000 kilometres (186,000 miles) a second.

This was the speed of light, known from measurement. Light was already understood to be a wave, Maxwell in effect revealed it as a form of electromagnetic wave. This was a dramatic result.

The Spectrum

In Maxwell's theory, what distinguished light from radio waves was only frequency. Light was electromagnetic waves at a much higher frequency than radio waves. When Hertz confirmed that radio waves existed, they joined light in what came to be known as the electromagnetic spectrum.

But they offered an enormous contrast in properties. Light was visible, radio waves were invisible. Light reflected off most material objects, cast shadows and travelled in straight lines, radio waves passed through brick walls, around mountains, and over the horizon. This was astonishing, even to scientists, who thought radio waves, apart from being invisible, would behave in other respects like light.

Frequency was known to make a difference even within the spectrum of visible light. It made the difference between red, green and blue, representing low, medium and high visible frequencies.

In the same way, radio frequencies could be classed as low, medium and high, and although the waves were not visible, there were recognisable differences. This was in the way the waves travelled, or propagated, around the earth. If they were to be used for communications, these differences had to be studied, because the possibility of communications in given circumstances depended on the frequency.

The early pioneers soon came to the conclusion that radio waves' ability to travel large distances was greater at lower frequencies, and they focused their efforts on generating them.

Moreover they realised that the radio waves generated by any spark would affect any apparatus set up for detection within working range. In other words, only one channel of communication was possible in a given locality, for two or more transmissions would come through together, that is to say interfere with each other, at the receiver.

The only hope of disentangling simultaneous radio communications lay in the use of different frequencies. The apparatus had to be 'tuned' to transmit and receive a specific frequency and reject others. Only differently tuned transmitters and receivers could work in the same locality without mutual interference. Unfortunately the spark inherently generated a wide band of frequencies and tuning spark

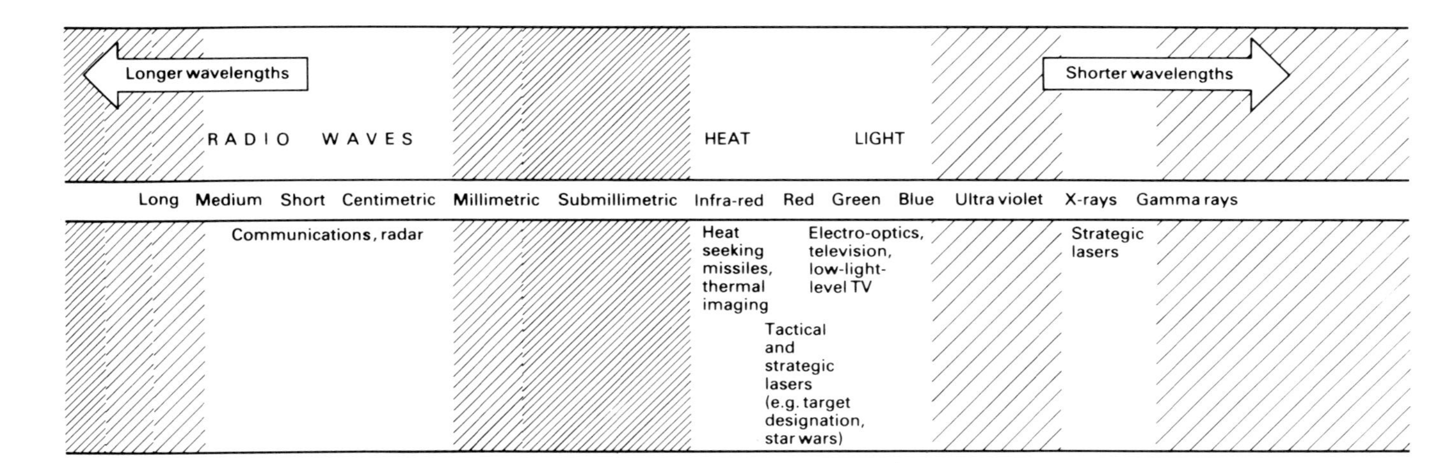

FIG 2.2 **The Electromagnetic Spectrum in Warfare** The electromagnetic spectrum is sometimes described as the commanding height of the electronic battlefield. The aim of electronic warfare is to exploit the spectrum oneself and deny it to the enemy. The spectrum is indefinite in extent but only certain sectors have been exploited, as indicated – heavy shading indicating least military exploitation. Active exploitation is dominated by two sectors which have not quite joined up, despite attempts to find military use for millimetric and sub-millimetric waves. On the far right, another sector of exploitation may emerge.

apparatus was not easy. Hertz attempted it from the beginning, but the battle for better tuning went on for many years, right to the end of the spark transmitter era.

The Hub of Electronic Warfare

Frequency was irrelevant to 19th century wire telegraphy. Steady currents were used, either 'on' or 'off', and the message went where the wires went. By contrast, frequency was the indispensable basis of radio. It was destined to become the hub about which practically the whole of electronic warfare revolved in the 20th century.

The crucial difference between the electronic warfare of the 19th and 20th centuries can be expressed in one simple way: that frequency was irrelevant in the 19th century but dominating in the 20th.

The progress of electronic warfare in the 20th century can be represented as progress in extending the usable frequency spectrum. Beginning with the effort to control frequency and produce specific frequencies, it turned into an upwards progress from low and medium radio frequencies to higher ones.

It has not always been a steady progress. Sometimes it has jumped. From the radio frequencies it eventually took a tremendous leap to the infra-red, the region of the electromagnetic spectrum just below the frequency of visible light but a long way above radio waves. Not even today has this gap been closed.

Occasionally electronic warfare goes downwards, using lower frequencies.

Not surprisingly, it is often said that the electromagnetic spectrum is the commanding height of the electronic battlefield. To control it for oneself, and to deny its use to the enemy, is one way of expressing the general strategic aim of electronic warfare.

Sometimes electromagnetic waves are absent from electronic warfare, as in much of underwater warfare. But it is a remarkable fact that the truth of the preceding statement is preserved by replacing 'electromagnetic spectrum' by 'frequency spectrum'.

What matters fundamentally is the ability of oscillations to carry information. The oscillations can be projected in any convenient way: acoustically through air or water, or by means of electromagnetic waves. Radio first highlighted the importance of oscillations and the mythical ether remains the principal medium for carrying them. But pressure waves in air or water are an alternative. The common factor between oscillations of every kind is the idea of frequency.

By comparison with radio frequencies, the typical frequencies of sound in air or water – audio frequencies – are extremely low. Middle C in music corresponds to about 271 vibrations per second. The audio frequency range finishes at the limit of human hearing, about 15,000 to 20,000 vibrations a second. But some of the radio frequencies used in the experiments of Hertz were about 560 million.

In honour of Hertz his name has become the unit of frequency, with the meaning of so many vibrations, or oscillations, per second. Thus middle C can be expressed as 271 hertz, contracted to Hz. A thousand hertz is a kilohertz, kHz, a million hertz a megahertz, MHz, and a thousand million hertz a gigahertz, GHz.

As early radio came to grips with frequency, it came to grips with another problem which, like frequency, was irrelevant to wire telegraphy.

The telegraph connected places A and B by a long electric circuit. There was only one circuit involved. The current went along one wire and returned along another, but both wires were part of the same continuous electrical circuit. True, it was possible to dispense with one of the wires, by making use of the earth's ability to conduct current – the 'earth return' – but this did not alter the principle of one continuous circuit. Many telegraphs utilised a single wire, such as the Black Sea cable, for the sake of the obvious economy in materials.[2]

In consequence, the electrical flow at one end of the telegraph – the strength of the signal – was the same as at the other. The same amount of electricity flowed at all places around the circuit. With radio, the position was quite different. There were two circuits, not one. There were physically distinct and separate circuits at transmitting and receiving terminals. In one the signal was very strong, in the other very feeble.

Antennas and Amplification

Radio could, in fact, be described without any reference to electromagnetic waves, as simply the discovery that signals can be sent from A to B without connecting A and B with a single long electric circuit. Two separate circuits, one at A and one at B, are enough. In some amazing way, space does the rest. A powerful signal in the circuit at A is reproduced in the circuit at B. In the nature of things, however, and it is a big however, the signal at B is very much weaker than the originating signal. How much weaker depends on the distance.

For radio to cope with this problem, it had to develop its own technology much more sophisticated than wire telegraphy. At first it attempted to increase the strength of the signal transmitted from A to B by exposing the transmitting and receiving circuits above the earth in some favourable manner, as 'aerials' or 'antennas'.

The heart of the transmitter was the sparking metal spheres. By linking the spheres to an antenna, raised to tens of metres height, the

PLATE 2.2 **A Triumph of Receiver Technology** At a time when amplification was impossible, the magnetic detector, in use from 1902, was a dazzling invention which enabled wireless telegraphy from a spark transmitter to be received reliably at 30 words a minute – fully competitive with cable telegraphy. It utilised a continuous band of soft iron wires, wound by clockwork at 7/8 centimetres per second past the poles of two permanent magnets. Here it also ran through primary and secondary transformer windings. The primary was connected to the antenna and the secondary to the headphones, making the signals audible. The magnetic detector was not completely superseded until the 1920s.

PLATE 2.3 **Tuning in 1907** This tuner, which was patented in 1907, worked in conjunction with a magnetic detector as a receiver of wireless telegraphy signals. In the spark transmitter era, tuning could not be as precise as it became with electron tubes. This instrument was designed to tune to all wavelengths from 2000 to 80 metres (that is from 150 KHz to 3.75 MHz), giving a good indication of the operational frequency range of early radio.

transmission became far more effective. The oscillating current extended into the antenna and radiated electromagnetic waves from it more intensely than from the actual spark. The spark's job was merely to cause the oscillations. Connecting the spheres between the antenna above and the earth below further improved matters.

But the radiated power was sent out in all directions and the antenna raised at the receiving end, which might be tens or hundreds of miles away, never collected anything more than the tiniest proportion of it, just as a distant observer only senses a tiny proportion of the total light and heat emitted by a blazing beacon on a hilltop. Radio had the problem of sensing the tiny electrical effects generated in the receiving antenna. Initially this was done by a variety of devices which have all but passed out of present memory.

Indeed if the problem was set in a modern electronics examination to design a radio receiver without using transistors, electron tubes or any amplifying device, many of the candidates would probably have a bad fright. But it could be done.

One solution is a tube of metal powder, loosely packed, connected between the receiving antenna and the earth. A current from a battery is passed through the powder. When the antenna receives radio waves, the tiny but rapid electrical oscillations suddenly cause the resistance of the metal powder to drop. This is shown by the battery current rising. This is the action of the 'coherer'.[3]

Usually the coherer was engineered to operate a simple printer, operating on a narrow strip of paper. The output of early radio was not auditory, but visual, a series of long or short marks corresponding to dashes and dots. This gave a written record just like the ordinary telegraph. In effect it made early radio a derivative of telegraphy, to which the appellation 'wireless telegraphy' was given (abbreviated W/T).

For all its other advantages, wireless telegraphy was a long way behind the ordinary telegraph in speed; at the turn of the century it could print out about ten words per minute compared to the forty of the land telegraph.

Possibly the most important invention in wireless telegraphy was Marconi's magnetiser, based on a loop of constantly circulating soft iron tape. This came after the coherer and provided the most effective means of detecting the faint signals received in radio antennas. It helped to close the speed gap between radio and conventional wire telegraphy.

Eventually came an advance which – helped by the pressure of military rather than civilian needs – transformed radio in all kinds of ways. It swept the era of the spark transmitter into oblivion. This was the advent of the thermionic valve, or electron tube.

3

The Passing of the Spark

THE BASIC electrical words date from the 17th century, but it was not until nearly the end of the 19th that the word 'electron', which had spawned them in the first place, entered the dictionary on its own account.

When J. J. Thomson showed in 1897 that electricity was composed of elementary particles, the name electrons was given to them, and they became the first of all the family of elementary particles recognised in modern physics.

Thomson's discovery was based on experiments with a type of apparatus which was a product of the glass-blower's art. It was a globe or tube with metallic wires passing through the glass, the glass forming a tight seal around them. One version is the ordinary electric light bulb. Devices of this sort had become quite common at the end of the 19th century.

For scientific purposes air was evacuated from the globe. The metallic leads were not connected together inside the globe, as with a light bulb, but terminated in the vacuum. Called 'electrodes', they were linked to sources of electric tension. Because of the vacuum, electricity – electrons – could stream through the space between them.

This was the beginning of electronics, though the general, modern use of the word was still fifty years away. The electrons, flowing through space, could be influenced by attraction or repulsion, according to the positive or negative charges on the electrodes. Or else they could be influenced by electric or magnetic fields applied from outside the tube. The stream of electrons could be focused, deflected, made to impinge on a luminescent area. The strength of the flow could be controlled.

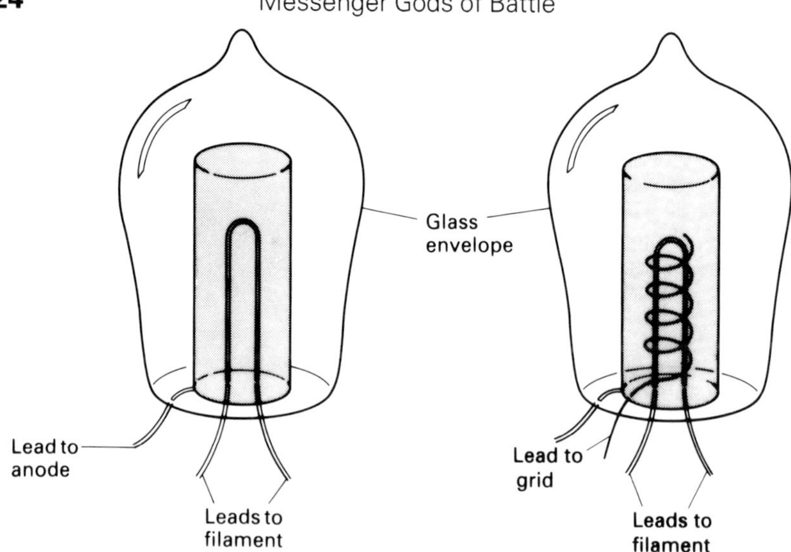

FIG. 3.1 **Diode and Triode** The first electron tubes ('valves') developed from the incandescent lamp. The diode (above left) contained a heated filament as the cathode and a surrounding metal anode. Electrons given off by the filament could flow through the vacuum to the anode, but the reverse flow was not possible. Therefore, as a one-way conducting device, the diode turned an oscillatory signal into a detectable one-way current. If an audio-frequency signal was amplitude-modulated on to the basic signal, this also would be detected, as a periodic variation in the current. The triode (right) included an open-mesh grid between cathode and anode. It was found that a weak signal applied between grid and cathode would control the flow of electrons through the vacuum, causing the signal to reappear greatly amplified in the anode/cathode circuit. Diode/triode technology developed in the decade before the First World War, culminating in 1913. It was just ready for the immense stimulus which the war gave to radio, bringing the spark transmitter/magnetic detector era to an end.

Undoubtedly the evacuated glass tube with embedded metal electrodes has been one of the most creative devices in history. It was the basic means of handling electrons and observing their effects. It made electrons useful, manageable, and practical.

These devices began to interest the early radio pioneers. Eventually they became basic components of radio equipment, called 'electron tubes', or in Britain 'valves'. Another term was 'thermionic tube', referring to the fact that tubes for radio contained an electrically heated filament to provide an especially copious source of electrons.

There were several variants of the thermionic tube. One, patented by Fleming in Britain in 1904, contained two electrodes and was called a diode. Another developed in the United States by Lee de Forest a little later, in 1906, contained three electrodes and was called a triode. The early devices were about the size of lamp bulbs, moreover, like lamps, they contained glowing filaments. The name 'lamp' occasionally survives as an alternative to 'valve' or 'tube', for example in Russia (*lampa*).

Yet another varient was the cathode ray tube (or CRT), invented by Braun in Germany, where it is still known as the Braun tube. It had been noticed that glass fluoresces where a beam of electrons impinges upon it; the Braun tube improved on this effect by introducing special fluorescent coatings.

This century-old invention is nowadays familiar as the screen of television sets, and it is still the main display in the majority of computer applications. In the Second World War it became vital because radar demanded the visual display of information, revealing very small time intervals which could not be measured in any other way. The historical importance of the CRT or Braun tube in electronic warfare simply cannot be over-estimated.

Military Motivation

The earliest radio equipment did not make use of electron tubes, but during the First World War they became the main distinguishing feature of radio equipment. Military needs were the motive force for this development. They brought a solution to radio's problem of sensing the antenna's tiny currents by amplifying them – making them vastly more powerful. They solved the tuning problem too, by making it possible to generate highly specific frequencies. But while they spelt the end of the spark transmitter, it was many years before the name 'electronic engineering' or 'electronics' began to be used instead of radio engineering.

This only happened when the techniques of radio engineering began to be applied to non-radio requirements, for example computing. It came during and after the Second World War. Ironically the advent of the transistor was then about to spell the end of electron tubes in the majority of their applications. But this did not invalidate the name electronics.[1]

While military radio equipment in the First World War was certainly electronic, in that it had begun to use electron tubes, it was not called so at the time. Only in retrospect is it electronic. But in retrospect much else is seen to be electronic, and even the ordinary spark is seen to be a manifestation of electrons. The only consistent principle is to apply modern terminology wherever appropriate, and by this standard electronic warfare goes right back to Schilling's 'electric exploder'.

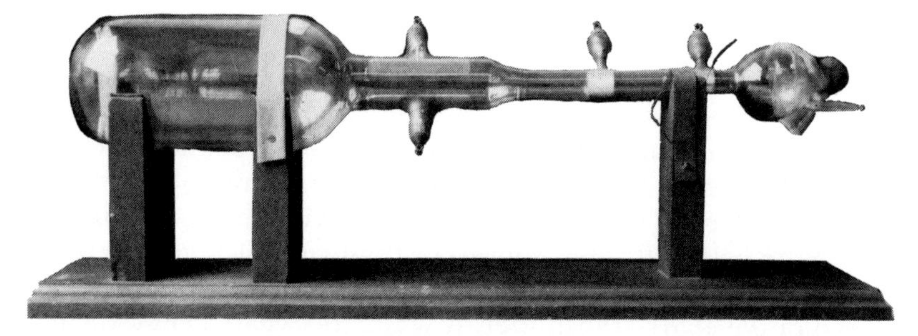

PLATE 3.1 **An Early Cathode Ray Tube** Few devices have had as much significance for electronic warfare as the cathode ray tube. From the Second World War onwards, it was a basic element of radar. Today, despite the advent of liquid crystals and light-emitting diodes, it is still paramount for the display of information of all kinds. It was invented by F. Braun, a German, in 1897. This early example is a Braun–Zenneck tube incorporating improvements by Zenneck. (*Photo: By courtesy of GEC–Marconi*)

Telegraphy had never depended on the electron tube. Instead it had produced a different device.

Although telegraphy could connect places A and B with a single long circuit, it was not practicable to set up in advance single circuits connecting every conceivable A and B that might need to be in communication with each other.

In other words the telegraph needed a network. The network could be much larger than its individual links. But it had to be switched in whatever way was necessary to provide the desired connection.

Therefore there was a need to pass on signals from one circuit to another and to use one circuit to control others. This was done by using the signal in one circuit to operate a switch to open and close another circuit – that is, to 'relay' the signal. In telegraphy, relays paralleled the 'active' role of electron tubes in radio.

Relays had already long been used in telegraphy when electron tubes started to be used in radio. This was 'electromechanical engineering', which remained a world apart from radio engineering, similar in some ways, different in others.[2]

Both electromechanical and radio engineering were destined to play their part in electronic warfare, but while some things could be done both by relays and electron tubes, relays containing mechanical moving parts could not react as rapidly as electron tubes. As will be later seen, this became crucial in the Second World War when code-breaking apparatus based on electron tubes was pitted against the German cipher machines constructed on electromechanical principles. Electromechanical engineering could not withstand the attack of electronics.[3]

Legacy

The 19th century bequeathed to the 20th all the essentials for electronic warfare – a legacy either awesome or exciting, according to which way one looks at it. What exactly did it consist of?

Undoubtedly the biggest, ready-to-use contribution was the electric telegraph, with its electromechanical engineering, stations and cable networks.

By 1900 this was a mature technology, developed on a world-wide scale. It was for commercial purposes, but the military applications were realised. There had been plenty of practical examples.

To the telegraph must be added the telephone, though this had not yet played a significant military role. The telephone had been invented in the United States in 1876, a few years after the Franco–Prussian war. Although the telegraph featured prominently in that war, the telephone did not make the same military impact. There were a number of reasons.

One was that wire telegraphy spanned big distances, but telephony by wire was limited in range. The telephone, using the same electromechanical engineering as the telegraph, inspired remarkable developments such as the Strowger automatic exchange, but these were still based on switches and relays and lacked any means of sensitive amplification.

Amplification was not necessary for the simple on–off signals of telegraphy ('digital' signals), but the telephone relied on reproducing the audio-frequencies of the human voice ('analogue' signals), and these could not travel far over a network of cable and electromechanical switches without distortion. Although for example telegraph signals were passed through transatlantic cables from 1866, it was almost another hundred years before the telephone could use transatlantic cables, thanks to amplification with submerged 'repeaters'.

Another, even more important reason, was that telegraphy offered something which telephony could not: the hope of secrecy. A telegraphic message prepared for transmission can be encrypted by codes or ciphers. Telephony does not easily lend itself to anything similar. Even today the 'scrambling' of a telephone conversation leaves much to be desired.

The need for secrecy in telegraphic communications was not unique to the military. It began as a business necessity. The telegraph gave a commercial fillip to the age-old diplomatic art of cryptography. Military users could therefore draw on commercial cryptography, but while commercial users merely had to guard against business embarrassments or financial losses, what was at stake for military and political users was stupendous. It was everything they were fighting for.

The 19th century's second contribution was radio, in its infancy as compared with wire telegraphy, but firing human imagination as no other invention before or since.

Radio started with spark transmitters and borrowed telegraphy's on–off, dot–dash codes as its working principle. Telegraphy was combined into radio as wireless telegraphy. It cannot be said that this was the dawn of electronic warfare, which as already described came almost a century earlier, nevertheless the advent of wireless telegraphy was the greatest single event in electronic warfare's entire history. It came in the early years of the 20th century.

Wireless telegraphy's function was to bring vast new scale and scope. It immediately became a communications medium so invaluable for the conduct of war that it could not be disregarded, but by very virtue of this fact it became at the same time a medium in which warring sides could attempt to intercept and read their opponents' military communications, or prevent them from getting through. It became a medium through which enemy locations might be discovered by direction finding, enemy movements followed, and swift information passed, enabling surprise strikes.

This was unprecedented in military history. It was electronic warfare's greatest bid so far to change the whole character of war. Wireless telegraphy offered military opportunities in abundance, and has never ceased to do so.

An Equal Partner

One effect of wireless telegraphy was to promote cryptography to the status of a fully equal partner in electronic warfare. Far more messages were sent to far more recipients, particularly warships, and recording them seldom presented much difficulty to the enemy, whereas with the telegraph it was at least necessary to gain access to the cables. Cryptography was called upon to provide much tighter security than for telegraphy by wire.

The coming of electron tubes meant that radio could at last borrow transmission of speech from the telephone. This was radio telephony, abbreviated 'R/T'. It came during the First World War. Radio telephony was demanded principally for aviation.

The need for radio telephony was only one of the military pressures behind the adoption of electron tubes. The main military advantage of electron tubes was that they enabled strong transmissions on accurately controlled, continuously generated frequencies. They solved the problem of tuning.

The ether ceased to be a single or double carriageway and became a multi-lane highway, with as many lanes or communications channels as the variety of frequencies could provide. As time went on this variety increased. It was chiefly used to supply the needs of communication via wireless telegraphy. In general wireless telegraphy remained an extremely powerful communications technique for military purposes. It has only ever made limited concessions to radio telephony.

The reason why spark transmitter radio could not carry telephony but only telegraphy was as follows.

In wireless telegraphy, the signal is very rapid oscillations which are turned on or off in the same way as the steady current in a telegraph wire is turned on or off. Telephony is not concerned with turning the signal on or off; it was developed by using the wire to convey the audio-frequency oscillations corresponding to speech. But it was a different matter to convey these oscillations by radio.

In theory it could be done by modulating the relatively slow audio-frequency oscillations of the telephone signal on to the far more rapid

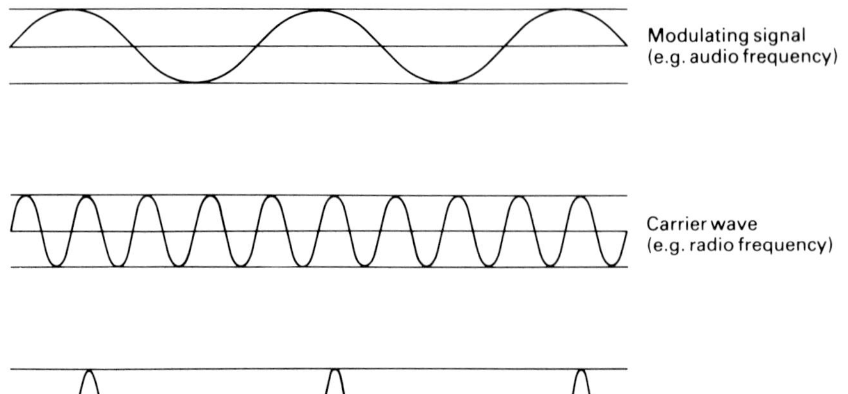

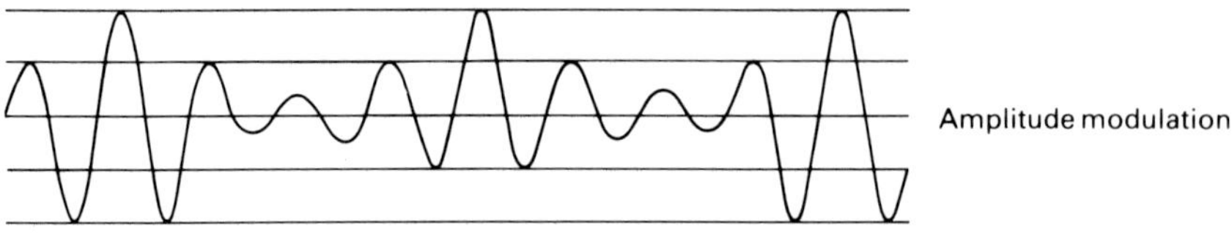

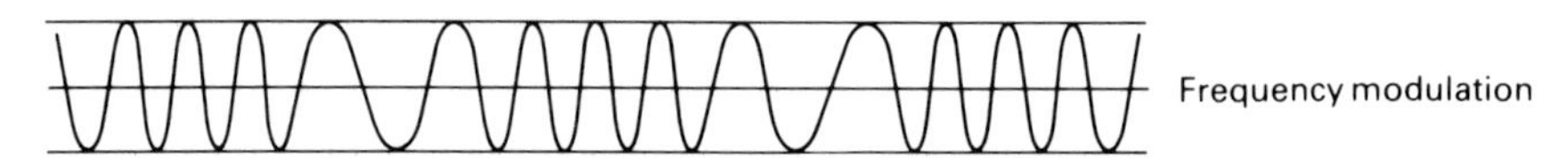

FIG. 3.2 **Modulation** Modulating one signal on to another, for example an audio frequency on to a radio frequency, made radio telephony (R/T) possible. The basic radio frequency became a carrier wave for speech. This development was forced by the needs of aviation in the First World War. Modulation later became important in other military electronic applications (e.g. Y-Gerät). Amplitude modulation (AM) was the primary means, but frequency modulation (FM), invented in the United States, began to prove its value in the Second World War for use in higher frequency bands, being less prone to interference.

oscillations of the radio signal, for example by making the basic radio signal vary in strength (amplitude), according to the audio frequency. This is amplitude modulation (AM). Other forms of modulation are possible, such as frequency modulation (FM). When the amplitude-modulated or frequency-modulated signal is received, the original audio frequencies can be extracted from it.

The trouble with the spark, however, was that it was not a smooth stable oscillation, which is what was wanted to convey speech without distortion. The listener heard the spark rather than the speech.

Circuits containing electron tubes provided everything that the spark did not: stable continuous radio frequencies, and easy means of modulating one signal on to another as well. The triode was the key to this. This was its role in the transmitter. The diode played its part in the receiver, enabling detection of the modulated signal. Triodes were needed in both transmitters and receivers for amplification.

Eventually, modulating one frequency on to a higher one became common practice, not only audio frequencies on to radio frequencies, but lower radio frequencies on to higher ones. This was a giant stride of equal importance for civilian radio and electronic warfare.

The historical dividing line between spark transmitters and electron tubes came during the First World War. It was not an immediate transition; there was an overlap. The United States was ahead of Europe with electron tubes, thanks to Lee de Forest's triode, but while military needs were the chief driving force in the development of radio, the United States was not at first a combatant. The European powers began the battle using the technology available to them.

4

The Coming of HF

THE 19TH CENTURY's legacy included the idea of frequency. Frequency could be looked at the other way round, in terms of wavelength. In fact this was the most popular way of referring to the main divisions of the radio spectrum, known in the beginning as long, medium and short waves.

Regarded as mere markings on the radio receiver's wave-band switch, which is probably how most people become familiar with them, these seem rather abstract concepts. But the reality is otherwise; they are concrete concepts in a militarily most important way. They are reflected in the size and power requirement of radio equipment.

The difference in dimensions is basically from the same cause as the difference in dimensions between the pipes in an organ loft. Larger pipes are needed to generate lower notes. In other words the pipe size is proportional to the wavelength. Middle C, at the middle of the musical scale, has a wavelength of about one and a third metres, but three octaves below middle C the wavelength is about 10 metres.

With radio frequencies the contrast is much greater. A typical long wave of 200 kilohertz has a wavelength of 1,500 metres, that is about a mile. Higher up in the electromagnetic spectrum radio wavelengths are measured in centimetres.

As with notes sounded on an organ pipe, so with radio waves transmitted from an antenna. To transmit efficiently the size of the antenna needs to be comparable with the wavelength. Not necessarily equal, but often half. For long waves, this means that a powerful transmitting site will be hundreds of metres in size.

This fact was relevant to early radio researchers, Marconi among them, trying to find the range over which communications were possible. At first sight it seemed that this should be no more than the range over which light from a beacon could be seen, since light and radio waves were ultimately the same thing.

But Marconi showed that with long waves, for reasons not then understood, the range was very much greater. In some mysterious way, long waves passed over the horizon, which cut off light rays, and continued curving around the earth. Because of this effect, he considered that the future of radio lay with longer waves for communications over any considerable distance. Shorter waves did not seem to offer the same prospects.

For these reasons, a radio installation designed to communicate to great distance required both high power and a large transmitting antenna. This was in the form of an array to increase the transmission strength. The receiver did not need comparable power, but it still needed a large antenna.

The main use of radio from 1900 to the First World War was communications with ships at sea. Fortunately, fixed shore-based transmitters could be built large and powered accordingly, while ships were big enough to carry reasonably long antennas strung between masts, and operate their own medium-power transmitters.

The typical scale of the land installations used by Marconi is illustrated by his site at Poldhu, Cornwall, in Britain, which had twenty masts 61 metres (200 feet) high and an oil-fuelled alternator providing up to 25 kilowatts.

Poldhu initially worked at a wavelength, so far as it could be ascertained, of 366 metres, though this is still a matter of controversy. 366 metres would have been in the medium waveband, better performance would have come with longer waves, and whatever its initial wavelength may have been, Poldhu was eventually modified to work in the range 1,100 to 1,650 metres.[1]

Progress

With installations such as this on either side, the Atlantic could be spanned. This was achieved in 1901, an astonishing progress from the metre ranges of Hertz's experiments only thirteen years earlier. Shore-to-ship ranges, limited by the smaller shipborne installations, were initially of the order of a few hundred kilometres, but ranges grew steadily and it was not long before a ship crossing the Atlantic could receive signals from the land installations on either side when in mid-ocean.

Marine radio developed rapidly in the early 1900s and naval radio was in the van of the advance. Radio transformed naval warfare but armies, needing mobile equipment were not equally well served. The British attempted to exploit wireless telegraphy in the Boer War, using equipment powered by chemical batteries, but without worthwhile results. In Europe it was the German Army which showed most enthusiasm for acquiring horse-drawn wireless stations.

PLATE 4.1 **Marconi Transmitter at Poldhu** The first transatlantic radio transmissions were made from Poldhu in 1901. This photograph conveys the size of the antenna installation, comprising twenty 200-foot masts and driven by a 25 kilowatt alternator. Unfortunately a gale blew the masts down just before the first test transmissions in December 1901, which were nevertheless successful using a hastily-rigged two-mast antenna. The receiving antenna in Newfoundland was held aloft by a kite. Early the following year Poldhu communicated through its rebuilt antenna with a ship installation on the *Philadelphia* out to 700 miles in daylight and 1,550/2,100 miles at night, a demonstration of immense consequence for naval warfare as well as passenger liners. (*Photo: By courtesy GEC–Marconi*)

This remained the pattern through to the beginning of the First World War. The war at last stimulated land and airborne use of radio and, by the end of the war, radio frequencies had advanced up the spectrum to about 1 megahertz, though significantly higher on the German side.

One megahertz was a wavelength of 300 metres, still no higher than the lower end of the medium wave band. These relatively low frequencies did not bring to land and air warfare the same dramatic impact as they brought at sea.

After the First World War radio experimenters turned to explore higher frequencies. Awaiting them was the most exciting discovery since that of radio itself: the amazing properties of the short wave, or high frequency band. These were destined to revolutionise all war, and through war the history of the 20th century.

The high frequency band, HF, is a specific designation for frequencies from 3 megahertz up to 30 megahertz. As the frequency goes up, the wavelength goes down, i.e. gets shorter, so HF corresponds to wavelengths from 100 metres down to 10 metres. (The frequency and wavelength multiplied together must equal the velocity of electromagnetic waves, 300,000 kilometres a second.)

The bands below HF are low frequency, LF (otherwise long wave band), and medium frequency, MF (otherwise medium wave band). LF is from 30 kilohertz up to 300 kilohertz and MF is from 300 kilohertz to 3 megahertz. These are the bands in which practical radio started, valued for their ability to propagate to great distances.

The key discovery that came in the middle of the 1920s about HF was that it too could range to great distances. It does this in a different way to long and medium waves. It does not curve around the earth's

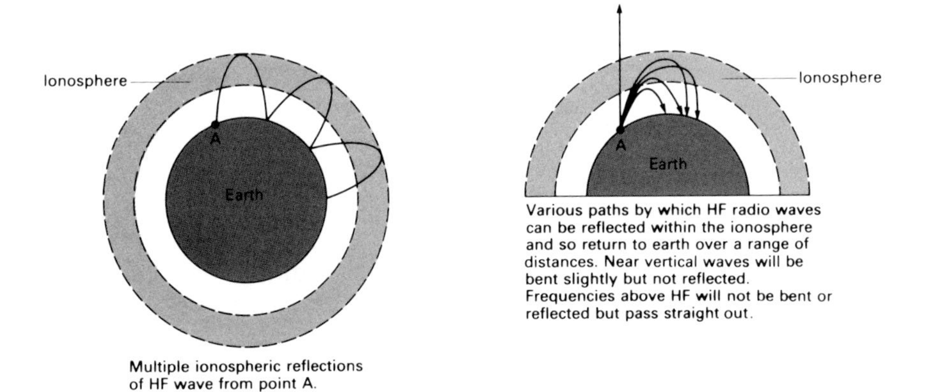

Fig. 4.1 **The Characteristics of High Frequency Radio Waves**

surface, as they do, but gradually rises from the surface, to bounce off the ionosphere.

The ionosphere is formed by layers of gas ionised by the sun in the upper regions of the earth's atmosphere. Ionisation makes these layers conductive to electricity, and as a result they reflect radio waves. They prevent them from escaping into space. Reflection happens up to a certain frequency somewhere in HF, the actual value depending on the ionospheric conditions prevailing, which vary from day to day and day to night.

Like LF and MF, HF is receivable up to a certain distance from the transmitter by the 'ground wave'. While the ground wave with LF reaches to thousands of kilometres, and with MF to several hundreds, with HF it reaches no more than a few hundred kilometres, enough for many purposes but not for long-range communication.

The Advantages of HF

Then the HF signal disappears. However, from about 700–1,000 kilometres it reappears. This is the 'sky wave' coming back down from the ionosphere. It remains receivable up to several thousand kilometres. At greater distances the signal will again disappear. But the ground reflects HF back up to the ionosphere, and still further away the signal may again reappear, having bounced once more.

Therefore HF can ultimately range further than LF and MF. Nor is this its only advantage. Because the wavelength is so much shorter, the dimensions of both the transmitter and receiver antennas shrink as compared with LF and MF, and the transmitter power requirement shrinks even more than the dimensions.

It was discovered that, with small installations for both transmitting and receiving, and no more power than chemical batteries or a small generator could provide, HF could equal and exceed the communications range offered by LF and MF.

Marconi, having been a pioneer of LF and MF, turned his attention to HF in the 1920s, and found the need for tens of kilowatts of transmitting power vanished. He received stronger signals at greater distances with under a kilowatt of transmitter power. With modern apparatus HF goes around the world on a few tens of watts. At the shorter ranges a few watts is adequate, the power of a pocket torch.

The only price that is paid is that HF communications by sky wave depend on the state of the ionosphere, and the ionosphere depends on the sun. Sometimes they are good, sometimes there is much fading and distortion. But the price is far outweighed by the advantages.

HF transformed radio for armies and air forces. The tactical and strategic revolution that radio had already brought to naval warfare took another leap. Germany ahead of other countries realised this. The result was seen in the Second World War. HF also impacted upon naval warfare, but the contrast was not so great because the strategic adaptation to radio had already happened.

Beyond HF, still higher frequencies came along, such as very high frequency, VHF, ultra high frequency, UHF, and super high frequency, SHF. This quickening progression up the frequency scale dominates electronic warfare in the Second World War.

This is true not only in relation to radio, but to another celebrated technology which the Second World War brought: radar.

As a concept radar was yet another part of the 19th century's legacy, an idea expressed by Nikola Tesla amongst others. By 1904 it had even been patented and demonstrated under the name 'telemobiloscope' by Christian Hulsmeyer in Germany. But it was not a practical proposition until the 1930s. The advent of radar forms the subject of Chapter 7. Radar began with HF (in Britain) but pushed up the frequency scale even further than radio.

Despite the exploration of still higher frequency bands, HF retained its uniqueness. It does so to the present day. It is irreplaceable in certain applications, both in radar and in radio.

Bandwidths and the Availability of Channels

There is yet a further advantage to HF, by comparison with LF and MF. This is greater available bandwidth – the ability to offer more independent simultaneous communication channels.

This arises because any transmission on a nominal frequency channel, say 1 megahertz, has in practice to occupy a small range of frequencies, which may typically be 5,000 hertz up and down from the 'carrier frequency'. So the adjoining frequency channel must be sufficiently far apart for no mutual interference to occur. It has to be at least 10,000 hertz away from the first nominal frequency.

When transmissions are spaced out at this interval, the LF band, which is 270,000 hertz wide, has room for only 27 channels, MF, 2,700,000 hertz wide, for 270 channels, but HF, 27,000,000 hertz wide, has room for 2,700 channels.

Thus HF multiplies the number of radio channels which may be simultaneously in use. This is of great military importance. Channel spacings are not always at 10,000 cycle intervals, but whatever interval applies, the principle is the same.

By the same reasoning of course higher frequency bands than HF have more channels still. But they do not go round the world. On the contrary their range is severely limited.[2]

In summary, among all the radio frequency bands, those above and those below, HF is unique in its combination of properties. It travels around the globe. It makes possible mobile transmitter and receiver stations of small size and power. It contributes to both radio and radar. It could not fail to play a pivotal role in the story of electronic warfare and, in fact, marks the main electronic difference between the First World War and the Second.

The Significance of Antennas

The military significance of HF is pursued in Chapter 6. HF was known to the 19th century radio researchers, but they were unaware of its potential. Although the early experimenters had no trouble in generating HF with sparks, they could not have exploited it, even if they had been aware of what it offered. They saw their problem as one of getting away from higher frequencies towards lower ones.

The shrinking of dimensions which occurs when passing from LF to MF and HF is but one example of the overwhelming importance of lengths and sizes which is a recurrent theme throughout electronic warfare. It is mainly seen in antennas, emphasising their special role. Still today as in the first days of radio, the transmitting and receiving antennas are the electric circuits which are in contact with each other through space over distances up to thousands of kilometres, be it with friend or foe. Electronics makes no distinction.

In time of war the antenna is the electronic warrior's gun. Like a gun, it points to the action. Like a gun, it has an external shape which reveals its function. This is vividly apparent from a comparison of old and modern warships. The old warship had a profile dominated by a variety of gun barrels. The size of these reflected their purpose, the projectile they were made for. The 16-inch main armament could not be interchanged with small calibre weapons. By contrast the modern warship has a profile dominated by a variety of radio and radar antennas. The size and shape of these also reflect their purpose, the kind of electromagnetic projectile they are intended to launch into or receive out of space. They are not interchangeable either.

At its simplest an antenna is a metal rod, fed with current. Electrons surge up and down in it. A rod antenna may be a 'half-wave dipole' – with a length half the wavelength of the radiation. Simple metal rod antennas a few metres long are common in military applications. They work well in the VHF band typically used for short-range communications. Vertical rod antennas are often a quarter wavelength long – the antenna is in effect reflected in the ground, as if it was standing on a mirror; this makes its dimension up to a full half-wavelength.

Rod antennas are not the only type, but fortunately all other antennas can be understood as if they were made up of simple rod antennas. For example, a loop antenna may be thought of as a series of short rods linked in a circle. Rather amazingly, the effect of all these adds up to make the loop antenna the equivalent of one single rod antenna lying on its side in the middle of the loop, along its axis. Sometimes it is more convenient to use a loop antenna than the equivalent rod.

By contrast, a slot antenna is simply a space cut in a metal surround. As such it is the logical opposite of a rod, which is a strip of metal surrounded by space. But in effect it behaves the same. Each type is particularly suited to certain applications. The slot antenna is obviously better suited to use on aircraft than the rod, which would give rise to excessive air resistance.

The parabolic antenna, which figures so prominently in electronic warfare, is like a torch or searchlight reflector, in that it is a curved surface which produces a directed beam from a radiation source at its focus. This is valuable in many applications, especially radar.

The electromagnetic wave is linked with the antenna that generates it not only through its size, but through 'polarity'. A vertical rod is said to generate a vertically polarised wave. The vertically polarised wave needs a vertical receiving antenna. It would not be picked up by a horizontal one.

This is true over short distances. But over long distances when the electromagnetic wave may pass through regions such as the ionosphere, the direction of polarisation may change. In this case the orientation of the receiving antenna needs to be adjusted accordingly. Or else an antenna needs to be used which can receive equally well at all directions of polarisation, as do some spiral or helical types.

Antennas play a particularly crucial role in electronic warfare. Versatile antennas are important because they are able to receive over wide frequency ranges or in different planes of polarisation.

Simple rod or slot antennas may be combined in arrays. There are many kinds of array antenna. By positioning simple antennas in geometrically calculated ways it is possible to transmit electromagnetic waves in specific directions and patterns. The pattern in which waves are radiated is called the 'polar diagram' of the antenna.

In the early days of radar, arrays comprising rows of rod antennas were typical. Today, array radars sometimes comprise rows of slots. These are much smaller than the former rods, in keeping with the higher frequencies being employed.

All antennas are subject to the law of size in relation to wavelength. Electronic warfare is always dominated by ordinary geometry. This simple fact is often overlooked. It may mean that airborne electronic warfare equipment cannot outmatch the ground equipment pitted against it because antennas on aircraft are always limited in size compared with those on the ground.

In warfare, God is on the side of the big battalions. In electronic warfare, God is on the side of the big dimensions.

The only qualification is that the size of the dimensions depends on the frequency being used. A small system using a higher frequency may have the advantage over a larger system using a lower frequency. If lower frequencies are essential, the only recourse may be antennas several kilometres wide. This is the case, for example, in communicating with submarines at some depth below the sea surface. Only frequencies in the extra low band, ELF, below 30 hertz can penetrate down to them. Such huge antennas need enormous power.

5

Radio Revolution

The 20th century began tense. Conflicts soon occurred. All the leading powers went to war or were drawn into it: Austria, Britain, France, Germany, Italy, Japan, Russia, the United States. The 15 years from the beginning of the Russo-Japanese War, in 1904, to the end of the First World War, in 1918, form a sharply distinct period, in which electronics begins to change war's whole aspect.

The changes were most obvious at sea. Elsewhere they came more slowly, but by the end of the period their consequences were profound. Radio was new, cable already a mature technology. Radio had its main effect on navies, in battle; cable globally, through politics.

The Pioneers

The most celebrated man to apply Hertz's discovery of radiowaves was the Italian, Marconi. His work began in 1895. Italy did not provide the necessary prospect of support. Marconi went to Britain, where he founded the company bearing his name. Britain was unique in many ways. It was the centre of a vast shipping network, connecting the world's largest empire and many other countries. It also had the world's largest navy, with global interests to protect.

Marconi was alert to the communications needs which sprang from these facts. He believed that radio had an international role to play alongside Britain's cable links. Marconi had rivals in other countries, notably Braun in Germany and Popov in Russia. Popov is credited with being the most serious contender for priority in inventing radio, but his work did not bear long-lasting fruit. Russia did not value Popov – at that time.

Braun on the other hand was destined to share a Nobel Prize with Marconi in 1909. Germany's scientific and industrial potential challenged all other European nations and the German Telefunken system became Marconi's main international competitor. Telefunken was a union of two earlier German companies, Braun-Siemens and Slaby-Arco, which linked in 1903.

From Britain, Marconi's ideas travelled to other countries. Sometimes this was through associate companies which later became separate, such as the Radio Corporation of America. But other companies sprang up independently, particularly in America and France. The technology developed with remarkable speed and could never be described as any one person's or company's monopoly.

Marconi probably possessed most of the master patents, though this did not enable him to control the global spread of radio. It was on the other hand a source of ineffective, time-wasting litigation. But while radio continued to excite the world, Marconi continued to be the chief focus of the excitement, through such publicity-conscious feats as transmissions across the Atlantic. Meanwhile contributions by other researchers and companies increased.

In the United States the main impetus for radio came from commerce, but in Europe, overshadowed by approaching war, military needs were dominant. Both the Marconi company in Britain and Telefunken in Germany had a large volume of business in the early 1900s in equipping navies with radio.

Marconi equipped the British and Italian navies; Telefunken the German, Swedish, American and largely the Russian. Telefunken's naval orders far outweighed the rest of its business. Both companies also produced radio equipment for armies; this proved to be far bigger business for Telefunken in Germany than for Marconi in Britain.

Standpoints

The history of this period can be looked at from the naval, the army, the aviation and the diplomatic standpoints. From the naval standpoint, radio communications implied a major break with the past. This was a break all the greater in that it had not been heralded in any way by the cable telegraph, whereas land warfare had already absorbed the telegraph's impact.

The War at Sea

The naval implication of radio was seen from the start. This is shown by Marconi's and Telefunken's naval contracts. Moreover navies conducted their own radio research. The British Admiralty was in the radio business as long as Marconi himself, and even contested his patents, unsuccessfully.

In July 1903 the British Admiralty conceded to Marconi an 11-year agreement for the use of his system. One year later, Telefunken could already claim 75 ship installations of various types supplied to or being completed by the German Navy, as well as 11 naval coastal stations.

Although the naval implication was seen sufficiently for radio to be regarded as a necessity on warships, its full significance could not be appreciated at the beginning. It turned out to be many-sided.

What was appreciated at the beginning was the facility radio offered for short-range inter-ship and longer-range ship-to-shore communications, though how these would operate in combat was not so easy to imagine. But it became clear that naval actions could be co-ordinated on a larger scale no longer dominated by visual signalling. Land-based command would no longer lose touch with distant fleets for indefinite intervals. The reality of combat eventually proved to be that land-based command directly participated in fleet actions.

Cryptography soared into the ascendant. Naval wireless telegraphy was unthinkable without it. Time and again, the fortunes of war were destined to hang on the work of naval code-breakers. None were more celebrated than those of the British Admiralty's Room 40, though their German counterparts at Neumunster were not without very considerable success. Radio direction finding joined cryptography as a means of extracting military intelligence from hostile transmissions. This was what is now called 'signals intelligence' or 'sigint'.

Land-based command acquired an extra role as the main location for cryptography and direction finding. For this reason, land-based naval high command gained a day-to-day, even hour-to-hour importance. Electronic warfare made it for the first time part of the battlezone. It would often be aware of changes in the naval situation before the admirals at sea.

The impact of radio is demonstrated by two great naval battles, of Tsushima at the beginning of the 1904–18 period, and Jutland towards the end of it, as described later in this chapter.

What is remarkable about Tsushima is that both the Japanese and Russian fleets were operationally equipped in 1905 with something only invented in 1895. Radio had arrived in time for the biggest clash of warships since Trafalgar one hundred years before.[1]

Radio played a significant although simple tactical role, working in favour of Japan. It could have played a bigger, strategic role, in favour of Russia, but imagination did not rise to this. If radio had not been invented, Japan's victory at Tsushima would have hung on the slender chance of a lucky interception. If radio had been used as it should have been by the losing Russians, who ironically were better equipped with it, the battle would have been avoided altogether.

Eleven years later, at Jutland, the possibilities of radio had been more fully grasped. It was basic to the control of both the British and German fleets, even though co-existing with visual signalling by flags, lights and rockets. It was not yet as instinctively understood as traditional signalling. It could do things which traditional signalling could not do, but it was not yet completely trusted.

This failure to integrate radio in combat helped to shape the outcome of Jutland. It caused a conflict in signalling on the British side which was the last thing the British could afford.

Radio brought the battle about. It did not enable either side to win. It may have saved one side from losing. Its conclusive influence came after the battle, in making such a battle unlikely to be fought again.

The War on Land

Radio produced no comparable revolution during the same period in land warfare. This was because it came in addition to army techniques of signalling over landlines which were already well-established. In the First World War these techniques were used in northern France much as they had been in the Franco-Prussian War almost half a century previously. Under the circumstances of largely static trench warfare, they continued to be adequate; it would have been a different matter if the battle had become mobile.

Germany went into the war with more interest in army radio than her opponents on the Western Front. There was a German belief that radio had a potential advantage in distributing orders instantly and simultaneously to as many units as had receivers, whereas telegraphy required time-consuming repetitions throughout a network. This was true to some extent, but required complete faith in cryptography's ability to guarantee security, a faith history was destined to deal with sadly.

France and Britain tended to see radio as an emergency alternative to cable, when shelling had temporarily cut land lines.

Despite the massive deadlock, the confrontation on the Western Front gave some scope for communications warfare between the armies, hinging on telegraphs and telephones as well as radio. But there was no major premium on it. Tactical results sometimes ensued, but the line never swayed.

The premium was bigger on the more fluid Eastern Front, with its bigger distances. Radio was in use by both Germany and Austria on the one side and Russia on the other. Russia outclassed Austria but was

PLATES 5.1, 5.2 AND 5.3 **Electronic Warfare in the Horse-Drawn Age** Plates 5.1 and 5.2 show a very early field radio equipment made by Telefunken for the German Army before the First World War. Plate 5.3 illustrates a $1\frac{1}{2}$ kilowatt mobile radio station of about that period offered by Marconi.

outclassed by Germany. Radio played a prominent part in worsening the fortunes of war for Russia.

Air Warfare

An aspect of the war in the West was the emergence of aviation in support of naval and land operations and as an offensive means in its own right. From the beginning Germany deployed large gas-filled dirigible Zeppelins able to carry radio. They were used for naval scouting and, later, strategic bombing away from the battle-zone.

Initial attempts at tactical bombing in the battlezone showed Zeppelins to be excessively vulnerable. By contrast the battlezone encouraged the use of aircraft, initially for reconnaissance, later for combat and tactical bombing. Eventually aircraft took over the strategic bombing role.

Military aviation was never a decisive aspect of the war, but it produced the beginnings of what was to become one of electronic warfare's best known, most famous branches – airborne radio and electronics, subsequently known as avionics.

Radio made the German use of Zeppelins for naval reconnaissance vastly more effective. Zeppelins also used radio whilst on strategic bombing missions. Low and medium frequencies meant a need for large antennas and equipments, but this did not represent a problem for craft which might be hundreds of metres long, with 15 or more crew. The radio operator was one of the most important crew members, with about a third of a ton of radio equipment and a special sound-proofed cabin. A long antenna trailed behind the airship, being wound in during electrical storms or when under attack.

Zeppelins gave Germany her first operational experience of long-range bombing. Initially this was by day and at low altitude. Given the slow speed or hover capability of Zeppelins, visual target recognition was possible. At night, target cities were still lit up as in peacetime. But such easy conditions swiftly vanished.

Radio Navigation and Telephony

Zeppelins began to face the problems which were to become familiar in the Second World War. As defensive guns and fighters drove them to greater altitudes, they had to determine position above cloud or in darkness. This was the radio operator's task.[2] He would establish contact with base stations in Germany or German-occupied territory, which would direction-find on his signals and transmit bearings back to him. These would then be plotted aboard the Zeppelin to find the intersection. Several base stations were used for this purpose. The German navy and the German army each operated their own stations and Zeppelins.

It was the slow speed of Zeppelins which allowed this to be a practicable method of position-finding. But it left much to be desired. Errors were typically up to 100 kilometres. Sometimes bearings reported to a Zeppelin failed to intersect at all. 'Night effect' played a role: the apparent bearing of a distant station changes slightly as between day and night. This was connected with changes in the ionosphere, something that was not understood at the time.

Thanks to the Zeppelins' radio transmissions, their progress was followed from direction finding stations in Britain and France. Numerous examples of accurate plotting are on record. This was signals intelligence.

Later in the war, Zeppelins discontinued transmitting for navigation. Instead they measured the directions of special navigational signals transmitted to them from Continental stations, which were in effect the first military radio-navigational beacons. This prevented their opponents from plotting their courses, but did little to improve accuracy. It was more difficult and less accurate to make directional measurements on board a Zeppelin than at a ground station.[3]

At this time Germany was undoubtedly ahead of her opponents with airborne radio. Countries other than Germany used dirigible balloons for military purposes but without the same degree of development, especially in radio.[4]

Towards the end of the war, the rising role of aircraft began to stimulate the development of radio telephony. At the beginning radio had been, for practical purposes, restricted to wireless telegraphy. This was entirely adequate for navies. It was adequate for reporting from Zeppelins and aircraft with numerous crew. But the single-seater aircraft was a different matter.

The pilot could not operate a Morse key for extended periods. Moreover instantaneous communication was often vital, particularly to other accompanying aircraft. In this aviation demonstrated its ability to force the technical pace – as it did again in the Second World War.

The need to introduce radio telephony emphasised the obsolescence of the spark transmitter. This had become remarkably refined. It had steadily responded to the demand for improved tuning. But it was not equal to telephony. Fundamentally sparks remained crackling sparks.

Radio telephony needed a steady, smooth, continuous source of radio waves on to which the voice frequencies could be modulated. This was possible using the electric arc as a source of continuous radio waves. The arc was essentially a stable spark. But the arc had practical disadvantages including limited power.

The Triode

The warring European powers increasingly turned to the technology of the thermionic tube, in particular the triode, a form of thermionic tube invented, as already mentioned, by Lee de Forest in the United States in 1906. Its significance was twofold. It was a means of amplifying small signals and also a means of generating continuous oscillations. But its overwhelming importance for the future of radio was not realised until 1913.

Its introduction was gradual during the war – until radio telephony was required. At this point it became indispensable. The German company Telefunken was well abreast of progress in tube technology, nevertheless it was the Allies who introduced airborne radio telephony.

At the same time airborne radio demanded smaller, lighter equipments. On the Allied side operational frequencies rose to about 1 megahertz, but German airborne wireless telegraphy went as high as 4 megahertz. In other words it fully explored the MF band up to 3 megahertz, and tentatively ventured into HF. These frequencies were entirely adequate for the ranges over which they were used. Electronic

---

MAP 5.1 **German Zeppelin Sorties Against Britain, 27–28 November 1916** Note: Routes of Zeppelins marked I, M, RI, T and U. †RIP = Zeppelin destroyed. Numbers are timings.

These tracks were plotted by direction-finding, from British Marconi stations, from transmissions on the Zeppelins' radios. This was *signals intelligence (SIGINT)*. The German base stations also plotted the Zeppelins' positions by the same method and reported them back to the Zeppelins. This was *radio navigation*, helping the Zeppelins to find their targets. Experience from the First World War convinced the Germans that radio navigation was necessary to enable aircraft to find targets at night. In consequence, Germany entered the Second World War with a number of advanced radio aids to bombing. These enabled the German night *blitz* on Britain to be immediately effective in 1940. Britain neglected this matter and, until 1942, only a small proportion of British bombs fell anywhere near their intended targets. On the other hand, Britain made extensive use of signals intelligence against radio transmissions from intruding aircraft formations during the Battle of Britain. The surviving evidence suggests that this often provided earlier and more detailed information about impending raids than the coastal radar chain. (*Illustration: By courtesy GEC-Marconi*)

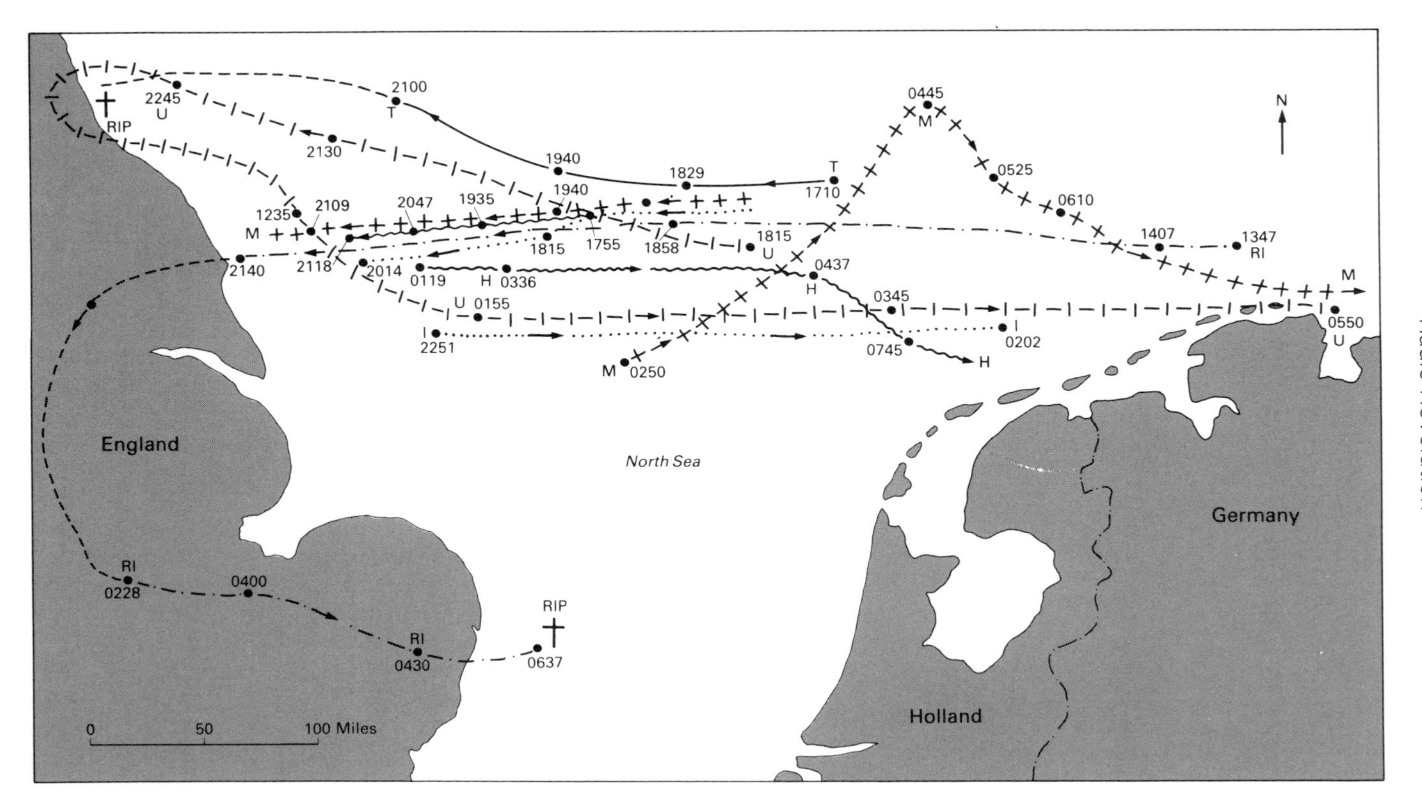
N
England
North Sea
Holland
Germany
0
50
100 Miles
RIP
2245
U
2100
T
2130
1940
1829
1710
T
0445
M
0525
0610
1407
1347
RI
M
1940
1235
2109
2047
1935
M
1815
1755
1858
1815
U
2140
2118
2014
0119
H
0336
0437
H
0345
U
0155
0550
U
2251
0202
0745
H
M
0250
RI
0228
0400
RI
0430
RIP
0637

PLATE 5.4 **Airborne Radio Telephony in the First World War** The increasing role of single-seater aircraft in the First World War put a premium on direct speech transmission (radio telephony), forcing the development of equipment based upon electron tubes (or 'valves') which alone could provide it. This wireless telephone from Marconi's Aircraft Division is dated 1921. Radio telephony (R/T) communications to, from and between aircraft were 'in clear' i.e.: not encoded, an exception to general military practice. The international standard aircraft frequency, post-First World War, was 333 kHz. There was an alternative emergency frequency of 500 kHz. Maximum permissible power was 700 watts. With this equipment Marconi guaranteed a range of 100 miles. (*Photo: By courtesy of GEC-Marconi*)

warfare in the First World War never hinged on the different propagation effects of radio waves at various frequencies, as it did in the Second.

Radio telephony could not offer the secrecy available through cryptography to wireless telegraphy. But for military aviation it did not seem to matter. At this time messages began to be transmitted 'in clear' by radio telephony. This remained a remarkable exception to the general rule of communications secrecy in war.

Cryptography in Diplomacy

But elsewhere cryptography became a vastly more important issue. International diplomacy is high strategy. In the 19th century it had started to become dependent on cable communications. The secrecy of diplomatic cables was always a potential target.

In the First World War it became a prime target. Britain exploited her position poised over the main international cable routes. The possible scale of political damage if secrecy was penetrated was never more vividly demonstrated than by British interception and deciphering of the Zimmermann telegram. This finally brought the United States into the First World War on the anti-German side. It was a strategic coup decisive for the outcome of the war, and arguably for the history of the rest of the 20th century.

The Russo-Japanese War

The Russo-Japanese War started as Russian and Japanese territorial expansion collided, with Manchuria and Korea as the immediate objects of avarice. Its background was the steady rise of Japan as an industrial and military power, and the decay of tsarist Russia.

For Japan, power projection by naval means was the essence of her strategy. She began the war with a night-time naval assault on the Russian fleet squadron in Port Arthur, main base of Russia's territorial concession in North West China (February 1904). This was followed up by the maritime blockade of Port Arthur and troop landings on the nearby coast and in Korea.

Russia had remote and difficult land access to the disputed areas, which were at a distance of 9000 kilometres from the Russian heartland. Thanks to the sea, Japan's access was much easier. The outbreak of war caught Russia with inadequate regional naval strength to contest Japanese supremacy. An attempt during 1904 by the squadron in Port Arthur to break out through the blockade ended disastrously.

Attempts to intervene by the naval squadron at Vladivostok, Russia's far eastern naval base, achieved minor successes but fared little better.

In sum, Russia was by geographic circumstances the weaker side. Unless she could break Japan's naval grip, her position was untenable. This was the reasoning behind a remarkable project: to send a powerful naval force around the world from the Baltic to the Pacific.

Inevitably, long-range communications were essential to this concept. Here for the first time history was offering radio the chance to play a crucial role in affairs of war, maintaining fleet communications links that would have been previously impossible.

Amazingly, this was realised. The Russian fleet was extensively equipped with German Slaby-Arco radio. Moreover it included one special auxiliary vessel, the *Ural*, as well fitted with radio as was possible according to the standards of the day. The *Ural* was the largest ship in the fleet at 13.818 tonnes, although not heavily armed (eight 4.7-inch guns). She was the world's first radio-dedicated warship to go into battle.

Thus there was balanced tactical and strategic capability: radio could be used for inter-ship and short-range signalling, but the fleet also possessed good equipment for long-range radio communications. More was not possible. The radio provision was well thought out.

What would the *Ural's* operational range have been? What possibilities were open to it?

Civil possibilities of maritime radio were evident from the Atlantic. Marconi had demonstrated transatlantic radio in 1901, and in 1904 the *Cunard Bulletin* appeared as the first regular daily newspaper at sea. Admittedly the Atlantic was better served with powerful shore stations than any other ocean of the world, and these were primarily on British and North American territory.

But there was no lack of shore stations elsewhere in Europe. Moreover there was a considerable number of stations elsewhere in the world, including the Far East. Telefunken had supplied Russia with a 1000-kilometre range coastal station in Manchuria. Marconi had supplied Russia with stations at both St Petersburg and Vladivostok. By the end of October 1904 the fortress at Vladivostok had radio communications with the outside world.

The range of low and medium frequencies is variable, better at night than during the day. It depends on transmitter power and the receiving apparatus. It depends on atmospheric conditions. It is better over water than land. By the standards of the time the *Ural* could expect to communicate over several hundred kilometres by day, perhaps up to 1000.

This range could not be guaranteed at any specific time, but probably could be guaranteed at some time in any 24-hour period. Moreover the night range might exceptionally be up to a few thousand kilometres. The *Ural* should sometimes have been able to establish contact with its destination port Vladivostok whilst still remote from Japanese waters.

But as the ships left Europe, rounded southern Africa, crossed the Indian Ocean and sailed past Indo-China and China, radio did not have to span the ranges to the Russian homeland unaided. The world cable network was well developed. For the most part the Russian fleet did not have to depart as far from coasts as liners crossing the Atlantic. Between cable and radio, the Russian fleet could and did remain in contact with the Russian capital St Petersburg.

This possibility could have been exploited in various ways. One necessity was to keep the basic strategy of the expedition under review, for over a long period the military situation could change in such a way as to make the initial objectives dubious or no longer attainable. In this case continuing inflexibly with the expedition as originally planned might put more at hazard than anything it could hope to gain.

This is exactly what happened. Between 2 October 1904 when the fleet left the Baltic port of Libaya, and 27 May 1905 when it reached Tsushima having sailed 30,000 kilometres, Port Arthur fell to the Japanese. The Russian fleet learnt of this, thanks to cable, whilst at Madagascar in December.

Strategic Transformation

All the fundamental assumptions had been swept away. The fall of Port Arthur gained for the Japanese their primary objective, removed the naval strength with which their own warships had been engaged, and opened the way to pursuit of whatever other objective might prove to be within reach.

On the Russian side, global strategic thinking was called for – and for the first time in history global communications were ready to facilitate it. But the necessary reassessment was never made. Not because communications between the fleet and St Petersburg were not established; we know for a fact that off Indo-China communications were established by radio to Saigon and thence by cable to St Petersburg; but because the idea of using radio for strategic reappraisal never occurred to them.

Doomed as the Russians were to be the losers at Tsushima, they paradoxically emerged triumphant on the literary plane. Never has any nation better documented its own nemesis. While the Japanese left the details of their victory all but unrecorded, the Russian defeat became one of the glories of Russian literature.

The Russian writer Novikov-Priboi wrote a brilliant eye-witness account of the expedition from beginning to disastrous end: *Tsushima.*

From its pages, devoid of a single word of anti-Japanese prejudice but justly candid about Russian failure, we have no doubt that radio was in regular use, and equally that no strategic debate was ever conducted.

The Russian admiral, Rozhestvensky, dutifully pursued his orders whilst increasingly appreciating that the chances were against him. In this he was but following the traditions of so many admirals in the past, who earned admiration for their valour in persisting with their assigned missions regardless of the odds.

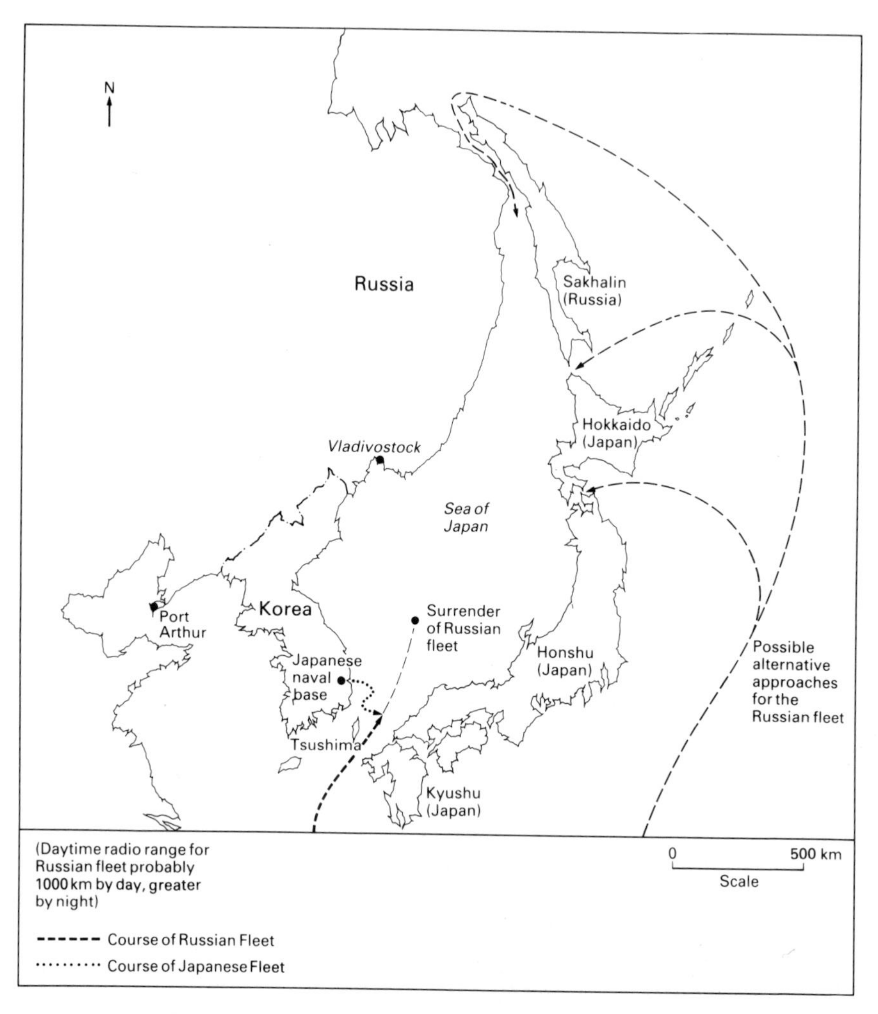

Map 5.2 **The Battle of Tsushima, 27–28 May 1905**

He never reviewed his orders or his plans with his captains, but in truth the necessity was to review them with land-based command which alone could take a broad strategic view and authorise him to alter them. This is the fundamental contrast of Tsushima with Jutland. The technical capability of radio did not change all that much in eleven years, but the strategic difference was the constant flow of messages which developed between land-based and seaborne command and the flexibility thereby introduced. Even if, as at Jutland, the contributions of land-based command were not always gratefully received.

The approach of the Russian fleet presented Japan with an excellent opportunity. If she could bar the way to Vladivostok and compel a battle, she could well overwhelm it at its weakest. The Japanese could be sure that after five months at sea, the Russian fleet would be more in need of rest and refit than a fight. This was certainly the case: the 59 ships that left the Baltic were down to 30, despite reinforcements. If they were destroyed, Japan could proceed to strike at Russian territory wherever she pleased.

For this reason, the real strategic necessity for the Russian fleet was merely to keep itself in being. By fighting a battle and losing it, it could throw away more than anything it might hope to gain if the outcome was favourable.

Evasion or Confrontation

As the Russian fleet steamed towards the Straits of Korea, the most southerly entry to the Sea of Japan, radio offered to both sides the main hope of accomplishing their respective objectives, evasion in the one case, confrontation in the other.

The Russian fleet's aim was to drop anchor at Vladivostok, but Vladivostok was on the furthest shore of the largely land-locked sea. Altogether there were only some three or four narrow entrances. None was more than a few tens of kilometres wide and any of them could be the setting for ambush and a battle.

One obvious use of radio would be to try and obtain forewarning. Japanese warships ahead might well be revealed by Japanese radio traffic. This would be a classic example of signals intelligence – deriving information about hostile forces by listening to their transmissions, studying the transmission characteristics, recording and if possible deciphering wireless telegraphy.

For the Japanese on the other hand, radio offered the possibility of patrolling the key passages with single ships. These could discover the approach of the Russian fleet and then summon the main force wherever it was needed. Without this, the chances of intercepting the Russian fleet would have been much slimmer.

The most direct passage to Vladivostok was through the first and widest entry, the Straits of Korea. There was a considerable premium on getting through it, but for this very reason it was hazardous. The Japanese navy could not neglect guarding it. In naval terms it had already proved to be the strategic cross-roads of the entire war zone, and was dominated by a nearby Japanese naval base, Mesampo Bay, in Korea.

Rozhestvensky chose to try and slip past unnoticed. He gambled on a single surprise move of his entire fleet through the Straits of Korea. Having taken this decision, he needed to look to radio to give him warning of Japanese naval activity ahead. So it did. The Japanese warships' transmissions were picked up by the Russians two days before they reached the straits.

Rozhestvensky might have decided to try one of the other entries to the Sea of Japan. But he stuck to his first intention. In an effort to conceal the presence of his fleet, he imposed radio silence on his own ships – the first recorded use of what has become a classical tactic of electronic warfare. Earlier he had neglected the strategic options radio offered, now he clearly understood that radio was a tactical factor which could only help the Japanese.

There was a hope of avoiding the Japanese in the sea mists although this was offset by short nights. The hope conclusively disappeared with the most dramatically ominous message yet transmitted in radio's ten-year history, sent by the Japanese auxiliary cruiser *Sinano Maru* just after 05.00 hours on the morning of 27 May 1905: 'The enemy is in square 203 and is evidently making for the eastern channel.' The reference is to one of the two channels into which the straits are divided by the island of Tsushima.

The *Sinano Maru* turned away, but within two hours the light cruiser *Idzumo* arrived to steam parallel with the Russian fleet.

The instruments of the Russian wireless operators began to register a string of 'incomprehensible messages – obviously cipher dispatches to Admiral Togo, acquainting him with our position, speed, course and formation'.[5]

Later still, from 10.00 hours, four more Japanese warships arrived to continue the *Idzumo's* duties. At this time *Ural* suggested the possibility of using its powerful radio to block the Japanese transmissions, but Rozhestvensky refused permission.

Jamming

Evidently another basic ploy of electronic warfare was already understood: jamming, to obliterate the enemy's signals. It is sometimes debated when this idea first occurred, but the fact is that mutual interference or obliteration of signals was as old as radio itself. Radio's first problem, stemming from the inherent lack of tune of the spark transmitter, was to keep signals from being entangled with each other.

A brochure published by Telefunken in 1904 analyses the problem in lucid detail, pointing out that interference depends on the geometrical relationship of the transmitters to the receiver, and the tuning capability. Where two transmitters are close together, communicating to a distant receiver, interference is inevitable.[6]

This was the situation obtaining when the *Ural* had the option of jamming Japanese transmissions. The Russian operators obviously recognised that they were favourably placed to do so. It was not the first time that such a tactic was considered or used during the course of the war, for there were numerous smaller naval actions in which radio played a role, albeit less well recorded. Undoubtedly however it was the most momentous. But by the time the question arose, it could no longer make much difference. The Japanese were well alerted.

The time to consider jamming was when the *Sinano Maru* first appeared alongside the Russian fleet. It would have meant an instant reversal of the policy of radio silence, a psychologically difficult decision to take. Moreover the ensuing pandemonium in the ether would have hardly been less effective in attracting attention at Admiral Togo's base.

The *Ural* was with little doubt the warship best equipped with radio on either side. What is known of the Japanese radio?

Whereas Russia looked to Germany for support, Japan looked to Britain and America. Her main warships were British-built, or in some cases Italian-built. Her radio was not Marconi-supplied, but not surprisingly rumour had it that the Japanese radio was a copy of Marconi equipment. Though the Marconi Company made every effort to confirm this, it never succeeded. What are on record are descriptions and comments by the British Naval Attaché in Japan.

We learn for example that the wireless telegraphy gaff on the *Asahi* was 234 feet long and 140 feet above deck (71.3 metres and 42.7 metres respectively). The upper limit of range was normally 180 miles (290 kilometres) but that 390 and 500 miles had been reported (467 and 805 kilometres). These figures would have been completely in keeping with general European maritime standards, and for Japanese naval purposes, with limited range requirements, entirely adequate.

Battle commenced at 13.49. hours.[7] The adventures of radio did not finish with its onset.

One Russian warship *Bedovi* was boarded by the Japanese, having already surrendered. Alarm was caused when the leading Japanese officer unsheathed his sword as his foot touched the Russian deck.

But it quickly became evident that what he intended to attack and disable was the radio installation.

Some Russian warships escaped, thanks to superior speed or good fortune. The *Grozni* reached Askold Island (south of Vladivostok) and radioed to Vladivostok for help, which was sent. The *Izumrud* hastened away so fast and blindly that it overshot Vladivostok and ran aground well to the north. Here it was blown up and the crew set out on an overland trek. As Novikov-Priboi points out, it also should have radioed Vladivostok.

Despite the *Izumrud's* unnecessary end, it showed what the whole fleet should have tried to do, that is reach the seas north of Vladivostok. The *Izumrud* was able to do this being marginally faster than any Japanese warship. The fleet would have needed to steer clear of danger, swinging away from Japan altogether and approaching around the northern tip of Sakhalin. It would have been more difficult for the Japanese to intercept such a move. Approaching from the north and establishing radio contact, the Russian fleet could have received help from the naval squadron in Vladivostok.

With the main Russian naval strength gone, Japan could prepare her next move at leisure. This was the invasion of Sakhalin, beginning on 7 July 1905, directly underlining Russia's strategic folly in allowing the battle of Tsushima to be fought. When peace was restored, through the Peace of Portsmouth (USA), signed in September 1905, southern Sakhalin remained a Japanese possession.

Subsequent Russian analyses of the disaster produced a tendency to blame the radio equipment, as being inferior to the Japanese equipment. But there cannot be the slightest sympathy for this idea. The failure was not in the equipment, but in the use made of it.

The First World War and Jutland

The principal naval powers opposing each other ten years later in the First World War, Britain and Germany, were at the forefront of science and technology. They were better equipped than Russia and Japan had been.

Throughout these years steady technical progress had been made. The spark transmitter had become more accurately tunable. Germany had maintained a high reputation for manufacturing radio apparatus. Despite commercial rivalries the Marconi Company and Telefunken had agreed to exchange of technical information.

Both countries long foresaw the approaching conflict. Both built powerful home and overseas radio stations to supplement cable communications. With war imminent the strategic significance of radio was in no doubt. Both governments commandeered all key radio resources.

Geography gave the British a positional advantage, in communications no less than in the exercise of naval power.

In 1914 the British began to build up a chain of radio direction-finding stations around the British Isles. These enabled the bearings of hostile or unidentified transmissions to be taken. By locating where the different bearings for a particular transmission intersected, its approximate point of origin could be determined. This is one of the most fundamental operations of electronic warfare and a crucial function of signals intelligence.

Directional accuracy to one and a half degrees was attained. Precision in locating an unknown transmitter depended also on the range. At typical ranges of a few hundred kilometres across the North Sea, the transmitter could be located within a box having sides of some tens of kilometres.

To improve matters the British operated a clandestine direction finding station from the attic of a small hotel in Oslo, capital of neutral Norway, much nearer the key German naval bases of Kiel and Wilhelmshaven. It could 'see' them from a better angle. It survived undiscovered for six months.[8] Direction-finding stations were also set up in France, with similar advantages.

From the beginning the British understood not only the strategic importance of long-range communications to themselves, but the importance of denying them to their opponents. With the First World War not one day old, they brought off the first great strategic coup of electronic warfare: on 5 August, 1914 the cable ship *Telconia* raised five German undersea cables from the sea bed off Emden, and severed them. This stroke was swiftly followed by naval bombardments or raiding party attacks on German overseas radio stations.

An accompanying measure could have been to jam Germany's main transmitting station at Nauen, west of Berlin. But this would have been a questionable move. Nauen was the world's most powerful installation, working on 200 kilowatts. To jam it remotely from the British Isles would have demanded considerable resources with little certainty of effective results. At best there would have been variable interference depending on the geographic location of the receiver.

Even a small measure of success might have entrained unfortunate consequences: it might have encouraged Germany to believe there was nothing better to do with Nauen than jam British communications. The most likely outcome would have been an escalating power war between rival transmitters. The passive alternative, in practice adopted, was simply for each side to listen to what the other transmitted.

This was not merely an inevitable result in default of active measures, but had a positive logic of its own. Useful information might be obtained. This option, first faced at the outset of the First World War, has become classical in electronic warfare: to jam the enemy, or listen to what he says. There is no standard answer. Everything depends on particular circumstances.

Germany's long-range communications became limited and difficult. She was constrained to use cable channels passing through neutral countries, principally Scandinavian. This in turn exposed her communications to increased risk of undetected interception.

The Impact of Radio on the War at Sea

The First World War began with several naval incidents and battles which spectacularly demonstrated the new importance of radio. German warships scattered on many oceans threatened British shipping and British allies. At the same time they sought to evade confrontation with heavier British squadrons. Forces were coordinated by radio, radio provided the trail which hunters followed, shore radio stations became strategic targets which sometimes perished, sometimes lured to doom, sometimes even in the moment of their own destruction sealed the fate of the attacker.

On the last day of peace between Britain and Germany, 4 August 1914, a tense situation existed in the Mediterranean. The German cruisers *Goeben* and *Breslau* were being shadowed by British forces. In principle these were capable of destroying them, and were only awaiting confirmation by radio that a state of war existed. This would trigger instant attack. For the German vessels a message of war meant doom.

Or should have done. But the expected denouement never came. The British forces, poised to kill, let their quarry escape. Failures in radio signalling have been held responsible, but the main reason was a failure in command for which the principal British naval officer was court-martialled.

In the Indian Ocean the lone German raider *Emden* was successful for three months in destroying commerce in the Indian Ocean. But early in November 1914 it moved to bombard the British radio and cable station on Cocos Island, and before putting the station off the air was recognised and reported. As a result, it was intercepted and sunk by the Australian cruiser *Sydney*.

A squadron of five German raiders under Admiral von Spee was formed in South American waters, including the powerful cruisers *Scharnhorst* and *Gneisenau*. Radio was fundamental to its operation and its long-range contact with Germany. Its transmissions were picked up from time to time by the British. In turn, it countered the threat which radio direction-finding posed by separating one ship from the rest in order to transmit.

It destroyed a British hunting force which engaged it on unequal terms at the Battle of Coronel, off Chile. But shortly afterwards, converging to attack the radio station at Port Stanley in the Falkland Islands, it was surprised by a superior force which emerged from the harbour. In the ensuing battle, named after the islands, four of the five German ships were sunk.

Following this early phase of the war, swiftly terminated in Britain's favour, naval strategy focused on the waters of the North Sea. Could the British fleet, the world's largest, deny operational freedom to the German fleet, which though smaller was extremely powerful? If the German fleet could gain free access to the oceans, Britain might be forced out of the war.

This issue was fiercely contested. After initial skirmishing an increasingly static naval balance emerged. The Germans kept their fleet in being and thereby kept the threat which it posed in being. The threat gave them the initiative. The British had at all times to keep the German fleet from breaking out. They needed to do this if possible without being forced to maintain distant patrols amidst minefields and submarine haunts, which would have led to continuing losses by attrition. Signals intelligence from radio was their main hope.

In turn, radio helped the Germans by speeding intelligence from Zeppelin naval reconnaissance.

In this way, radio helped both sides to avoid serious mistakes. It tended to promote stability. This stability was consolidated by the Battle of Jutland in May 1916.

A Premium on Swift Response

The German fleet was based on the northwest German coast, near Wilhelmshaven, approaches to which were heavily protected by minefields. The British fleet was based on the Scottish coast, from Scapa Flow to the Forth estuary, where it was poised to react to German sallies. At this range there was a premium on reacting as swiftly as possible.

The Germans made more intensive use of naval radio than the British. Continuous monitoring of German naval radio signals, the British realised, was the key to their ability to react swiftly. In practice they put their fleet to sea whenever signalling at Wilhelmshaven indicated imminent naval activity.

The Germans gradually realised that radio was a source of intelligence for their opponents. Yet with large, complex fleets including submarines, and long-range manoeuvres, including night operations, radio signalling was indispensable. Low-powered transmissions did not guarantee limitation of range. Only occasionally and temporarily could radio silence be observed.

As British attacks on German communications increased, the Germans learnt the need for ever-tighter communications security. Electronic warfare was joined by cryptography and cryptanalysis on a massive scale: the effort to devise unbreakable codes and ciphers on one hand, the effort to break them on the other.

The Role of Cryptography

Cryptography was thousands of years old. The coming of the cable telegraph had already stimulated a vast development. Systems had been devised to handle copious message flows. Now radio multiplied the problem many times over.

There was an inherent security in cables in that interception meant somehow tapping the cable, or corrupting an official of the cable company. This tended to limit the prospects for cryptanalysis. But radio put enormous volumes of encrypted messages directly into the hands of the enemy. The cryptographers had much more material to work on.

At the same time, the geographic scale of the war increased the number of users needing regular and rapid methods of encrypting radio messages. It increased their dispersion by land, sea and air. The physical risk of codebooks sometimes falling into enemy hands increased. It would not always be known when this had happened.

Above all, although encrypted messages were being transmitted from many separate and widely distant points, radio permitted them to be intercepted, accumulated, and subjected to cryptanalysis at one central station. Here all the resources of the counter-attack could be concentrated, particularly highly skilled personnel with specific abilities.

Nothing endangers the security of an encrypted message so much as other messages encrypted in the same way with which it can be compared. Moreover, mistakes made in encryption by operators working under stress in combat conditions often give the code away, and one encrypted message so broken compromises all other uses of the same code, however far away they are.

Other cryptographic disasters can occur. Some messages go out for wide distribution. One sender may prefer for safety's sake to encrypt such a message in passing it on, but later another sender, believing that the need for security is past, may transmit 'in clear'.

No formal security breach is entailed, and the message itself may not be sensitive, but comparison of message lengths at a central interception point will often suggest what has happened. The cryptographers realise that they have in their hands both the plain text and the encrypted text of the same message. In this case the code may well have been given away completely. All other messages sent in it, including those previously sent and recorded even though not decipherable at the time, can be read. Some of this material is likely to be highly sensitive.

Advantages of Centralised Control

The large mass of material the cryptanalytic teams had to work with inevitably contained abundant examples of such security flaws. In practice central code-breakers can work at a higher intellectual level and with all kinds of advantages against dispersed code-users in the field.

The older European states, particularly France, Austria and Britain, were ancient practitioners in the black art of reading other states' secret messages. They had long-standing skills to build on.

Britain was additionally fortunate to get a flying start in war-time cryptanalysis. The German cruiser *Magdeburg* was lost in the Baltic to the Russians, who recovered her codebooks and promptly transferred them to the British Admiralty. This gift, received by Winston Churchill scarcely a month after the war began, led him to set up the organisation which became famous as Room 40. The code books did not instantly solve every problem of reading German transmissions, but provided a basis for progress. Further similar if less spectacular incidents added to the fund of material for study.

Success in cryptanalysis grows like a snowball. Once some codes have been broken more follow. The process is interrupted when the enemy introduces a new code, but it is difficult for any code-user to break away completely from systems already in use. Thus cryptanalysts can often leap from the codes they know to the codes the enemy tries next. There may be a time delay varying from hours to years before they are broken, meanwhile even partial solutions are valuable.

The Pay-Off

The blossoming of cryptanalysis at the beginning of the First World War was a spectacular outgrowth of signals intelligence. But the combatants vigorously applied other, more basic, signals intelligence techniques, such as recording the number, direction, strength and kind of all the transmissions they could pick up. This, by itself, offered a copious volume of information, even when the transmissions could not be read. It could still indicate probable areas of troop or ship concentrations, directions of movement, and force build-ups preceding an attack.

German naval tactics in the North Sea took the form of provocative but short-duration sallies, such as sending limited squadrons to bombard towns on the English east coast. No worthwhile targets were available, but this did not matter; such actions were bound to bring British warships out and the aim was to inflict losses by submarines or mines, or by leading back on to a superior force. Both sides were wary and no crucial engagement developed out of these forays.

Strategically, the British aim was to play for a general action between the main fleets under conditions in which they could expect to win by virtue of numerical superiority, faster ships and heavier guns. This could only happen if the German High Seas Fleet came out, which above all else the British watched for. Correspondingly, if the German High Seas Fleet was to be used aggressively, in the hope of surprising and destroying a weaker British squadron, it would have to come out without being observed. In practice, 'observed' meant 'being detected by radio intercepts'.

This phase of the naval war culminated in a major deployment of the German High Seas Fleet at the end of May 1916, leading to the Battle of Jutland. Electronic warfare played the main role in bringing the battle about. On 30 May the British detected intensified signalling and a warship movement in the mouth of the Jade river, the naval harbour near Wilhelmshaven. They also detected intensified Zeppelin naval reconnaissance patrols. They intercepted and decoded signals which suggested the imminence of a German fleet movement.

A Simple Stroke Brings Advantage

On the combined strength of all these indications, the Admiralty ordered the British Grand Fleet into the North Sea in readiness. It put

---

MAP 5.3 **The Battle of Jutland, 1916. Situation on 31 May** This map shows the convergence of the British and German naval forces on 31 May 1916 which led to the Battle of Jutland, and the movement of German Zeppelin scouts off Wilhelmshaven on the previous day, plotted by British direction-finding stations. This activity was one of the indications to the British, obtained by signals intelligence, of an impending German naval operation. The British navy was alerted at about 1700 hours on 30 May and sailed at midnight (compare these timings with those of the Zeppelin flights).

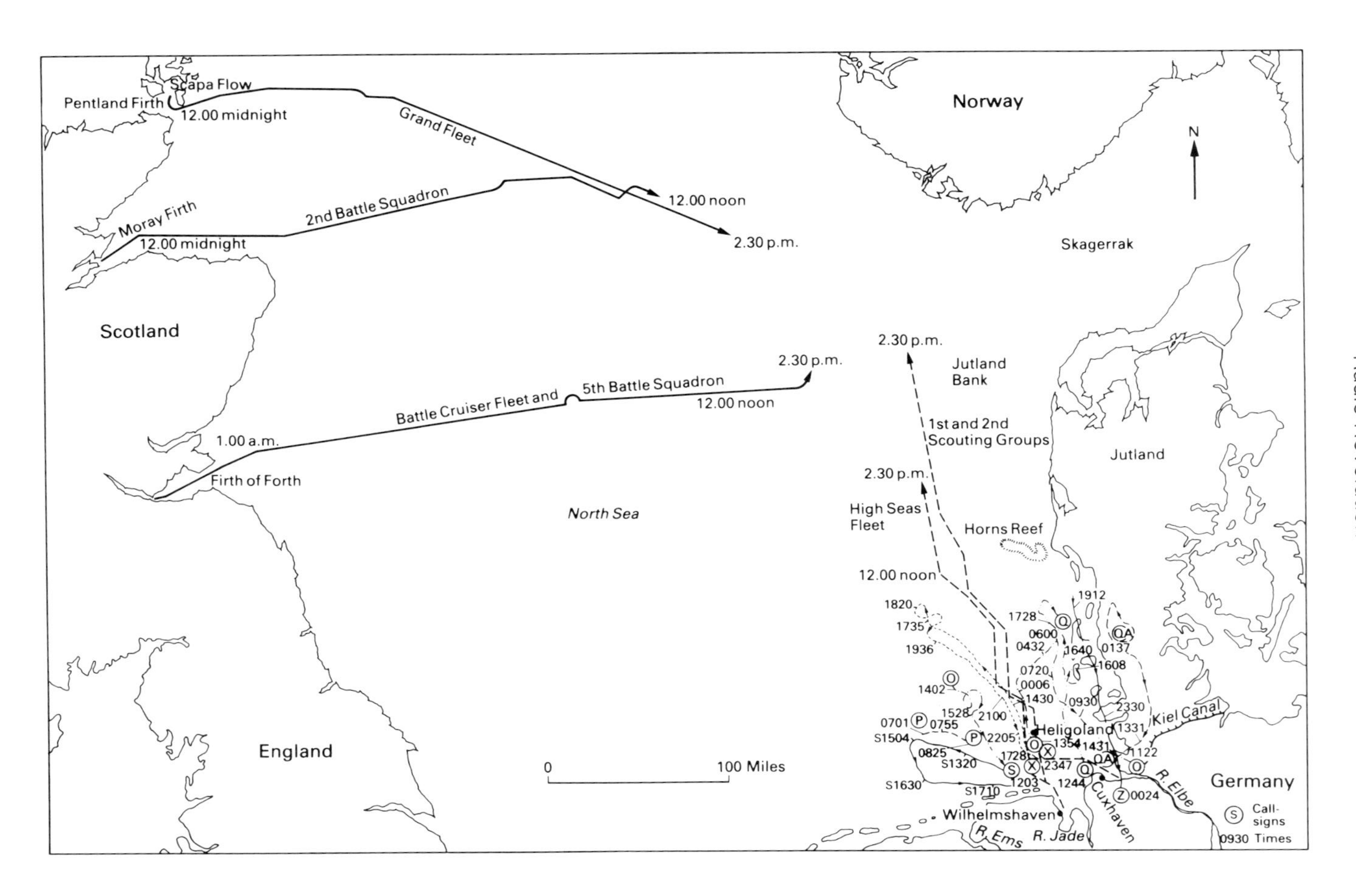

Scapa Flow
Pentland Firth
12.00 midnight
Grand Fleet
12.00 noon
2.30 p.m.
Norway
N
Moray Firth
2nd Battle Squadron
12.00 midnight
2.30 p.m.
Skagerrak
Scotland
2.30 p.m.
2.30 p.m.
Jutland Bank
Battle Cruiser Fleet and 5th Battle Squadron
12.00 noon
1st and 2nd Scouting Groups
1.00 a.m.
Jutland
2.30 p.m.
Firth of Forth
High Seas Fleet
North Sea
Horns Reef
12.00 noon
Heligoland
Kiel Canal
England
0
100 Miles
Germany
Wilhelmshaven
Cuxhaven
R. Elbe
R. Ems
R. Jade
S Call-signs
0930 Times

to sea on the evening of 30 May when the German High Seas Fleet was doing likewise. Neither command knew for sure what the other side was up to.

In executing their plan, the Germans brought off a brilliantly simple stroke of electronic warfare. The German flagship *Friedrich der Grosse* transferred its call sign to the naval shore station at Wilhelmshaven. As a result, long after the flagship had led the German High Seas fleet out of the Jade River, the shore station's continued signalling created the impression that *Friedrich der Grosse* was still where it had been. The British Admiralty radioed to its fleet at 12.35 hours on 31 May: 'Directionals place flagship in Jade at 11.10 a.m.' ('directionals' meaning bearings taken on German signals).

At the time this signal was received, British expectations that the German fleet might be encountered were beginning to diminish. The day was half gone. The signal appeared to suggest that the British fleet might as well consider turning for home.

The British vanguard was ranging far ahead of the main fleet, by some 65 miles. At 14.15 hours it began to turn back. But within the next quarter-hour, sightings of German activity were reported to its commander. He changed course again to investigate. This led to a clash with the German vanguard. This clash was the celebrated battle between the battlecruiser squadrons which preceded the main battle of Jutland.

The British battlecruiser commander, Beatty, had overwhelming strength available to him. But his ships were in two groups, and his back-up strength, the Fifth Battle Squadron, failed to follow its commander when he changed course towards the GErman warships.

This happened *because of a failure to read signal flags*. Radio gave independent confirmation of the commander's changed course and eventually the error was corrected. But not before an excessive gap had opened up and the chance of a swift, decisive action had been lost. This confusion, the tendency to rate visual above wireless signalling, even when visual signalling had become difficult, is symptomatic of the British story at Jutland.

Radio performed its strategic function before the battle. But in the battle it could not perform its tactical function unhindered. Presumably the conflict of signalling methods arose from centuries of reliance on visual signallings. Only when radio had the field to itself, that is when ranges were too great for any form of visual signalling, were its signals respected.

Despite the split in the British force, the British battlecruisers were aggressive. They sustained heavy initial losses, but compelled the German battlecruisers to turn away. The British gave chase.

Then, thanks to the earlier radio deception, the Germans were able to spring a surprise: they led the British battlecruisers on to their High Seas fleet. It was the British battlecruisers' cue to turn away towards their own main force.

In effect it was their turn to become the decoy, leading on the Germans, and it was the Germans' turn to be surprised, by the British Grand Fleet. The scene was set for a general engagement.

The battle developed some 80 kilometres or more off the Norwegian and Danish coasts. Its scale was far more awesome than Tsushima.[9] Numerical superiority and armament favoured the British. But for various reasons the outcome was inconclusive.

The Causes of Misinformation

It was late in the day. Striving to reconcile the continuing conflict of visual and radio signalling, the British command at sea, under Admiral Jellicoe, was cautious. Underlying this cautiousness was uncertainty about the reliability of radio intelligence from the British Admiralty. The supply was copious, and vital to interpretation of the situation. But the initial misinformation planted by the Germans continued to do its work. Doubts always persisted.

Nevertheless as night fell the British Fleet positioned itself favourably for renewed engagement on the following day. The German Admiral Scheer found his fleet to the west of the British fleet, cut off from retreat. This was highly dangerous. He had no wish to face a renewed engagement.

At 21.14 hours, as darkness came, he issued a signal by radio to the whole German fleet which could hardly have been issued in any other way: 'Our own main body is to proceed in. Maintain course SSE $\frac{1}{4}$ E; speed 16 knots.' He proposed to use the cover of darkness to extricate his fleet from hazard.

The British Admiralty recorded Scheer's signal, deciphered it and retransmitted in code at 22.41 hours. The Admiralty transmission was received on the British flagship *Iron Duke*, decoded and handed to Jellicoe at about 23.30 hours.

It made the German strategy clear, and also the fact that the possible lines of German retreat which he was covering did not in fact include the one which the Germans had chosen. But it offered the possibility of setting a new interception course calculated for a daylight battle.

Meanwhile British orders transmitted after the fall of darkness had been intercepted by the German listening post at Neumunster. At 22.10 hours Neumunster reported to Scheer: 'Destroyers have taken up position five sea miles astern of the enemy's main fleet.' Jellicoe had separated the destroyers from the capital ships.

Jellicoe took no immediate action on the intelligence which had reached him by radio. He discounted it as being in the same class as the advice that the German flagship was still in harbour at 11.10 hours. Consequently, as the German fleet drove homewards through the night, it crashed through the British destroyer flotillas following five miles behind the battleships. Eventually what was happening became clear. The British Grand Fleet turned at 02.30 hours on 1 June, but by then it was already too late. There was no hope of renewing the engagement.

Thus, at Jutland, radio was an ever-present positive and negative factor for both sides. But the Germans scored more points through electronic warfare than they gave away. Recognising British capabilities in signals intelligence, they exploited them in setting a trap at the outset. They signalled effectively during the action. The British correctly anticipated the possible German sally but were thrown off the scent. They lacked the tactical confidence in radio which would have been necessary for a more conclusive result.

More than one incident testifies to British dissatisfaction with radio intelligence. The crowning irony came when the German light cruiser *Regensburg*, in the rear of the retreating fleet, inadvertently misreported its own position by over ten miles. The signal was read by the British Admiralty and passed on to the British command at sea. The latter well knew where *Regensburg* really was, and attributed folly to the Admiralty rather than the *Regensburg*. By this time the matter was irrelevant.

Stalemate

Although this was not the last German sally, after Jutland the importance of the North Sea as the arena for a potentially decisive fleet action declined. Radio was a factor contributing to the stalemate. Its role in naval signalling and intelligence was far from perfected, yet its effect was undeniable. Neither side could sufficiently escape notice to manoeuvre strong forces into position for a surprise. Neither side could be deceived into serious mis-deployment. Intelligence flowed too swiftly.

A new pattern of naval conflict began to emerge, leading away from fleet actions and leaving the field to submarine warfare as the primary form of naval action. Before Jutland, submarines had intervened in such dramatic ways as the sinking of the *Lusitania* in 1915. Even at this time, radio's defensive role was highlighted by the warnings broadcast to *Lusitania* during its fatal voyage – insufficiently heeded, as it proved.

As Germany began to place a greater stake on submarine warfare, the Allied powers introduced convoys as a means of controlling the threat to merchant shipping. Radio contributed both to the control of submarine operations and to the control and defensive routing of convoys. The electronic battle at sea continued.

Developments within Land Battles

The naval history of the First World War highlights the electronic clash of Britain and Germany. Because it was spectacular it overshadows the electronic land conflict in northern France.

As noted above, the German army was well prepared to use radio communications. France was able to exploit this use on land, as Britain had been able to exploit it at sea, by extracting a considerable amount of signals intelligence: positions, identities, strengths of military units on the other side of the fighting line, operational intentions. France was at a comparable technical level in radio, indeed in some respects, notably electron tube manufacture, she was ahead of Britain.

The British and French were confident that their preference for cable landlines spared them from the danger that the Germans might do to their communications what they were doing to the Germans'. Their confidence proved to be illusory.

An unrealised weakness of the cable system was the use of 'earth returns'. Instead of having two wires to connect points A and B, making an unbroken round circuit, a single wire was used, and the circuit completed through the earth, which carried the current on its return journey.

It was not realised that this use of the earth might be detectable at some considerable distance, up to five kilometres, from either A or B, by the use of sensitive instruments which would enable messages to be read. It was the Germans who made this fascinating discovery on the other side of the front line.

On the Western Front, French, British and German armies all gradually realised that in one way or another their communications security was failing, and tightened it. At no time however did failures in communications security impose a new pattern on the land war. Lives were paid for leakages but the balance was never tipped.

Cryptography and cryptanalysis mounted in significance towards the end of the war, during 1918, with attempts by both sides to mount offensives. This began to restore some fluidity to long-static positions. The celebrated German ADFGVX radio code, using these letters only, related to this time. The French broke it, to their considerable advantage.

On the Eastern Front, Russian and German armies used radio. Russian disregard for the demands of radio security was often total. It cost them very dear. In the earliest part of the war, the Russian thrust along the south of the Baltic posed a serious threat to Germany. Germany parried it at the battles of Tannenberg and the Masurian Lakes, thanks to the interception of Russian radio signals. These made Russian intentions and weaknesses apparent.

The Russian war effort collapsed amidst munitions shortages and other organisational chaos. This proved temporary. Amazingly, a revival occurred, but although it included the introduction of new codes, Russia never managed to make her use of radio secure. Ultimately, the Revolution supervened, and probably the traumas which had been suffered encouraged the Bolshevik state to place a high premium on cryptography. The scene was set for the espionage conflict which was to break out many years later.

The Zimmermann Telegram

Germany's cryptanalysis was assisted by the traditions of her Austrian ally. As one of the older European states, Austria had a long background of code- and cipher-breaking. Both the Austrian and French schools of cryptanalysis played their role on, or rather behind, the diplomatic stage before the outbreak of the First World War.

There is nothing to suggest that either of them significantly influenced the course of history. But this claim can be made for the British coup which lead to the interception and deciphering of what became known as the Zimmermann telegram.

The telegram was sent by the German Foreign Minister, Artur Zimmermann, to the German Minister in Mexico in January 1917. In the event of the United States entering the war against Germany, it authorised him to offer Mexico a military alliance. This would hold out hope to Mexico for the return of 'lost territories in Texas, New Mexico and Arizona'.

Because of the British stranglehold on international cable communications, Germany was obliged to send this signal in two devious ways: by courtesy of Sweden, and by courtesy of the United States itself, through its embassy in Berlin. Both countries were sufficiently trusting to accept the encrypted telegram. But the cable routes employed passed through Britain. Thus it reached Room 40, and the encryption was eventually broken.

Before diplomatic use could be made of it, the tracks whereby it had fallen into British hands had to be disguised, and arguments prepared to induce the Americans to accept the decoding as genuine. This was done by the end of February 1917. When the telegram became public knowledge, it caused an uproar. It was specifically referred to by President Wilson of the United States on 2 April in asking Congress to endorse a state of war with Germany.

This diplomatic disaster had several elements. Germany's basic aim should have been to keep the United States out of the war. She did not appreciate this sufficiently. Britain's basic aim was to induce the United States to come off the fence.

Britain achieved her aim as the cumulative result of two coups. Firstly the preliminary cutting of German undersea cables at the beginning of the war. Secondly the inspired cryptanalysis of the messages thereby diverted through British cable stations.

Conclusion

The First World War ended 20 months later. From Germany's viewpoint, Russia's elimination from the war had been swiftly offset by the acquisition of the United States as a new opponent. Without the Zimmermann telegram, matters might have taken a different course.

The electronic warfare of the First World War was chiefly in the field of communications. It was fought over the security of encoded messages. The Zimmermann telegram was its most spectacular single passage of arms. It showed that a failure in communications warfare could be fatal, even for such a powerful country as Germany.

Germany had begun with remarkable strength. She had the naval strength to challenge Britain, formerly undisputed in control of the seas. She had the army strength to win on the Eastern Front against Russia and to thrust the Western Front onto French territory and hold it there. It was a demonstration of underlying economic, industrial and often technical pre-eminence.

A balance was struck between Germany and her West European opponents. Radio stabilised this balance. It prevented either side from making gross mistakes. On the Eastern Front, the balance was more precarious. Radio destabilised it in favour of Germany. But on the grand strategic front, failure in the communications war brought Germany's collapse.

6

Revolution Upon Revolution

REVOLUTION is no doubt an overworked word. Yet there is no other adequately describing the changes in war which came in with the 20th century.

The evolutionary process speeded up. Many technologies contributed to the ever-faster tempo. Steam made the mechanised navy possible. The internal combustion engine made the mechanised army and aviation possible. But what these were to man's military muscle, electronics was to man's military mind. It combined and controlled almost everything else.

Thanks to electronics there was not one revolution but a sequence of revolutions.

Electronics progressed regardless of peace or war. Peace or war merely determined its applications. But progress made in time of peace was turned to account in time of war. For this reason electronics in warfare moved by a leap between the two World Wars. It lapsed after the first but soared with the second. History repeated itself on a grander scale and with more facets to the action.

What distinguished the period of electronic warfare beginning with the Russo-Japanese War was the coming of radio. Radio joined cable. It was relatively crude but more combat-capable. It brought revolution but only to naval war.

What distinguished the next period, beginning with the Second World War, was the coming of radar. Radar is locating objects, such as aircraft and ships, by the way they reflect radio waves projected at them. It is not only direction finding, as practised for signals intelligence, but ranging, and it works against a passive target, that is one which does not itself actively transmit.

Radar was born out of radio by the threat of war. Once again the new technology brought revolution, but this time it was revolution upon revolution. It was the radar revolution on top of the radio revolution. For as events were to show, when radar arrived the radio revolution had not spent itself. It had only begun.

This time the twin revolutions were not restricted in impact mainly to one military sphere of action, the naval one. They penetrated every aspect. Paradoxically, in view of this universal presence, their fighting profile was low. No high ranks or commands were conferred for their sake. On the contrary, the ranks that were conferred were not as high as they might have been. This was a strategic mistake, born of underestimation.

Nevertheless radio and radar were among the war's dominant influences. They enabled it to be fought in a way different to any previous war. Were they ultimately above all? Was the Second World War, in the final analysis, the world war of electronics? The case is tempting to argue. Some believe it to be so.

Realistically however the technologies used in the war cannot be judged in isolation. Nor were technologies the only thing that mattered. The very idea of the 'war-winning weapon' is suspect. Both radar and the atomic bomb have been put forward as candidates.

By definition a war-winning weapon is one that fights for the winning side. The atomic bomb fought for the winning side, but it arrived when the win was already a foregone conclusion. Radar arrived at the beginning, and fought on both sides. It is popularly seen however as fighting for the winning side. This is a lopsided viewpoint. Moreover it ignores the contribution of radio.

In the Second World War radar stole the limelight from radio. Admittedly, this was limited limelight until the war was over and military secrets began to be divulged to the public. Yet radar's post-war glory left radio in darkness. It obscured the fact that the radio revolution which had begun in the First World War was only a start.

'The Wizard War'

The First World War ended as the pace of radio progress was speeding up. The war was the cause of this, but the momentum carried over into peace. As a result, when radio was applied again to military use, it was ready, even without radar, to revolutionise the Second World War and did so.

Ironically, the world missed this. Popular interest after the war, chiefly in the Anglo-American world, fixated on radar, with which were associated such electronic countermeasures as 'bending the beams', the whole being collectively termed 'the wizard war', in Winston Churchill's expressive term.

In reality much of beam technology and beam-bending belonged to radio and was devised independently of radar. There were other important aspects of the radio war which remained little known for thirty years. These included signals intelligence, above all the battle with the German Enigma machine. When it became known, it was scanned more for sensation value than the maturer historical view it was capable of giving.

Like radar, 'Ultra' – the often copious information flow from intercepted German signals – was initially seen as confirmation of British pre-eminence in electronic warfare. Its revelation during the 1970s came with a fanfare reminiscent of the post-war excitement about radar.

In truth, the British wartime achievement in signals intelligence was in most respects more impressive, from the viewpoint of military results, than the British wartime achievement in radar. But neither should be focused on to the exclusion of each other, or to German and American achievements in the same sphere. These were impressive also.

What was special about the British achievement in signals intelligence was that it was against something equally special: namely the most massive and sophisticated employment of radio yet seen in war. This was the military use of radio by Germany. The American achievement in signals intelligence against the Japanese, which brought spectacular results, and more rapidly became public knowledge, was against an opponent far less advanced, technically or militarily, than Germany.

British successes in signals intelligence, coming later in the war, have tended to obscure that at the beginning Germany was ahead in signals intelligence. Ignoring this introduces distortions.

The distortions are greater because the Second World War was above all a cultural war. When it was over, the victories of some and the defeats of others were explained in cultural terms. Scientific achievements were cultural achievements and as such were subjected to the same pattern of interpretation, regardless of whether it was justifiable. Much first-class German technical achievement was down-rated or ignored. Complacent assumptions were made which were never challenged before they solidified into accepted truth.

Consequently 'the wizard war' was marvelled at, but the fuller significance of electronic warfare in the Second World War was not recognised. It alters the whole perspective in which the war is seen. Part of the readjustment is getting the impacts of radio and radar into proper balance.

In the 20 years between the two world wars, civilian radio gave rise to mass public broadcasting, defied the global economic crisis of the late 1920s/early 1930s with uninterrupted growth, and produced television.

The underlying advance in basic radio technology was correspondingly great. The properties of HF were discovered in the 1920s. Practical, public-service use of the frequency spectrum moved upwards into HF and lower VHF, that is from a few megahertz up to over thirty. Broadcast television was introduced in Britain on 45 megahertz. Experimental use went higher. Such developments occurred simultaneously though in varying degrees in the leading European countries, the United States and Japan.

Changing Patterns of Research

Military radio developments followed at first a different pattern. After the First World War military expenditures fell sharply. Military interest in radio went into eclipse. In the stable circumstances of peace, the older technology of cable was generally adequate for military communications. Military use of radio was mainly confined to medium frequencies, as in the First World War. The military were, for the time being, no longer pioneers.

Navies were the only partial exception. Naval expenditures were restrained but radio's special significance for naval operations continued to inspire research. This was particularly the case in the United States navy and the British navy.

Already in the 1920s Japan ceased to be an ally of the United States and began to loom, distantly, as a potential enemy. There was at this time no renewed threat to Britain from the German navy, which had been totally self-destroyed at the end of the First World War. But the British navy continued to have a world-wide empire to patrol, and because Britain's traditional friendship with Japan was disintegrating, it bore increased responsibility in the Far East. Nevertheless, neither in the US navy nor the British navy was radio research driven by a sense of immediate urgency.

In the 1930s this pattern changed. It changed abruptly in Europe with the birth of the Third German Reich. In the Far East, Japan annexed Manchuria and invaded China. Diplomatically if not militarily, the Americans took China's side.

As the pendulum began to swing away from peace, military doctrine digested the lessons of the last war and prepared for the next. Germany paid particular attention to radio. The advance brought by HF was integrated into military practice. Armies were mechanised and mechanised armies needed radio. A quarter-century before, the same combination of mechanisation and radio had revolutionised naval warfare. The corresponding revolution was about to unfold in war on land. Germany was its pioneer.

At the same time aviation reached a point in its progress where air forces became an especially menacing new arm of war. This point had never been approached in the First World War. The new arm demanded radio no less insistently than either of the others. Without radio communications its potential could not be realised. HF radio, compact and achieving good ranges with low power, provided exactly what was necessary.

The increasing tension of the 1930s could not fail to affect navies. The warship legacy of the First World War was outdated even where it had survived. New naval construction gathered pace in several countries, especially Germany, Britain, the United States and Japan. The revolution started by radio in war at sea was set to continue. But there was a new circumstance. Navies were confronted with the most formidable challenge in the whole history of sea power.

The warship's supremacy in its own element was questioned by the new air arm. The speed and range of aircraft gave them the initiative. Moreover aircraft might be launched to attack a warship from another warship. This meant that being a long way from shore was no protection. Nor was the newly-created aircraft carrier itself invulnerable. Without means of warning, it could be overwhelmed by surprise air attack before it could launch its own aircraft in self-defence.

The warship's need to anticipate and ward off air attack became a condition of survival. Radar alone answered this need. The defensive motive was reinforced by radar's potential to increase offensive capability at sea. It promised to locate surface targets at night, in limited daytime visibility, or beyond the visual horizon. The value of radar was seen first by navies.

Radar – The Pressing Need for Progress

The principles of radar were almost as old as radio itself, but for a long time the technical barriers to development were too great. The nature of these barriers is the subject of the next chapter. For the present, it is only relevant to note that with the simultaneous arrival of much higher frequencies in the 1930s and the new urgency of naval defence, the scene was at last set for them to be overcome.

The space limitations of the shipborne environment, and its climatic severity, drove naval radar engineering in what proved to be the right direction. That is towards higher frequencies as a way of achieving compact, robust construction. Impressive early results came in Germany. From a project started in 1933, the Seetakt radar was developed and fitted on the pocket battleship *Admiral Graf Spee* by 1938, providing gunnery control. It operated with a compact masthead antenna on the remarkably high frequency of 375 megahertz.

Naval radar also actively developed in Britain and the United States. The British navy had radar 'in its sights' from the late 1920s, but despite having the strongest research resources of all the British armed forces, did not begin a practical radar project until 1935. In this year the British air force got away to a slightly earlier start.

The British air force project was for a chain of land-based warning stations around the coast. This became the world's first strategic area-defence radar network. Individual stations began to become operational during 1937, and by the end of August 1938 five permanent stations in south east England had been combined for network operation with central reporting. These were intended to give cover against air attack. Other stations gave isolated sectors of cover further north. A year later, by September 1939, connected coverage through eight stations had been established along the east and part of the south coast of Britain.

The reason why the British air force project leapfrogged British naval radar was undoubtedly that the strength of the German air force had alarmed Britain, whereas in the absence of strong German naval surface forces, the surface naval threat was down-rated. The British *Chain Home* stations worked in the upper part of the HF band, typically about 27.5 megahertz. They were effective against aircraft at medium or high altitude approaching the coast, but not against ships.

At approximately the same time as the British coastal chain was being readied for war, a German coastal chain, conceived by the navy for coastal defence, was also beginning deployment. A string of radar stations began to appear along Germany's relatively short North Sea coastline. These were intended for tactical or local area defence against both ships and aircraft. Doubtless there was memory of British incursions into these waters in the First World War.

Initially the German stations were not integrated into a strategic chain. The operational range was about half that of the British system. The radar was *Freya*, in some respects similar to but larger than *Seetakt*. As in the British system, eight stations were operational at the outbreak of war in September 1939.

Radar's debut in war casts the historical spotlight uniquely on Germany and Britain. There were other countries, in Europe and outside it, with strong technical capabilities, already taking an interest in radar. Some of these were no less powerful but were waiting in the wings. Others were less powerful and were destined for tragic roles. When the storm broke Britain's European allies soon collapsed. So far as the immediate development of radar and its application in war were concerned, Germany and Britain were left confronting each other, poised to continue their electronic rivalry of the First World War.

Investment in Technology

Despite the radar deployments, when the Second World War started the practical emphasis fell first on radio. This was because of the energy which Germany had applied to harnessing radio for war purposes. In Britain the development of radar was the main electronic investment made in preparation for war, but in Germany investment in radar was secondary to investment in radio. Even so German radar was technically ahead of British radar. It was based on higher frequencies.

German developments

Germany's basic science and technology were roughly equivalent to their British counterparts. But in radio and radar, German appreciation of possibilities, understanding of military requirements, thoroughness, extent of use, and quality of engineering solutions were, at the beginning of the war, in advance.

Why this was so is an important question, for differences in national levels of technology have become a key issue in electronic warfare.

An interesting sidelight is cast by the 'Oslo Report'. This was an anonymous report from a source in Germany delivered to the British Embassy in Norway shortly after the outbreak of war. It contained a resumé of German technical military developments. Its chief content was electronic developments. Surprisingly for such a rich intelligence treasure, it received little attention in Britain.

The reason is probably that the technology it described was, to say the least, a little incredible by British standards at that time. It included reference to the role of radar – without using the term which had not then been thought up – in guarding the German coast at Wilhelmshaven. It explained how British aircraft losses had already been suffered in this area on radar's account.

The significance of this reference was not immediately understood; amazingly, in Britain the question whether Germany possessed anything comparable to British radar did not arise; it was a pre-judged issue; Germany did not. Not only was the Oslo report generally ignored,[1] but so was the evidence afforded by the opportunity to examine a Seetakt radar when the German pocket battleship *Graf Spee* was scuttled just outside Montevideo harbour in December 1939.

It needs to be said that the technology of what is now called radar – in Anglo-American usage – was not then specifically distinguished from radio of which it was still a branch. It might, according to country, be called something like radio direction finding, but this did not differentiate it from long-existing methods of locating active radio transmitters.

Germany's main use of radio technology required none of the sweeping technical advances that radar did. It was the technology of using HF radio which had developed in the 1920s. What it did require on the other hand was military foresight, planning and energetic procurement.

HF made equipment smaller, particularly the transmitter, required less power, increased the number of communications channels, and where necessary offered extended range. It made possible a vast expansion in the number of users able both to transmit and receive. It streamlined military communications. This was exactly what the German armed forces needed.

Germany understood HF radio as being primarily for operational use. In other words, in support of combat. Users were organised into radio nets. A net included users with a common interest, for example members of the same unit dispersed over various locations. A net shared a common frequency, and was managed from one station.

HF radio did not replace landlines as the preferred channel for regular internal defence communications. Once a military operation was completed, communications links reverted to landlines as soon as possible. For example the German invasion of France was accompanied by intensive use of HF radio, but the volume of transmissions steeply declined when the fighting was over.

MF, 300 kilohertz to 3 megahertz, the main radio band of the First World War, which continued in use in the 1920s, was not obsolete. It required larger and more powerful transmitters than HF but was suitable when only one transmitter was required to serve a number of receivers, that is in such functions as providing radio beacons for air navigation. LF was also in use for this purpose. MF radio links were used to some extent for interior communications; low power MF transmissions had limited range.

British Trends

British military radio technology followed a similar pattern to German but without, initially, anything approaching a corresponding scale of investment. Britain's reorientation from peace to war came later than Germany's, and the increased investment went mainly into the air force secondly into the navy. It lagged markedly in the army, even though the British army, like the German, procured a variety of vehicles for mobile radio communications. It was in the British navy and air force that a pioneering attitude was to be found towards radio and its emerging offshoot radar.

Table 6.1 *Frequency Bands of Electromagnetic Radiation*

Designation		Frequency and corresponding wavelength		Wavelength designation	Propagation	Military history and importance
ELF	*Extra Low Frequency*	3 to 30 hertz	100,000 to 10,000 kilometres	extra long waves	uninterrupted global range penetrating surface of sea, requiring extreme power	Naval use in submarine communications, post-WW2, for slow one-way transmission to submerged vessels.
SLF	*Super low Frequency*	30 to 300 hertz	10,000 to 1,000 kilometres	super long waves	These bands are of little importance as electromagnetic wavelengths. The frequencies are however important as audio or acoustic frequencies, propagating in air or water, or modulated on to higher frequency radio waves.	
ILF	*Infra Low Frequency*	300 to 3000 hertz	1,000 to 100 kilometres	ultra long waves		
VLF	*Very Low Frequency*	3 to 30 kilohertz	100 to 10 kilometres	very long waves	uninterrupted global range, requiring high power	Naval use post-WW2
LF	*Low Frequency*	30 to 300 kilohertz	10 to 1 kilometre	long waves	uninterrupted range over land and sea to thousands of kilometres, at high power	General military use in WW1.
MF	**Medium Frequency**	300 kilohertz to 3 megahertz	1 kilometre to 100 metres	medium waves	uninterrupted range over land and sea to many hundreds of kilometres, at considerable power	Naval use in Russo–Japanese War, dominant all-purposes military band of WW1.

HF	**High Frequency**	3 to 30 megahertz	100 to 10 metres	short waves	dual range, short'medium and global, both with low power	Some airborne use in WW1, revolutionised military radio in WW2, remains vital for military radio and over-the-horizon radar.
VHF	Very High Frequency	30 to 300 megahertz	10 to 1 metre	metric	line-of-sight and into space	In WW2 for radio and radar, remains vital for military radio.
UHF	Ultra High Frequency	300 to 3,000 megahertz	100 to 10 centimetres	decimetric	line-of-sight and into space	In WW2 for radar, remains vital for radar, now also vital for military radio.
SHF	**Super High Frequency**	3,000 to 30,000 megahertz	10 to 1 centimetre	centimetric	line-of-sight and into space (global via satellites)	Major radar innovation of WW2, later became major band for military satellite radio cummunications.
EHF	*Extra High Frequency*	30,000 to 300,000 megahertz	10 to 1 millimetre	millimetric	line-of-sight, range limited by atmospheric absorption	Limited use post-WW2, chiefly important for satellite radio cummunications.
–	*Submillimetric*	300 to 3,000* gigahertz	1 to 0.1 millimetre	sub-millimetric	line-of-sight, range limited by atmospheric absorption	Attempts at use in recent decades.
IR	**Infra-red**	3,000 to 428,500† gigahertz	0.1 to 0.0007 millimetre	–	line-of-sight, range dependent on state of atmosphere	Major importance since late 1950s for anti-aircraft targeting, from air and ground.
	Visible light	428,500 to 750,000 gigahertz	0.0007 to 0.0004 millimetre	–	line-of-sight, range dependent on state of atmosphere	Major growth of military optoelectronic technology, lasers, and television during 1970s and 1980s.

Notes

* There is no accepted boundary between submillimetric radio waves and infra-red. Sometimes it is set at 6,000 gigahertz corresponding to 0.05 millimetre wavelength. There is a gradual change of properties.

† The boundary between infra-red and visible light is not absolutely sharp. Figures given here assume that visible light is from 0.0007 to 0.0004 millimetre wavelength. 1 hertz = 1 cycle/second; 1,000 hertz = 1 kilohertz; 1,000 kilohertz = 1 megahertz; 1,000 megahertz = 1 gigahertz.

VHF

Britain was ahead of Germany in one respect. This was the use of VHF for radio. Very High Frequency, 30 MHz to 300 MHz, is the band immediately above HF. Germany exploited this band for radar, with for example Freya, which worked on approximately 125 megahertz, but neglected it for radio.

VHF has significantly different properties to HF. It behaves much more like light. It travels in straight lines though it still penetrates buildings. It has less tendency to curve around the earth's surface. It goes up and out through the ionosphere without reflection. Most importantly, it does not come back down anywhere else.

Its range is therefore restricted and a VHF receiver only picks up transmitters which are within line of sight, or within a ground range measured in a few tens of kilometres. Distant interference is eliminated. But between the ground and aircraft the range is much greater, depending on the height of the aircraft. It may be two, three, even four hundred kilometres. Between one aircraft and another the range is even greater.

These factors put a premium on VHF for radio telephony between aircraft. The voice comes through loud and clear, an important consideration in the presence of high engine noise and other operational difficulties. Moreover, just as HF offers bandwidth for more channels than MF, so VHF offers more bandwidth still. A generous abundance of frequency channels is available, and several pre-tuned channels can be set up in advance for push-button selection.

With VHF there is no need to fiddle with the tuning knob, as may happen with HF, to try and escape from some unknown interference which may be coming from a very distant source. An instant choice of channels helps to get best reception and avoid jamming. The introduction of VHF for aircraft ground-to-air and air-to-air radio telephony was made by Britain at the beginning of the Second World War.

At this time German aviation used HF. German fighters used it for radio telephony and Germany bombers used its for wireless telegraphy. This continued the practice of the First World War, when voice communications had been found necessary for single seater aircraft, while multi-crew aircraft and Zeppelins used telegraphy. This difference in German practice meant that fighters and bombers could not intercommunicate. It proved an operational drawback for the German air force.

This did not however reflect any lack of technical competence on Germany's part with VHF. Germany used VHF for radar before Britain did. Moreover, above VHF comes UHF, Ultra High Frequency, and in this, the highest frequency band in use up to the

PLATE 6.1 **T1154. The Main Radio Transmitter of the British Bomber Offensive in the Second World War** The main radio equipment carried by British bombers in the Second World War was the T1154/R1155 (T = Transmitter, R = Receiver). This photograph shows the T1154. It had four frequency bands: 2–500 KHz, 2.5–4.5, 4.5–8.7 and 8.7 to 16.7 MHz. Thus HF predominated. The receiver, on the other hand offered five bands: 75–200, 200–500, 600–1,500 KHZ and 3.0–7.5, 7.5–18 Khz.

beginning of the war and until about halfway through it, Germany was the pioneer both with radio and radar.

UHF

UHF is Ultra High Frequency, from 300 megahertz to 3000 megahertz (=3 gigahertz). UHF has the characteristics of VHF, but more sharply evident. It is still more light-like. Germany not ony used UHF for the Seetakt radar, working as noted above on 375 megahertz, but pioneered it for military radio in the form of microwave communications links. It was possible to focus beams of UHF from one parabolic antenna to another, just as light might be projected from a searchlight.

Such beams were used to supplement landlines for interior point-to-point communications. They had an advangage over landlines in that the bandwidth of UHF is very large, bigger again than VHF. Conventional telegraphic signalling over cables has to make do with limited bandwidth. To put it another way, a single UHF link could carry a much larger amount of information. The narrow beams created no danger of remote interception.

While Germany introduced this technology for the armed forces on an extensive scale, the capability was not unique to Germany. A commercial communications link working in UHF was installed between Britain and France in 1931, but the initiative seems to have led nowhere.

This development did nothing to displace conventional cable from its military role. In both the German and British armies the laying of landlines was mechanised to accompany the movement of troops. The mobile military field telephone exchange appeared.

Between cable and radio, armies at the beginning of the Second World War had far more versatile communications than hitherto. But it was uniquely radio that kept pace with the most dramatic military development of the 1930s: *blitzkrieg*.

It was in Germany that the potential of *blitzkrieg* was realised, lightning war with mechanised formations. It could roll rapidly across large territories and promised swift solutions. Correspondingly it was the German Army which saw that this kind of war would be as dependent on radio as on the internal combustion engine.

So it proved to be. The field commanders followed their armoured and motorised columns in personal vehicles which were radio-equipped. Radio was necessary both for the cohesive action of small fighting groups and for communications between group and field headquarters. Striking forces were area-dispersed beyond possibility of visual control and command.

Blitzkrieg meant a land war in sharp contrast to the First World War or any previous war. The communications needs of the armies on the ground were paralleled by those of the forces supporting *Blitzkrieg* from the air. *Blitzkrieg* demanded, as no previous technique of war had ever done, intercommunication between the commands of all formations, from tanks to artillery and tactical aviation.

'C^3I'

The unique ability of HF to answer the needs of *blitzkrieg* has already been described. In grasping this fact, in exploiting it with armed forces for the first time comprehensively equipped for radio communications, Germany recognised what has become one of the most important priorities of modern military practice. Today it is referred to in various ways, sometimes as control and communications, more comprehensively as command, control, communications and intelligence – contracted to C^3I.

Whatever the terminology, essentially it all comes to the same thing, though modern technology multiplies the ways in which it can be achieved. It means a system to guarantee the flow of all information necessary for the conduct of military operations, all across the battlefield, under all circumstances. Today many other links may be used as well as HF radio, including satellite links, but HF radio was the first link to make it possible. It could not be done with MF or LF.

Despite the role of landlines, the need for radio did not disappear even when Germany's battle lines became static. Because of *blitzkrieg* much of continental Europe fell under German control. Everywhere lines of communication were extended. The German air force and the German navy operated from remote bases. There was continuous rotation and redeployment of forces. A prodigious communications requirement continued.

Cable could not meet every requirement. Landlines reached across Europe to provide communications links wherever this was possible, particularly in or near the German homeland. But whenever landlines were lacking, and this was not infrequently, the only alternative was radio. Long-distance communications were often made of necessity over a series of consecutive links, not all of which could use cable.

Many operational communications had to pass through radio at some stage, particularly for the air force and the navy. Police and other non-military services sometimes used radio. Without radio, the command and administration of German-occupied Europe would have been impossible. As activity levels varied from one geographical sector to another, a rise in radio transmissions became the typical pointer to impending local movements.

The position at the beginning of the Second World War can be contrasted with that at the beginning of the First. Then both sides used radio for naval deployments and both applied signals intelligence to try and discover the other's intentions. At the beginning of the Second World War, radio was used on a far greater scale, even more by air and land than at sea. The use was largely one-sided – by Germany. Surprisingly this had neither been foreseen nor adequately prepared for. War, it had been thought in Britain, would probably bring radio silence.

Britain and France were thrown back heavily on their traditional skills in signals intelligence. At first little was done with it. What was done in France could not affect the brief course of France's war. It became a legacy for Britain.

But at this time German signals intelligence was being very successful. It was successful against the main British user of radio, the navy, particularly since British codes frequently fell into German hands through ship sinkings. It was successful against the main French user of radio, the army, particularly in the period preceding the invasion of France in May 1940. It accurately disclosed French strength and positions.

Eventually the pendulum began to swing the other way, through the sheer volume of intercepted messages falling into the hands of British cryptanalysts. One of the effects of extensive German use of HF was that radio messages from the majority of users were recordable. This was the task of the British Y services – listening services. The number of messages recorded in Britain climbed up through hundreds a day and reached a thousand. Ultimately it exceeded 2000 a day.

Because of range effects a message might not be recorded at all listening stations, but would usually be picked up somewhere. Longer range messages were often picked up extremely well. The task called for operators with considerable skill. They needed the ability to tune their receivers to faint signals, to follow small variations of frequency, to take down barely audible Morse. They needed to become familiar with the way German radio nets worked. They had to attach great importance to recording the preamble which preceded transmission of the encrypted message itself. The preamble provided vital clues to decryption.

Enigma

In developing radio for war, Germany realised that without encryption radio would be useless, that the volume of material requiring encryption would grow immensely, and that traditional methods of encrypting and decrypting would seriously hamper communications.

She responded accordingly. She streamlined the process by mechanisation. The principal equipment she introduced was the celebrated

Enigma machine. This was derived from a machine originally produced for commercial telegraphy. The mode of operation, based on electric switches or relays, was typical of electromechanical engineering.

Germany refined Enigma for military use, adding to its security, and mass-produced it. The machine was basically a typewriter keyboard which automatically gave an encrypted output.

The output was not on paper. The machine had a bank of lamps with letters. In response to each input key stroke, one of the letters instantly lit up – the letter to be used in the encrypted message. This output was transcribed and handed to the radio operator. The process of encrypting a message was not much slower than typing it.

What crowned the efficiency of Enigma was that the process was directly reversible. For example, one might type in the letter A and the letter X would light up. Had one typed X, the letter lighting up would have been A.

Consequently, providing the Enigma at the receiving end had been put into the same initial setting as the sending machine, the encrypted message could be directly typed into it and the output would be the message again 'in clear'. Therefore decrypting took no longer than encrypting.

What actual substitution occurred, whether it was X for A or some other letter for A, was determined by the machines' setting. Enigma's setting changed automatically with each letter typed. Having given X for A the first time, the machine would probably give some other letter for A if A was the input again on the second stroke. The only letter it would not give was A itself; it never returned the same letter.

The important thing was that, so long as the machines were set identically to start with, the sequence of settings that the sending machine went through was the same as the sequence that the receiving machine went through. At any point, the receiving machine was ready to give an instant decrypt of the letter transmitted to it, despite the immense complexity of the encryption process.

Thanks to Enigma the labour of hand-encrypting and decrypting messages was eliminated – and with it, the inevitable loss of time. With electromechanical encryption and decryption, results were instant. Without it, radio could not have kept pace with the progress of actions, and could not have played the role envisaged for it in *blitzkrieg*.

Machines such as Enigma were not unique to Germany. Sooner or later they were in use by most combatants, for example the British Typex machine. What was exceptional about Enigma was its methodical introduction and use alongside radio on an unprecedented scale. In terms of electronic war, it was a partnership between electronic and electromechanical technology.

Achilles heel

The basic essential of radio communications with Enigma machines was for the sender to provide enough information about the setting of his machine for the receiver to bring his machine into the same setting. This was Enigma's operational simplicity – and also its operational Achilles heel. The information was provided through the message preamble, which was why the preamble was the cryptanalysts' main point of attack.

Electromechanical cryptography became widely used. Germany was fundamentally correct in calculating that it was capable of providing adequate security to enable the war use of radio. Much use of Enigma defied cryptographers throughout the war. But much

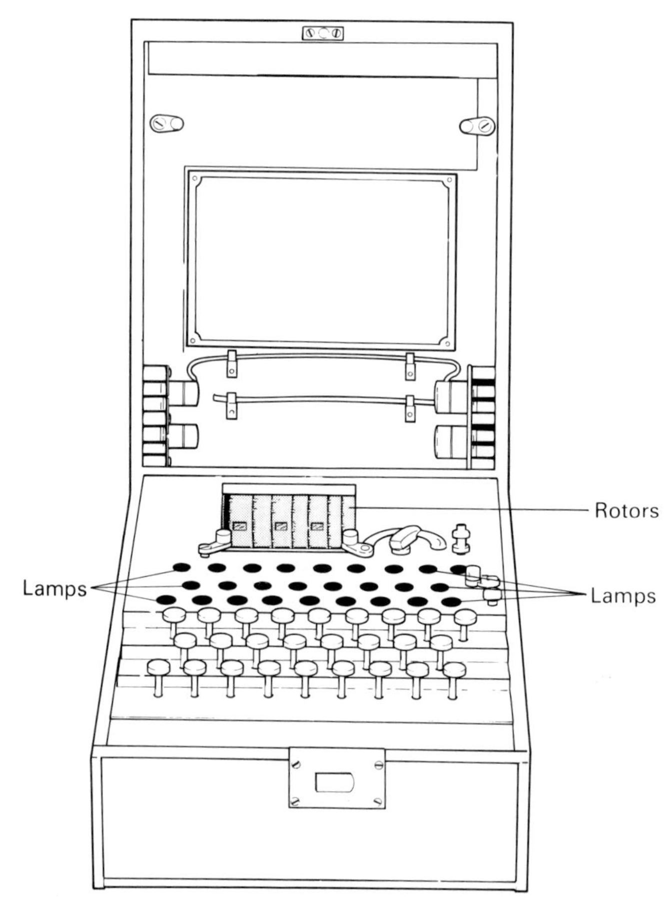

Fig. 6.1 **Enigma** Enigma machine showing typewriter keyboard (front), lamps which light up to show letters and rotors (back).

other use was eventually given away, chiefly by operator slackness, failure to adhere strictly to proper procedures. For this entirely human reason no refinements could make electromechanical cryptography entirely secure. Operator slackness was exploited by cryptographic efforts on a scale and with technology which Germany had not foreseen.

To obtain its alphabet-shuffling effects, Enigma used an alphabetic plugboard and a variable number of interchangeable internal rotors. Enigma had to be standardised for particular groups of users, the army, air force, navy and so forth. This was done by providing a particular group with its own rotor set. This might for example comprise five rotors. At any one time, three of these might be in use; to decrypt a message it would be necessary to know which three, and in what order they should be inserted in the machine. Additional information defining the setting would specify the initial positions of the rotors and the cross-pluggings of the plugboard.

In the circumstances the wiring of the rotors, and what is generally and rather loosely referred to as 'keys', that is the rotors in use at particular times together with rotor and plugboard positions, became an intelligence target. It was attacked in various ways.

Sometimes machines could be captured, in circumstances which left doubt about their fate. Destruction or throwing overboard of Enigma machines, rotors, and lists of keys, was top priority for the commander whose position, ship or submarine was overwhelmed. But it did not always happen.

The system was to some extent proofed against these inevitable contingencies by regular key changes, procedural changes, and above all change or addition of rotors. However it could never be completely proofed. Losses tended to have a cumulative effect. Ultimately it could never be known exactly what had been lost, and how much help it had given to hostile cryptanalysts. Changing the complete system was impossible; there was too much invested in it.

Many cryptographic battles were waged during the Second World War, but the most massive of all was undoubtedly that waged against Enigma. Its importance was first realised in Poland. The Polish attack on Enigma through the 1930s became a legacy for British cryptographers after Poland had fallen.

Other machines similar to Enigma were used by Germany, taking their inspiration from the commercial teletypewriters and teleprinters which enabled a message to be transmitted by cable in a single 'on line' operation. With teletypewriters and teleprinters the message, typed in at the sending end, was instantly turned into a code similar to Morse but known as Baudot and transmitted down the cable, where it gave an instant print-out.

This system was adapted to military needs by introducing rotors to encrypt the stream of Baudot signals and decrypt it at the receiving end, so that an instant print-out in clear was still obtained. The encrypted Baudot signals were often sent by radio. Geheimschreiber was perhaps the first machine to support this technique. While Enigma dominated field and operational cryptography and general military use, the teletype system was used by Germany for traffic at diplomatic or high command levels. Messages thus sent, and intercepted in Britain, were referred to as 'Fish' and were the most rewarding target for cryptanalysis.

Confronting an unimaginably copious flow of intercepted signals, the British responded, as they had in the First World War, by centralising their cryptanalytic forces at one point. In the Second World War this was at Bletchley, outside London. To Bletchley came a greater volume of German signals, recorded at many interception points within and without the British Isles, than came to any single point in Germany. Here unique developments occurred.

Computerisation

Formerly, cryptanalysis was a manual task, handled by gifted individuals. At Bletchley it became a team operation with ever-increasing assistance from at first mechanical, then electromechanical, and finally electronic equipment. In other words, the mechanisation of encryption was matched by the mechanisation and finally the computerisation of cryptanalysis.

Bletchley had a need for machines to reproduce Enigma's function; given the appropriate key and settings such equipment produced decrypts. Special cryptanalytic equipment was not necessary for this; the British Typex machine was adapted for the job. But most of the work of decryption was in making tests to find settings which would start to turn an encrypted message into recognisable German. The most formidable task facing Bletchley's cryptanalysts was to speed the process of finding these settings. Initially this was done by manual methods aided by electromechanical 'bombes'.

But the task became progressively tougher, above all against 'Fish' traffic. Necessity compelled the British to turn to the electron tube. The electron tube had never invaded the electromechanical domain of telegraphy and telephony from its own domain of radio because it was unnecessary. It would have been unduly complex and expensive. But when it was adapted to perform similar functions, it worked much more rapidly for it contained no moving mechanical parts.

It is now accepted that the electronic computer had its beginnings at Bletchley during the Second World War. This is where the advantage of electronics became clear. The security of an encryption machine could be measured by the complexity of the alphabet-shuffling it could perform in the time available, that is, in practice, as letters were typed into it. Electronic equipment used time much more productively than electromechanical equipment. It could test very rapidly.

This was the work of the electronic cryptanalytic computers designed by the British and called 'Colossus', ten of which were produced.[2] Ultimately it was possible to test-read messages for cryptanalysis at 25,000 characters a second, using parallel processing. In the last part of the war, the battle with teletype system encryption using the 'Colossi' became the major direction of British cryptanalysis.

Thus the battle of strategic signals intelligence culminated as a battle of the electronic era against the electromechanical era. The electronic era won.

Germany frequently and rigorously examined her cryptographic security. But she missed this turn of events, which undercut the assumptions on which her fundamental calculations of radio security were based.

Ironically, the fact that the electronic computer was the dawn of a new technological age was missed by the British. After the war, they never commercially exploited their achievement. Instead it was kept as the closest of state secrets.

The reason for this secrecy has been suggested as follows. The British, after the war, sold captured Enigma machines to a wide variety of users, some if not most of whom would be expected to use them to transmit diplomatic and military secrets. The British wished to conceal that the encryption which Enigma and teletype-system machines provided had become transparent to them.[3]

Be this as it may, the secrecy probably cost more than anything it gained. While it was being maintained, the electronic computer began to evolve elsewhere and Britain's wartime lead was lost.

Balanced Favours

Eventually, long after the war, the considerable British cryptographic success against German radio communications became widely known. This does not mean that radio worked uniquely in Britain's favour. At the beginning of the war, radio worked in Germany's favour. Germany could not have controlled her fighting machine without it. Moreover she was ready at this time with her own chain of radio intercept stations and applied the methods of signals intelligence with striking success.

Germany's intensive operational use of radio in the invasions of Norway, France, Belgium and Holland in 1940 far exceeded British expectations and preparedness. At this time Germany was breaking British naval codes while the British were unable to break either German navy or army codes. The British paid with the loss of numerous ships including the aircraft carrier *Glorious* off the Norwegian coast. This pattern was to be later repeated in the desert war in North Africa.

During the Norwegian campaign Britain did break into the German radio traffic called 'Red', which produced a flow rate of one thousand decrypted messages a day. This was Britain's first major cryptographic success in the Second World War. It made clear that Germany offered a big 'radio target' to Britain, bigger than Britain did to Germany.

From this point on signals intelligence increasingly became Britain's special weapon against Germany, rather as submarines were Germany's special weapon against Britain. The reasons were similar. Signals intelligence attacked Germany's crucial reliance on radio communications, just as submarines attacked Britain's crucial reliance on maritime communications.

In the First World War, what mainly hinged on the radio battle was the war at sea. The overall effect was for radio to prevent serious surprise or wrong guessing in this. It thereby made more certain the stalemate implicit in the approximate equivalence of forces. It was a stabilising factor.

In the Second World War very much more hinged on the radio battle. Radio enabled Germany's conquest of Europe and was indispensable to her continuing conduct of the war. But increasingly it became a drain of intelligence, damaging the German war effort. Germany used radio intensively but failed to protect radio security adequately – a classic syndrome of electronic warfare. As a result advantage in the radio battle swung from Germany in the beginning to Britain later. It was a serious advantage for Germany to concede.

In specific areas, such as naval warfare, it incurred operational penalties such as the sinking of submarines and supply ships whose patrol areas and rendezvous points were disclosed. In others it allowed Britain an improved appreciation of the way the war was developing and increased confidence in strategic decisions.

A Strategic Reassessment

This was particularly clear in 1941 and 1942, in the highly critical sequence of situations which transformed the war from the deadlock of Britain and Germany confronting each other alone to truly global conflict. This sequence began with the German invasion of Russia in June 1941. Britain's first requirement was to re-assess her own strategic position, most crucially the threat of invasion.

Conventional judgement was that Operation 'Barbarossa', the invasion of Russia, was a necessary preliminary to Operation 'Sealion', the invasion of Britain, which would be completed all the more speedily once Moscow had been taken.

At this time Britain obtained the only certain information of the progress of the war on the Russian front by signals intelligence, intercepting German air force and army traffic. Little information was forthcoming from Russia herself, though Russia was an ally.

In practice, the fact that intelligence was acquired from German signals added to the confidence with which it was evaluated. It indicated that within five or six weeks the invasion of Russia was lagging its timetable so seriously that the invasion of Britain could be discounted for the foreseeable future.

This vital strategic determination was swiftly followed by others as the war's whole aspect changed.

The United States and Japan went to war in December 1941, through Japan's attack on the US fleet in its base at Pearl Harbor. At this time the German–Russian struggle was reaching its climax in front of Moscow. But Japan, remembering defeats in 1938 and 1939 at the hands of Russian forces on the Manchurian border, did not hasten to declare war on Russia.

Japanese, American and British anxieties all alike focused on the outcome of the thrust towards Moscow. Its progress became a primary intelligence target for the three nations.

If Germany was prevailing, Japan could safely declar war on Russia. Signals intelligence revealed to the West what was happening. Decrypted German communications disclosed that the tide of battle was ceasing to flow in Germany's favour. In January 1942 intercepted Japanese diplomatic traffic from Berlin to Tokyo disclosed Japanese concern at the German retreat. The likelihood of Japan embroiling herself in war with Russia retreated too.

When the German offensive was at last renewed, it was concentrated towards the south of the Soviet Union and brought German arms to Stalingrad by August 1942. This threatened a German breakthrough into the Middle East, causing another crisis for the Allies. Emergency actions were considered. But long before the threat was removed by a manifest German collapse, the strain behind the German front was revealed by signals intelligence, and a German appeal for Japan to declare hostilities against Russia was intercepted.

This confirmed the changing direction of the war. It gave confidence to Allied strategy, which still had months to wait until the full scale of the German disaster at Stalingrad became evident in February 1943.

In this way signals intelligence related the significance of a particular battlefield to the overall struggle, and pointed in advance to the strategic turning point.

Later the contribution of electronic cryptanalysis against teletype system encryption was of special value to the Allies at the time of Operation 'Overlord', the invasion of France in 1944, in intercepting communications from the German high command in Paris.

Top-level eavesdropping

To compare with the strategic achievements of Allied signals intelligence, from September 1941 to early 1944 Germany was listening in to the radiotelephone link between Britain and the United States.

The only means of telephony across the Atlantic, first demonstrated by radio during the First World War, remained radio in the Second. It is technically difficult to provide adequate security on telephone calls. The technique of slicing the audio frequencies of the voice into a number of bands and scrambling these is anything but foolproof.

Germany established an interception station in Holland to record Anglo-American transatlantic telephone transmissions. A directional antenna array was used in Britain, but it was not possible to prevent a sufficiently strong signal reaching Holland. The return signal received from America would in any case have been about equally strong in Britain and Holland.

Germany was regularly successful in recording and unscrambling the conversations. On at least one occasion a call between Roosevelt and Churchill was eavesdropped. Interceptions such as this should have provided high-grade diplomatic information, but apparently little use was made of any information which was obtained.

A radio-cryptographic war flared between Germany and Russia with the German invasion in June 1941. The initial *Blitzkrieg* gave way to more static warfare. But given the vast distances of the front there was an undoubted premium on radio communications.

German evidence testifies that, initially, tactical Russian radio security gave much away. Russian evidence concedes that communications was the weakest area of their technology as compared with German.[4] This probably relates to the general quality, quantity, and variety of Russian communications equipment rather than cryptographic techniques.

To begin with Russia did not use cipher machines. These were later supplied to her by her Western allies, but hardly in sufficient quantity to make a significant difference. She also acquired German machines, by capture and from her allies. As the war progressed she undoubtedly broke the security of some German radio traffic.

As noted already, Britain began to intercept and read German military traffic from parts of the Eastern Front and from the start of the invasion. Some of this information was supplied to Russia, its origins disguised. Britain had little confidence in Russia's cryptographic security; this reflected earlier British penetration of some Russian codes.

Nevertheless Russia had evidently learnt to protect top-level diplomatic traffic before the war, otherwise her diplomacy would have been transparent whereas in fact it was opaque. Moreover thanks to thorough penetration of the British security services, including at Bletchley, Russia must have been aware of British capabilities.

Officially, Britain desisted from intercepting Russian communications as from the German invasion of Russia, when Russia became an ally. Considering the premium which soon arose on information from the Eastern Front this decision was questionable.

Probably, however, Russian military radio could not be satisfactorily intercepted from the British Isles. The case was evidently otherwise with German military radio. This point to differences in the frequencies of the equipment in use. Russia had not followed Germany's progress up the frequency scale. She was probably still using MF. For the British to intercept this a nearer listening post would have been necessary.

Whatever the truth of the matter, this would explain the fact that Russia, having allowed Britain to open a radio intercept station near Murmansk, ostensibly for listening to German military traffic, later closed it. Russian suspicions had been stirred that British enthusiasm for radio interception was not exclusively directly against the common enemy.

At all events, Russia went into the Second World War with a system of radio communications of variable cryptographic efficiency. Diplomatically, it was good. Militarily, it was sometimes good and sometimes bad. There was also another dimension – espionage.

Thanks to ideological sympathisers, Russia was able to exploit internal espionage to an extent not possible to any other country. This espionage often passed its results back by radio, as for example the Lucy Ring and the *Rote Kapelle* in Western Europe. Radio however was the weakness which ultimately betrayed these organisations to German signals intelligence, through direction finding.

The Germans unquestionably broke numerous Russian codes with advantage in the opening stages of the war, but this advantage declined. It is not known to what extent Russian cryptanalysts succeeded against the Enigma machine, but as the war progressed Russia was forced to improve the security of her radio cryptography.

The United States versus Japan

By contrast the drama of the radio-cryptographic conflict between Japan and the United States was rising years before fighting between these powers began. The United States directed increasing effort to intercept Japanese communications and to understand Japanese cryptographic techniques from the 1920s and through the 1930s. The conflict between the countries was basically maritime from beginning to end and forms one of the subjects of Chapter 11.

Japan received cryptographic assistance from Germany during the 1930s in the form of the Enigma machine, which was adapted to the special requirements of the Japanese language. Japanese language and culture both hindered and helped the task of cryptanalysis. Nevertheless American experts achieved remarkable success, reconstructing by inference from study of Japanese ciphers the general characteristics of Japanese cryptographic equipment and the way it worked. Japanese traffic was being intermittently read long before the onset of crisis – the Japanese attack on Pearl Harbor.

With hindsight, both signals intelligence and radar gave enough warning for the United States armed forces to have been on guard when the Japanese attacked. The blow was not averted because these instruments of electronic warfare were not highly enough rated at the time. But once war began in earnest, Japan's cryptographic inferiority became increasingly serious. In fact it doomed her.

Her strength was sapped by various incidents, none more spectacular than the loss of her foremost commander, Admiral Yamamoto, in April 1943, after 16 months of war. Following interception of radio messages, Yamamoto's plane was shot down by American fighters.

Yet the battle zone was such – the vast waters and scattered islands of the Pacific – that there was no alternative to radio for commanding and controlling Japanese forces. The Far Eastern theatre of war was as big as the European and North Atlantic one and it was no less dependent on radio communications.

Much more starkly for Japan than Germany, the imperative was to make radio communications secure, or else lose the war. The issue was as simple as that, even if it was never understood. Japan conceded to the United States in radar technology as well as in signals intelligence, and this compounded her difficulties.

It is in the nature of the radio intercept battle for its victims not to realise what they are losing, except when it is already too late. When loss of radio security is suspected, because many things have gone wrong, a bitter position arises. Investigations are pursued in many directions, sometimes wildly.

Radio cannot be dispensed with, but an investment in new codes and procedures demands prodigious time and effort. Even then, without knowing exactly how the leak has arisen, it is impossible to be sure that the right measures have been taken. Not surprisingly, there is a tendency to reach a formal conclusion, after much agonising and mutual recrimination, that nothing, after all, has gone wrong.

The Second World War even more vividly demonstrated the importance of military cryptography than the First. It remains second to none among the crucial arenas of electronic warfare.

7

The Challenge of Radar

THE RADAR BATTLE contrasted in every way with the radio battle. Radio was ready for the Second World War, but an intense scientific effort was needed to bring radar into being. Radar was developed from radio, but formidable problems had to be overcome such as radio never needed to tackle. Radar changed and developed during the war much more than radio. It absorbed by far the major proportion of electronic research and development.

Where do the technical difficulties of radar lie, as compared with radio?

Basically the idea of radar is simple. Radio waves, launched into space from an antenna, reflect off some objects. They ignore others. Conveniently for military purposes, they reflect strongly off such metallic objects as aircraft, tanks and ship – metallic objects that are good conductors of electricity.

What happens is that radio waves induce electric currents in such targets. These currents are minute compared with those in the originating antenna. Nevertheless they in turn radiate radio waves – much feebler. In effect the original radiation is scattered in many directions. This scattered radiation is what radar tries to detect. In detecting it, radar reveals the presence of the object. Good reflectors can be easily picked out against a less reflective background. Aircraft can be picked out against the sky or ships against the sea.

Although the principle was simple, to realise it in practice was another matter. The coming of radar had to wait on the advance of basic radio.

The first problem was power. Only a tiny part of the radiation from a transmitting antenna reaches a particular receiving antenna – unless the latter is extremely close, which is seldom the case. More usually the

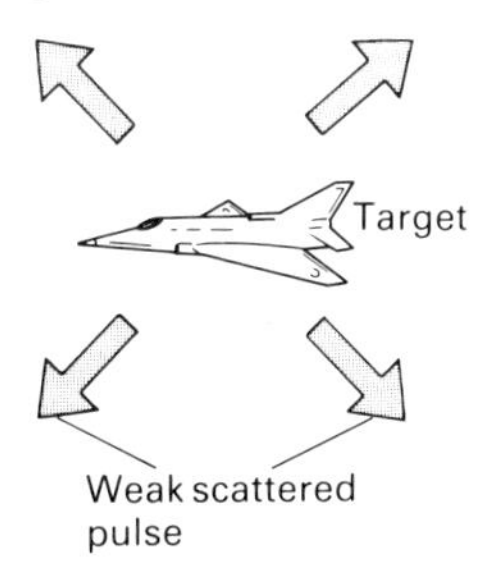

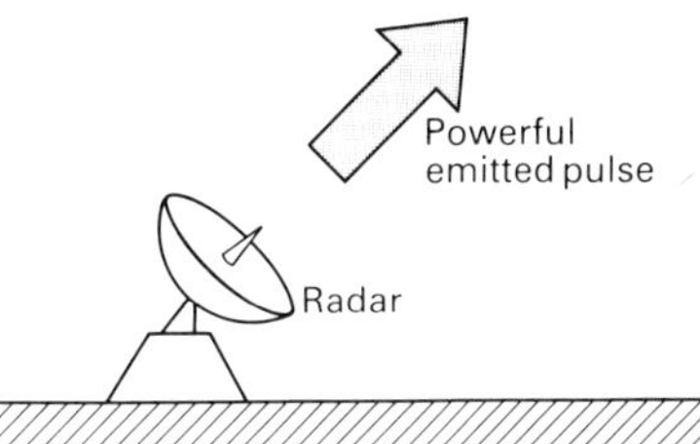

FIG. 7.1 **The Principle of Radar** A powerful pulse of radiation transmitted by the radar antenna induces electric currents in the target. These currents in turn radiate a pulse, but very much weaker, and scattered in all directions. Some of this scattered radiation returns to the radar antenna, which now functions as a receiving antenna. The time between the transmission and return of the pulse measures the target range. The return pulse is only detected when the radar is 'looking' at the target.

range is from tens to hundreds or thousands of kilometres. Radio copes with this circumstance by amplifying the received signal.

With radar, on the signal's outgoing leg, the target itself is the receiving antenna. As usual, only a tiny part of the transmitted power falls upon it. This tiny amount of power is not amplified, as it would be with radio. Then for the return leg, the target is cast in the role of the transmitting antenna, using only this weak unamplified power. It radiates, but by radio standards very feebly.

This is the signal which returns to the radar antenna – which started off as a transmitting antenna but becomes a receiving antenna. On this return leg its power is reduced again. It is reduced in exactly the same ratio as on the outgoing leg. It has become very weak indeed. If it is reduced a million times over the outgoing leg, it is reduced a million times again on the return leg – a thousand billion times over both.[1] This is the signal which radar must detect. Only at this point can amplification begin.

Therefore to make radar operate over worthwhile ranges, high power in the transmitter has to be combined with high amplification in the receiver. Power and amplification are combined to a degree unnecessary in radio.

Even high amplification is not enough by itself. There is a tendency for electron tubes to generate a certain amount of 'radio noise'. This noise, self-generated by the receiver, is amplified equally with the wanted signal. This puts a limit on the smallness of the signal that the receiver can detect, however high its amplification is. The radar receiver must operate as 'noiselessy' as possible.

The Radar Antenna

The second problem was the antenna itself. In radar the antenna is a far more critical component of the system than in radio. Simple rods or wires no longer suffice. To project enough power, channelling or focusing in a particular direction is required. For this purpose an array of rods or wires is necessary, or even a parabolic antenna. In the same way an array or parabola is necessary to pick up the faint return signal.

The fact that the antenna is directional gives a means of finding the direction from which the signal is being reflected. If the antenna can be rotated, scanning the horizon, it picks up the signal strongly only when it is 'looking' at the target. The larger and more elaborate the array,

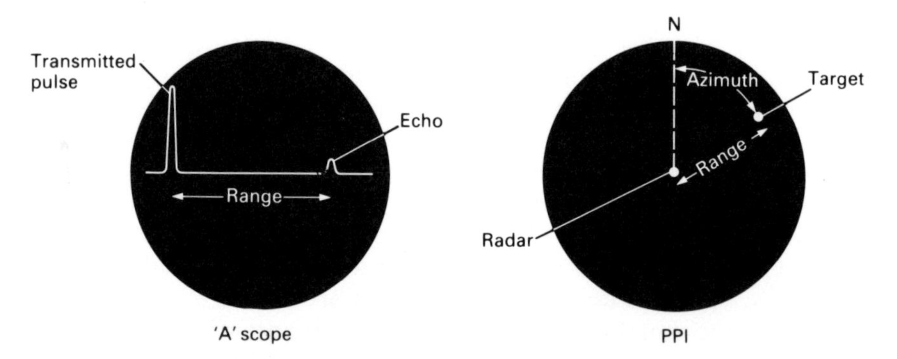

Fig. 7.2 **Forms of Radar Display** On the left above, the 'A' scope, with a baseline corresponding to a fixed time interval. The transmitted pulse registers at the left, the returned echo showing as a 'blip' at some distance to the right – the distance being proportional to the range to the target. On the right, the 'PPI' (plan position indicator), in which the radar is at the centre of the display, which shows not only distance but the direction of the target. In this illustration, North is assumed to be at the top.

within limits, the more directional and therefore efficient the antenna can be. A parabolic antenna can be very efficient. To summarise: radar put a premium upon large, rotatable antennas such as radio never required.

The third problem was frequency. Frequency determines the dimensions of the antenna. The law that applies to radio applies even more so to radar: to radiate efficiently the antenna's dimensions must be comparable with the wavelength of the radiation. Radar cannot get off as lightly as radio.

With radio it is generally enough if the antenna size is half the wavelength. But with radar, given the need to create a directional beam, the antenna size has to be several times the wavelength. The bigger the antenna is in relation to the wavelength, the more sharply directional is the beam, and the more accurately the position of a target can be resolved. Low and medium frequencies got radio started, but could contribute nothing to the beginning of radar, for in radar use they would necessitate gigantic antenna arrays, kilometres in size.

For the sake of practical antennas, radar needed frequencies in the VHF band of 80 to 100 megahertz or above. The antenna size then became a matter of metres or tens of metres. Early radar did use lower frequencies but the antenna size was inconvenient. Shipborne radar in particular had to start with VHF radar.

But to begin with, as the frequency scale was ascended, power fell off. Radio technology had not produced components which could keep up the same supply of power at frequencies in VHF and above as in lower frequency bands. Radar asked for a combination of frequency and power which radio had never attempted. The key components were electron tubes, and to make radar possible their frequency range and power output had to move upwards.

Other problems had to be solved. Radio was a continuous transmission of radiation. Early experiments approached radar in the same way. Some progress was made with continuous wave radar, but it soon became clear that radar really needed pulses – short repeated bursts of radiation at extremely high power.

If a short pulse was transmitted, the returning echo could be listened for against a background of silence. The interval between the sending of the pulse and its echo return was the time of the round trip to the target and back. The target's range could be measured.

However, to measure the interval between the pulse and the echo, it had to be visualised. Again in contrast to radio, radar needed a visual output, which the cathode ray tube provided. The cathode ray tube could analyse very small periods of time, by displaying a baseline corresponding to a brief known interval. On this the transmitted and received signals showed up as blips. The separation between the blips

TABLE 7.1 *Radar Band Designations*

Second World War	P	Originally signified 'pulsed', distinguishing radar from radio, later as radar progressed up the frequency spectrum became the lowest of several radar bands, signifying the VHF/lower UHF region, the others being:
	L	'Long', about 1 gigahertz
	S	'Short', the basic magnetron radar band, typically about 3 gigahertz (as in H_2S)
	X	About 3 times above S band, typically about 10 gigahertz (as in in H_2X)
	K	About 9 times above S band, typically about 25 gigahertz (as in in H_2K)
Post-War		With international use, civilian as well as military, the standard designations VHF and UHF were introduced, the bands required more accurate definition, and supplementary bands were required in SHF. At the same time, radar was restricted to narrow choices of frequencies within the bands. Thus UHF covered most of the old P band, the L band, and most of the S band, but the term 'UHF radar' meant a radar working at certain frequencies in the UHF below L band. *The practical significance of L, S, X, and K was unchanged*:
	VHF	133–144, 216–225 megahertz
	UHF	420–450, 890–942 megahertz
	L	1.215–1.4 gigahertz (nominal L band 1–2 gigahertz)
	S	2.3–2.5, 2.7–3.7 gigahertz (nominal S band 2–4 gigahertz)
	C	5.25–5.925 gigahertz (nominal C band 4–8 gigahertz)
	X	8.5–10.68 gigahertz (nominal X band 8–12 gigahertz)
	Ku	13.4–14, 15.7–17.7 gigahertz (nominal Ku band 12–18 gigahertz)
	K	24.05–24.25 gigahertz (nominal K band 18–27 gighertz)
	Ka	33.4–36 gigahertz (nominal Ka band 27–40 gigahertz)
US/NATO		Military system with letters A through M designating the whole frequency spectrum up to 100 gigahertz. The traditional L band becomes D band, S band becomes E/F band, X band becomes I/J band, K is unchanged.
	A	0–250 megahertz
	B	250–500 megahertz
	C	500–1000 megahertz
	D	1–2 gigahertz
	E	2–3 gigahertz

TABLE 7.1 CONTINUED *Radar Band Designations*

	F	3–4 gigahertz
	G	4–6 gigahertz
	H	6–8 gigahertz
	I	8–10 gigahertz
	J	10–20 gigahertz
	K	20–40 gigahertz
	L	40–60 gigahertz
	M	60–100 gigahertz
General practice	A mixture of systems is used, usually L and S with I and J replacing X and Ku. No ambiguity is entailed. But C band is ambiguous unless the context is clear.	

could be scaled off to indicate the echo interval, and therefore the target range.

Radar differs again from radio in using a single antenna. The same antenna is used to send the pulse and listen for the echo. This is not absolutely necessary: the type of radar which uses separate transmitting and receiving antennas, located some distance apart, is occasionally employed, being known as bistatic. But monostatic radar, on a single site and usually with a single antenna, is far more convenient and has become the general standard.

Duplex Working

Reaching this solution meant clearing another technical hurdle. It meant finding a way of isolating the receiver from the transmitter. For if both are connected to the same antenna, although the transmitter only operates for a tiny fraction of the total time while the pulse is being sent, the power during this time will wreck the supersensitive receiver.

Only gradually did various solutions to the problems of 'duplex working' appear. These disconnect the receiver from the antenna for a brief instant while the pulse is transmitted, then reconnect it so that it can listen for the echo.

The major part of radar's many problems broadly reduced to the single problem of frequency. When Germany, Britain, the United States and the Soviet Union tackled the challenges of radar in the 1930s, they found it possible to work in the frequency range from about 25 megahertz to 600 megahertz, that is in the HF and VHF bands and lower part of the UHF band.

In the UHF band Germany was undoubtedly ahead. She could work up to about 600 megahertz; the British navy followed the same path more slowly. Above this point everybody's technology reached a barrier: it was impossible to generate adequate power. But from 25 to

600 megahertz there was scope to solve the radar problems. A generation of equipments sprang up in this frequency range.

As explained in the previous chapter, in actual battle usage, Germany and Britain were the undoubted twin radar pioneers. But in these countries radar developed in contrasting ways. In Germany it followed one main stream and produced a number of classic solutions. In Britain it trifurcated, with spectacular variations of technology.

The German development started in earnest in 1933, when Dr Rudolph Kuhnhold began work on radar for the German navy. The Gema company was formed as a result in 1934 and the Freya radar was produced by Gema in 1936. Intended for coastal surveillance of surface vessels, Freya also proved effective against aircraft. Before the end of 1936 it was ordered by both the German navy and air force.

Freya operated on 125 megahertz, in VHF, and was on a design pattern which became classic. The antenna was formed of vertical radiating elements making up a flat, relatively compact array. The array contained two rows, one above the other, each containing six radiators (that is individual rod antennas), and was about 33 feet square. It was rotated to scan the horizon. Because the antenna elements were vertical the radiation was vertically polarised. Freya worked on a power of 20 kilowatts.

In Britain radar had a political start in 1935. At the beginning of this year Britain was surprised by a German claim to have achieved parity in air forces. It was soon realised that the German air force was in fact larger and that there was no immediate prospect of overtaking it. This put the British prime minister in an embarrassing position, for he had undertaken that this would not happen.

Suddenly there was an urgent requirement for homeland defence against air attack. This triggered the development of radar specifically for support of the British air force. The development was directly driven from the highest political level. This was in contrast to the development of radar in Germany, where it was not at this time a specific subject of top-level policy. It was also in contrast to the development of radar in the British navy, where it tended to be politically overlooked.

Watson-Watt and Chain Home

Responsibility for developing Britain's area-defence radar, in fulfilment of the political directive, was given to a team headed by Robert Watson-Watt, working mainly at a base at Bawdsey on the British east coast.

Watson-Watt's background was in the relatively academic field of radio research into the ionosphere. HF was used, because HF was uniquely able to probe the ionosphere. Higher frequencies went straight up through the ionosphere without returning.

Watson-Watt worked with what he understood. He swiftly adapted

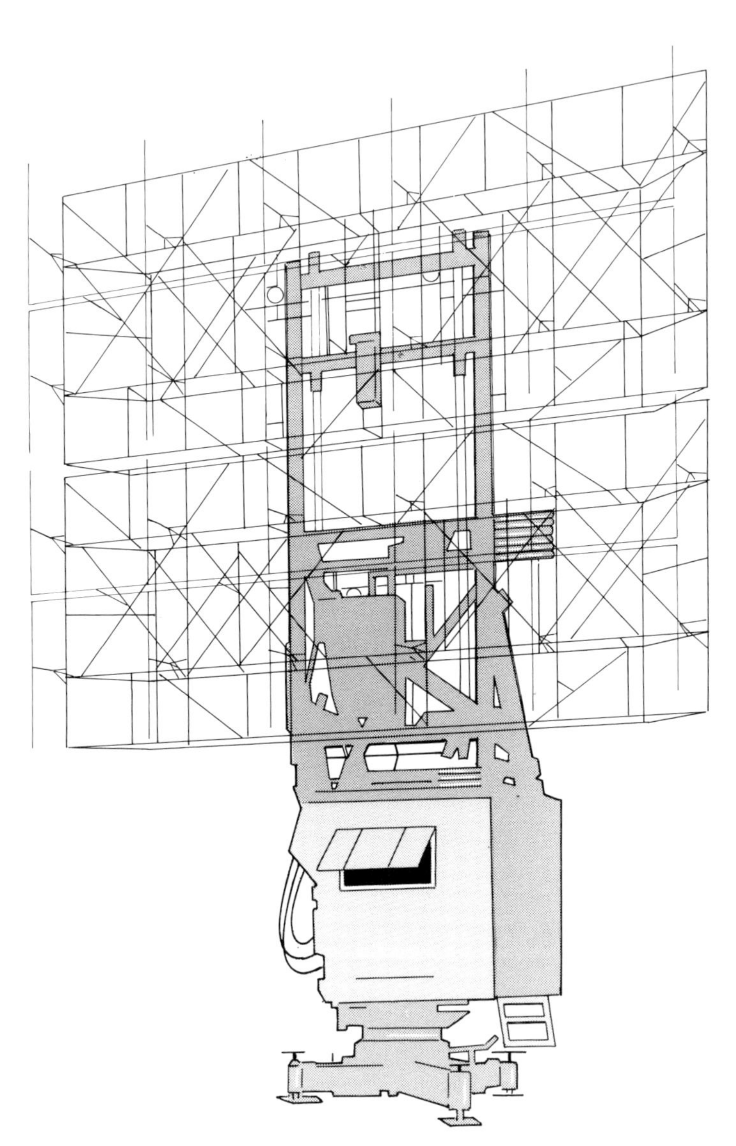

FIG. 7.3 **Freya** Working at about 125 MHz and rotating through 360 degrees, Freya was the main German surveillance radar throughout the Second World War, deployed for both coastal and inland surveillance.

his HF technology to defensive purposes. In any case he considered HF had special advantages. Driven by what was rightly seen as a matter of extreme urgency, the threat of war within an unknown but possibly very short time scale, he cut off introduction of new technology from the end of 1935.

The executive effectiveness of Watson-Watt's approach was unquestionable. By the actual outbreak of war in September 1939 the radar system he had devised was embodied in an operational chain of eight stations covering practically the entire eastern coast of Britain and half the southern coast. This was called Chain Home. The 'Home' emphasised that similar installations were planned elsewhere in the British Empire, notably on Malta in the Mediterranean.

Chain Home covered a much larger geographic span than the short stretch of German coast open to the North Sea which Freya covered – 1500 kilometres against 250, even though the number of Freya stations was the same – eight. Moreover the stations were linked by cable into a defensive communications network enabling centralised control of the British fighter force. This was an impressive feat of organisation.

It was also far-sighted, in that this central coordination was made a requirement from the start. Experience has since shown that any chain of defensive radar stations gathers extra strength from being centrally linked. It is able to react more quickly and effectively. The Freya coastal chain reacted rather slowly until increasing defensive urgency compelled central linking.

Nevertheless the initial choice of HF for Chain Home imposed practical limitations. The individual station left much to be desired compared with Freya.

HF implied relatively long wavelength and correspondingly large antenna arrays to radiate adequate power. Frequencies were typically from 20 to 30 megahertz, in the upper part of the HF band, with wavelengths from 15 to 10 metres. Transmission at any one station required four 360-foot-high masts, 180 feet apart, between which the antenna wires were strung horizontally at various heights. The radiation was therefore horizontally polarised, in distinction to Freya.

The returned signal was received, not by the same antenna array as with Freya, but on four separate 240-foot-high masts. These supported pairs of simple horizontal rod antennas, arranged cross-wise – 'crossed dipoles'. Separate transmitting and receiving antennas did not make Chain Home a bistatic radar, since the antennas were all on one site.

The whole installation was extremely large. It could not rotate as Freya did. The transmitter did not scan but spread each pulse of radiation simultaneously and fairly evenly over a fixed 100-degree sector of the horizon. In effect the sector was floodlit with radiation. For this reason more power was needed than with the narrow-beam Freya,

PLATE 7.1 **Chain Home** Chain Home provided the world's first strategic air defence radar network, erected along the east and south coasts of Britain (later extended to the west coast). It used High Frequency and consequently demanded large installations. 360-foot-high transmitter masts are seen on the left of the photograph above and 240-foot receiver masts on the right (*Photo: By courtesy of GEC-Marconi*)

up to a megawatt. Direction finding on the returned signal depended on comparing signal strengths in the crossed dipole antennas.

Detection of targets was possible only within the limits of the 100-degree sector. This of course was adequate to the needs of a coastal chain of stations in which each station covered one sector. The system was conceived for exactly this requirement.

The Filter Room

Problems and ambiguities of target identification might arise, but in principle these could be resolved by comparison between adjoining sectors, for the outward views overlapped considerably and incoming aircraft would normally show up in more than one sector. Inputs from various stations were passed back to a central 'Filter Room', and it was here that the indications provided by the various stations of the network were interpreted.

The Filter Room played a key role in the British Chain Home system. The individual station was not as effective in resolving and locating targets as a radar of Freya type, which rotated and worked on a frequency almost five times as high. It was the central Filter Room which countered this weakness.

Many criticisms may be offered of Chain Home but in practice it did what it had been designed to do. In the Battle of Britain in 1940 it gave the service it had been intended for. It thereby vindicated its creator, Watson-Watt. He set out in 1935 to build it not knowing how long fate was giving him. Eventually he beat fate by at least a year, possibly more.

Many others in history have failed where Watson-Watt succeeded. Freya was better technology, but the same race against time never applied to its development and introduction.

Limitations of the System

Having vindicated Watson-Watt once, Chain Home did not vindicate him again. It continued to be operated but it was not equal to the subsequent demands of the war.

Chain Home depended considerably upon the human factor – the skill of its operators. All radars depend to some degree on their operators, in ways which are not easily defined but are largely intuitive. Chain Home depended probably more than any other. By the same token it gave much scope to intuition and expertise. Women found themselves fighting in the front line of electronic warfare as Chain Home operators. Being intuitive, they displayed special aptitude.

Nevertheless Chain Home missed much that Freya offered. Freya functioned throughout the war, finally against a ferocity of attack that Chain Home never had to contend with. Freya proved to be a prototype of radar design valid in some ways to the present day. Chain Home on the other hand had no development potential. It was a dead end. This fact was apparent during the war itself, as various expedients were enforced upon the British to remedy its shortcomings, beginning from 1940.

The amazing thing about Chain Home however is that, dead end that it was, it took a long time to reach its end. It survived from the 1930s into the 1950s – long after Freya had vanished. It fell out of use at the end of the Second World War but was restored to operation in the 1950s when tension in Europe was rising again. Britain fulfilled a post-war export order to Argentina.

Chain Home is unchallenged as the maverick of radar history. Its 1950s revival can only have been politically inspired – just as its beginnings were – for its technical shortcomings by that time were starkly apparent and swiftly fatal.

Chain Home was designed for longer range than Freya, typically out to 200 kilometres against Freya's 120. This reflected Britain's need for maximum warning time.

Radar Horizon

Range with radar is dependent on pulse repetition frequency, the rate at which pulses are emitted – time is allowed for each pulse to travel outwards to the maximum desired range and come back before the next pulse is generated. Otherwise confusion occurs between the echoes. The faster the pulse repetition frequency, the shorter the range.

Range also depends on altitude. All radars can 'see' to a more distant horizon than the human eye. The human eye benefits from a slight bending of light waves, by the atmosphere, around the earth's surface. This puts the horizon about 8 per cent further away than it would be if light travelled strictly in straight lines. The bending effect with radio waves is greater.

Sometimes it can be so abnormally high with radar that the waves 'duct' around the earth's surface for vast distances. But normally the range to which a radar sited at sea level can detect targets which are also at sea level is limited. Ships have a massiveness which makes them good radar targets. Aircraft are far smaller targets, but their altitude increases the range at which radar can detect them. In other words they are above the horizon to a greater distance.

A useful rule of thumb for calculating radar range is that the distance in miles is the square root of twice the height in feet. For example: if an aircraft is at 20,000 feet, twice this equals 40,000, the square root of which is 200. So it is within range, to a radar station at approximately sea level, up to about 200 miles. If the radar is above sea level, the range appropriate to its own height is calculated and added to the range indicated by the target's height.

In practice, other factors have also to be considered, especially the way in which the radiowaves reflect off the target and other objects. For Chain Home, HF had been chosen in combination with horizontal polarisation. This choice had been based on the idea that it would correspond to the dimensions and aspect presented by approaching aircraft. The metal wings and fuselage, it was thought, would constitute a horizontal antenna of roughly the right length, and would therefore reflect strongly. But this turned out to be far from the whole truth.

HF reflection off an aircraft does not work in quite the way originally expected, moreover horizontal polarisation produces strong reflection from the ground in the form of echoes from large flat areas such as slopes and hills. This caused 'ground clutter' to appear on the screen. Ground clutter is always present to some degree with surveillance radars.

As a result, Chain Home could function looking out to sea, but over land, the strength of the wanted signal from the aircraft, in relation to the unwanted 'noise' from the background, was too weak for reliable detection at any considerable range. On the positive side, horizontal polarisation gave exceptionally long range over water, because strong reflection from the sea enhanced the radiation in the forward direction.

Chain Home stations were sited on the coast and the transmission pattern was designed to make them look out to sea – the transmission was strongest in this direction. This reduced the problem of ground clutter; in addition, each station was calibrated, so that the reflection pattern off local geographical features was known.

An additional problem showed up in that Chain Home's radiation did not reflect well off aircraft at low angles of elevation. The radar could pick up high altitude targets, typically 15,000 feet, but did not perform well against targets at low altitude – a few thousand feet.

By contrast, Freya working with vertical polarisation and a frequency five times higher, had a smaller problem with ground clutter. Relatively speaking, it obtained a stronger signal from the target, even at low altitudes. The signal could be picked out despite the clutter. As a consequence, Freya was a more versatile radar than Chain Home. It had acceptable performance on aircraft at most altitudes, whether in use at the coast, for which it was originally designed, or inland, where it was later used. By halving the pulse repetition frequency, it was found possible to double its range, to about 250 kilometres. Thanks to its narrow sweeping beam, it operated with far less power than Chain Home.

Chain Home and Freya may be compared with the only other surveillance radar of their time, the American SCR270. Like Chain Home, this radar used horizontal polarisation for the sake of long range over water, which was the main requirement, but in frequency it was close to Freya. It was therefore far more compact than Chain Home, but shared the same vulnerability to ground clutter. It did not scan and its directional capability was not high. Any fair comparison must put Freya well ahead of the other two.

Watson-Watt himself frankly listed the shortcomings of Chain Home. He pointed to the weakness in its method of finding direction. This was by comparing the signal strength in its crossed dipole – the two antennas at right angles to each other. The antenna were not rotated; instead the operator tested the relative strength by turning a knob to find a balance between them, from which the direction could be inferred. This was called 'swinging the gonio'. 'Gonio' was short for goniometer.

Candour

The goniometer was more of a scientific instrument than a combat-efficient device. With honourable candour Watson-Watt called his failure to provide something better than the goniometer 'my greatest mistake'. The goniometer was used in finding elevation as well as direction, and both of these functions left much to be desired in the operational Chain Home radar of 1940. Watson-Watt acknowledged this.

In practice the most serious of Chain Home's limitations was its confinement to the coast and the fact that it looked outwards but not inwards. Not the least evidence of this is provided by Winston Churchill. He refers to Chain Home several times in *The Second World War*, underlining its inability to look inward upon the scene of battle.

It is fair to point out that Churchill, before becoming Britain's prime minister, was a member of the committee which oversaw Chain Home radar's development, virtually from the beginning.

It is also fair to point out that the consequences of this limitation were kept within bounds by the tactical nature of air war in 1940. Providing early warning of the approach of attacking formations was received, defending aircraft could rise to meet them. Given visual flying conditions, the defenders would find the attackers without further assistance. In non-visual flying conditions they would never find them anyway.

The limitations did show up when German aircraft were reassembling over southern Britain for return flight in escorted formations. Chain Home could not track these movements.

Chain Home Low

In attempting to resolve the inadequacies of Chain Home, the British air force was led to its next advance in radar practice, centring upon the Chain Home Low radar described in the next chapter. Chain Home Low made the urgently necessary switch to a higher frequency – 200 megahertz. Otherwise it was in sequential development from Chain Home. Together Chain Home and Chain Home Low represent one prong of the trifurcating British development of radar.

British Naval Radar

Another prong was British naval radar. As already noted this began in 1935, shortly after the beginning of Chain Home. Not being driven by the same urgent political considerations, it was able to follow a more considered pattern of development. This was beneficial, in that it had more time to get its technical solutions right. It had to reject HF at the outset because HF would never solve the problems of shipborne radar. The dimensions would be too big.

British naval radar was forced to turn to VHF and UHF. It developed a series of radars from about 43 megahertz to 600 megahertz. In this respect it paralleled the pattern of German radar, although initially the arrays were simple by comparison, typically pairs of horizontal rods (indicating horizontal polarisation). To make up for this, power levels were high. British naval radar proved that electron tubes made in Britain enabled radar to work with adequate power up to 600 megahertz, in other words that power was not the serious constraint on frequency that it had hitherto been considered to be.

This should not have been surprising, for the British Admiralty's Signals School was the source of the country's most advanced electron

---

FIGS. 7.4, 7.5 AND 7.6 **Early British Naval Radars** Early British naval radars had simple antennas comprising two or four horizontal radiating dipoles accompanied by parallel rod reflectors. Fig. 7.4 shows the twin-dipole Type 79X, working on 43 megahertz; Fig. 7.5 is the four-dipole Type 281 (90 megahertz) and Fig. 7.6 the four-dipole Type 291 (240 megahertz). These were search radars and directional accuracy was not high, unlike German naval radar which was designed for gunnery control. The Germans used 'mattress' antennas with vertical radiators, rather like *Freya* (which was of naval origin) but smaller, as they were for masthead mounting. They worked on higher frequencies than the British e.g. 375 megahertz for *Seetakt*. Compare these early types with the Type 284 naval radar at Fig. 11.1.

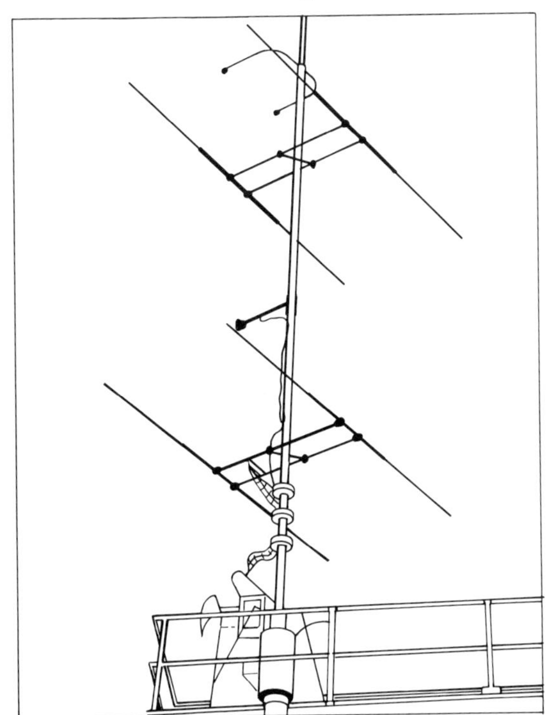

Fig. 7.4

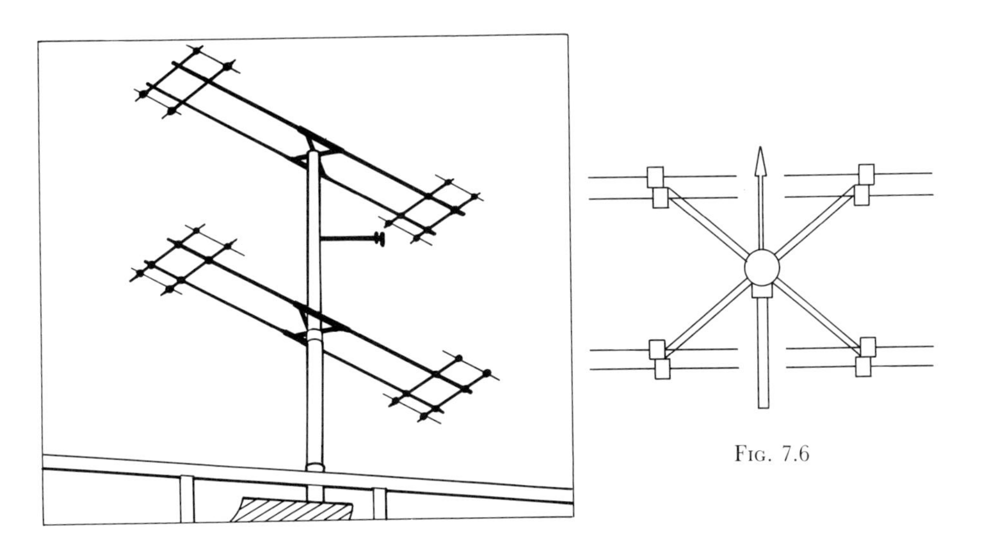

Fig. 7.5

Fig. 7.6

tubes (called 'Micropups'), and the navy was aware of its own capabilities. Strangely enough, British politicians were less aware of their navy's capabilities than of their air force's.

The most unconsciously ironic passage in Churchill's *The Second World War* is his remark on being shown the prototype Chain Home Low radar at Bawdsey: 'I cannot conceive why the Admiralty are not now hot upon this trail.' The Admiralty were in fact hot on equally good trails, even if they had not been given the same resources to pursue them.

The story of British naval radar is taken up in Chapter 11. *Seetakt* remained the prime example of German shipborne radar, for although other equipments were produced, the operational scope available to German surface naval forces contracted. Radars produced for surface use by submarines failed to provide the defensive capability needed. German radar was destined for its greatest achievements with ground-based and airborne air defence radars. Working within the same frequency range, up to 600 megahertz, but at lower powers than British radar, it teamed the ground Wurzburg radar with Freya, and created the airborne Lichtenstein.

Third prong

The third prong of British radar was the most spectacular of all, although it did not arrive operationally until halfway through the war. Shortly after the beginning of the war, in November 1939, an invention was made in Britain which had remarkable consequences. It was a new component for radar, a form of electron tube which leapt across the frequency barrier. This was the cavity magnetron.[2]

The cavity magnetron opened the way to the fascinating technical possibilities of radar in a previously inaccessible frequency band – Super High Frequency, SHF. SHF is from 3000 megahertz to 30,000 megahertz, or 3 gigahertz to 30 gigahertz.

The corresponding wavelengths are from 10 centimetres to 1 centimetre – hence the terms 'centrimetric wavelengths' and 'centrimetric radar'. Yet another term is microwaves.

Centimetric radar proved to be the biggest watershed in radar's history. But it did not happen all at once. It took three years to create the first militarily effective operational equipments around the new component. This work was done not only in Britain but in the United States. American research and industrial resources had much to contribute in speeding development.

The first cavity magnetron gave kilowatt power at a frequency of just over 3 gigahertz. Previously only one watt or so was available at such frequencies. In radar use, this would have been the equivalent of looking for an aircraft at night with a pocket torch. The magnetron changed the torch into a searchlight. SHF radar became a practical possibility.

SHF chiefly affected airborne radar. Britain pioneered airborne radar before SHF arrived, but SHF transformed it. Because the wavelength was much smaller, antenna dimensions were much smaller. A new generation of airborne equipments was born, using parabolic antennas. It was far more aggressive. It was applied in offensive roles.

1943 was the year of centimetric radar's airborne advent. Dramatic as this was, centimetric radar's full significance lay many years into the future, long after the Second World War, and it came in both civilian and military applications. Meanwhile in the middle of 1943 airborne centimetric radar brought the naval Battle of the Atlantic to an end and heralded a new phase of air war.

Despite these dramatic results, a balance must be preserved in judging centimetric radar's military significance. The story of centimetric radar continues in the following chapters. It will become clear that centimetric wavelengths did not invade every area of radar. During the Second World War they made little difference to ground-based defence radar; this became largely a German preserve.

After the war radar technology gradually re-based itself on the magnetron for most purposes. SHF eventually became a much-used band for ground-based defence and other forms of surveillance radar, such as civilian air traffic control radar.

By themselves, the terms UHF and SHF became rather too broad for convenient designation of radar frequency bands. Even during the war the practice began of referring to rather narrower sectors of the frequency spectrum spectrum, in use for radar, as 'L-band', 'S-band', 'X-band', 'P-band', 'K-band'. This had a security value at the time.

The practice has become permanent. The terms are often used but unfortunately many different interpretations now exist of what they mean. A list of radar frequency bands accompanies this text.

The implications of the cavity magnetron applied overwhelmingly to radar. Despite some attempts to use SHF, military radio communications remained based on HF, VHF and UHF. The rise of SHF military radio came much later, with communications satellites.

8

Radio Versus Radar

In the Second World War radar was electronics of the battlezone. It came into its own where ranges were short, where forces were in contact, where fighting flared. But in the strategic role it hardly challenged radio. Radio provided the communications by which the war was universally directed and reported.

Although radar was tactical, this was not to the exclusion of radio. Even tactically, radar sometimes left the field to radio. More usually in the heat of battle both radio and radar had their parts to play, in coordination with each other.

For this reason the battles of the Second World War have always to be seen from both the radio and radar aspects. An interesting process then comes to light: the changing relationship of radio and radar and the changing balance of their offensive and defensive roles.

Radar bred a much greater variety of apparatus – more complex, more costly, much larger. It also bred a different pattern of countermeasures, in other words a different pattern of electronic warfare.

Radio links can sometimes be jammed. This is noise jamming. Radar is not only vulnerable to noise jamming, but is open to deception jamming. Deception jamming has been something of a rarity with radio.

The main danger with radio is from signals intelligence. With radar there is no such risk as a crucial despatch being read by the enemy. Radar emissions can be detected, revealing the radar's presence, but this is a calculated risk that every radar user knows he takes. It is a quantifiable risk.

The consequences of a radio message being read are not so easily quantifiable. It depends on the message and the circumstances. Leakage of information may not come to light until much later. It may never be realised at all. But with radar the enemy's counter is generally immediately obvious or soon becomes so. Things go wrong fast.

At the beginning of the Second World War, from Germany's *blitzkrieg* on Poland in September 1939 to the occupation of Denmark and Norway and finally the invasion of Belgium, Holland and France in May and June 1940, radio dominated. During this period which saw the building of Germany's '*Festung Europa*' – 'Fortress Europe' – radio was an indispensable part of offensive operations.

Nevertheless radar was already in the war on the defensive. On both the British and German coasts it stood sentinel from the war's opening hours.

Britain mounted her first offensive operations against the German coast with daylight air attacks in September 1939, a day after the war began. She followed up with two further attacks in December 1939. An attack on 18 December was disastrous. Twenty-four British Wellington bombers approaching Wilhelmshaven were detected by German Freya radar at seventy miles range. As a result of the subsequent interception, by Messerschmitt 109s and 110s, only ten Wellingtons returned.

This experience convinced Britain of the vulnerability of bombers to fighters in daylight. This was correct so far as it went, but radar's contribution to the outcome was not realised. It is noteworthy that although the Oslo Report, received by the British in early November from an unknown German source, explained how the September Wilhelmshaven raids had been detected, the December raid was allowed to proceed.[1] Notwithstanding the Oslo Report, Britain did not then, nor for more than a year afterwards, credit Germany with possession of radar. Had she done so, she would have seen that daylight vulnerability was increased by radar's early warning. As it was, her bid to make a surprise attack against coastal targets was made in ignorance of the true odds against success.

After France fell the electronics battle flared more intensely. Germany gained a new, closer springboard for air operations against Britain, as well as an unexpected opportunity to try and force Britain out of the war by invasion. The German air force increased its intrusions into British airspace, escalating from tactical harassment to pursuit of strategic objectives.

From Day to Night

The first strategic objective led to the Battle of Britain. It was an attempt starting in mid-August 1940 to achieve air superiority over southern Britain with daylight air attacks. This was seen as providing the essential pre-condition for invasion. Accordingly the British air force itself was the target. The aim was to destroy its aircraft and airfields by air fighting and ground bombing. Daylight bombing raids compelled the British air force to give battle.

The second strategic objective led to the Blitz. It followed the recognition that after one month the first objective had made insufficient progress. An invasion of Britain had not been made possible. Mid-September had been reached, the days were shortening and the weather would worsen.

The Blitz represented a switch to the political objective of finishing the war through pressure on the civilian population. This objective was pursued by attacks on London and other cities. It also represented a switch from mainly daytime operations, in the Battle of Britain, to mainly night operations.

This change from day to night was highly significant for electronic warfare. It changed the character and magnified the scale of the electronic battle. Germany made the change in order to avoid high bomber loss rates. She like Britain, had to accept the daytime vulnerability of bombers, despite the massive fighter escorts which she, unlike Britain, was able to provide. The British fighter force, being defensive, was short-ranged. In the Battle of Britain it had concentrated on attacking German bombers; German fighter escorts had been unable to prevent this.

The Blitz continued through the early months of 1941. Together with the Battle of Britain, it formed a prolonged period of massed air offensive operations which gave radar its first opportunity to defend a national airspace, both by day and night.

For radio it was the second opportunity to support an air offensive – the first having come with German attacks into the same airspace in the First World War. The German air force deployed a variety of beacon- and beam-based radio navigation systems enabling aircraft to find their way by day and night, and in particular to bomb targets by night. These were much more sophisticated than the simple radio methods used in the previous conflict.

The British had not foreseen this development. They were driven to whatever spoiling methods they could quickly improvise. These were reactive and spontaneous but reasonably effective. Thus came the birth of electronic countermeasures in the Second World War. It was radio countermeasures in the defensive role. It was a black art. It joined radio's existing black art of signals intelligence.

This was the most intensive episode of electronic warfare history had yet witnessed. It was so intense, and introduced so many new features, that it seemed qualitatively different to anything that had happened before. In the narrow meaning of the term 'electronic warfare', it was the beginning.

But it in turn was dwarfed by the electronic struggle which developed in the skies of Germany as roles changed. Germany withdrew from the night bomber attack on Britain in mid-1941, at a time when the British were going increasingly on to the offensive themselves. From 1942 the British attack was progressively armed with new radar and radio bombing techniques. In 1943 it was joined by the Americans.

To this Allied onslaught the Germans responded with vigorous defence. Crescendo followed crescendo in the battle as it swung first one way then the other. Radar at last became the chief electronic aggressor. Cities were located by radar – and bombed. Aircraft were located by radar – and shot down. Without radar neither cities nor aircraft could be found.

Changing Roles

The air warfare which began over Britain and ended over Germany can be seen, according to preference, as two separate battles, or else as one continuous battle in which defensive and offensive roles were switched. The latter is more accurate in that the fighting overlapped whilst continuous progress occurred in electronic technology. Each side developed its own technology while learning from the technology of the other.

It should not be seen however as it often is seen, as two consecutive battles demonstrating first the claimed defensive superiority and then the claimed offensive superiority of the ultimate winning side. Nothing could be further from the truth than this popular picture.

In the early stage of the battle Germany pursued the offensive over Britain, inflicting considerable damage to cities and using radio navigation aids to find targets at night. British countermeasures sometimes mitigated but did not prevent these attacks. They did not prevent the German attack on Coventry in November 1940.

At the same period, and for more than a year afterwards, the British air force penetrated German night skies with similar objectives but with a complete failure to appreciate the necessity for electronic navigation and target-finding aids. For the lack of these aids by far the largest proportion of British bombs missed their targets by several miles.

Only when this fact was incontrovertibly established by the evidence of photographic reconnaissance, evidence that was reluctantly admitted after years of disbelief, were electronic navigation systems introduced. This delay happened even though Germany had obviously found them necessary. The British loftily attributed this latter circumstance to inferior pilot training. They had obviously forgotten Germany's use of radio for the same purpose in the First World War. While these complacent illusions were being cherished, night-time interception of British bombers over Germany was claiming a substantial number of victims thanks to radar, the existence of which in German hands was still denied.

The significance of these facts is entirely clear. At this stage in the war Britain was in many ways behind in using electronics but did not realise it. On the contrary she thought she was ahead because of her radar, and because of her success with radio countermeasures. In reality she had much catching up to do. She was eventually able to turn the tables on Germany in many respects, although not in all.

Germany never solved the problem of an unjammable electronic target-finding aid. When Britain finally did so, it was by using airborne radar rather than radio. Britain developed countermeasures against German radar as well as against German radio. But Germany countered in turn effectively. By the beginning of 1944 the losses suffered by Britain's Bomber Command, pursuing the offensive over Germany, outweighed any war contribution that the Command was making.

In reply to the question 'which side won the electronic war in the air?', it is only true to say that at one time and another each side was ahead. But these superiorities were generally short-lived and never became decisive. The air battle finally collapsed in the Allies' favour as the war drew near its end, but this was an inevitable part of Germany's general collapse. It resulted from her inability to stem simultaneous ground invasions from East and West. It had nothing to do with her inability to stay in the electronic warfare race.

Technologically the defeated Germany was in many ways ahead of her victors. This is a generalisation applying to various sectors of military technology, including some sectors of electronics such as ground-based warning radar and airborne countermeasures. Here her performance was strong.

This was true despite the claims sometimes made that the German Government failed to grasp the importance of electronics, and despite the self-disparaging remarks of many of Germany's wartime leaders. Understandably, accurate information and balanced judgement were rare in post-war Europe, while the losers had a tendency to look for any and every reason on which blame could be fixed. The resulting delusions have been persistent. For some reason, delusions are endemic in electronic warfare.

An Epic Confrontation

The air battle was obvious and dramatic. It was fought directly over the heads of civilian populations. It was the stimulus to amazing electronics ingenuity. Not surprisingly it has come down in history as the unsurpassed epic of electronic warfare. This is the repute it holds to this day. Rightly so; the air battle in Western Europe was the fiercest of all the Second World War's electronics confrontations.

Nevertheless electronic warfare was less decisive here than it was on some other fronts. True, the air battle could hardly have been fought at all without electronics. Without electronics the antagonists could not have found each other. But success in electronics was shared between the sides sufficiently evenly to prevent the air battle from tipping conclusively in either direction. If it had tipped, could it have forced an end to the war by itself? This remains an open question.

This was certainly the idea which lured first the German air force in 1940/1941, and afterwards the British and US air forces in 1943/1944. Total defensive collapse in the air would have left civilian populations completely at the mercy of bomber attacks. What might then have happened is conjectural. The possibilities were glimpsed during the period of the British attacks on Hamburg in July 1943.

This was due to the sudden introduction of a devastatingly effective tactic in the electronics war: the disruption of radar by 'window', that is strips of light metallic foil released from aircraft with effects as described in Chapter 10. It was a fearful warning of the consequences if electronics failed in defence. But the failure was not permanent. The electronics balance, and the balance of the air war, was restored.

Admittedly, the balance collapsed again towards the end, when Allied aircraft attacked Germany with increasing impunity both by day and night. This was when the worst damage was done; an attack on Dresden produced a similar result to the raids on Hamburg. But matters had already gone too far for this to have any significance in relation to the ending of the war.

It was otherwise in the naval battle. This was less visible to the populations of the warring countries but more vital to the outcome, in both the Atlantic and the Pacific. The roles played by radio and radar were also more vital. They form the main topic of Chapter 11, but for the sake of comparison it is appropriate to anticipate some conclusions of Chapter 11 in concise format here.

With submarines Germany came near to cutting the links across the Atlantic between the United States and Britain. What prevented this from happening was a combination of three electronic weapons. Two of them were applications of radio, the other of radar: signals intelligence, direction-finding on HF transmissions – HF DF or 'huff-duff', and anti-surface vessel radar.

As a result German submarines were exposed to a risk of surprise attack when surfaced. When airborne anti-surface vessel radar moved to the SHF band, thanks to the magnetron, this risk increased to the point of forcing withdrawal of German submarines from the Atlantic.

The German submarine arm never re-established its threat to make the Atlantic unsailable for Allied shipping.

Twin failures

The conflict between Japan and the United States hinged on the balance of naval strength in the Pacific. By her initial strike at Pearl Harbor Japan swung this in her own favour, but by her failure to protect radio security lost it again.

Japan had radar but derived negligible advantage from it. It was not as good as American radar but this does not explain Japan's failure to exploit it for what it was worth. This was an additional failure in electronic warfare on Japan's part, though not so significant as the failure to protect radio security.

But for these failures, the comparison of Japanese and American naval strength would have pointed to a much more prolonged struggle, until American economic superiority could prevail. In fact Japan began to lose the initiative she had won at Pearl Harbor quickly. She lost control of Pacific waters entirely by 1945. For an island power this military situation was impossible. The outcome was already inevitable when hastened by atomic bombs.[2]

In contrast to the rival forces in the Pacific, British and German surface forces were approximate electronic equals. They both understood radio and radar and effectively exploited them.

In the actions between them radar clearly showed its aggressive character.It found and pursued – but the quarry knew when he was being pursued. It could make escape by night or in poor visibility difficult or impossible – but the quarry knew that if escape was to be achieved the first necessity was to deceive the radar. Having brought forces to battle, radar controlled the course of the action.

Naval warfare between the Italians and the British in the Mediterranean exposed, as no other theatre of war did, the irrecoverable naval handicap imposed by the lack of radar. This was despite the considerable radar research that had been conducted in the homeland of Marconi.

From the days of the Second World War to the present time, radar's importance in naval use concedes nothing to any other application. The warship of today can only survive by virtue of radar. To say this is not to minimise the naval significance of radio. It is rather to emphasise the overwhelming significance of all forms of electronic warfare in naval operations. Electronic warfare began at sea with radio, it is at sea that its results have been most decisive, and today at sea it reaches its extreme development.

On the front between Germany and Russia, with its vast distances and areas, radio dominated, but radar's contribution is all too often overlooked. It was employed chiefly in the defensive ground-to-air role by both sides. On the German side, this meant tactical use in coordination with air forces supporting army operations. On the Russian side radar appeared in the defence of Moscow against air attack, from late 1941 to early 1942. It was used for early warning of approaching aircraft and for gun-laying of anti-aircraft batteries.

Moscow was probably better defended than either London or Berlin. Damage was minimal in spite of intensive attacks mounted from short range. But many measures contributed to its impregnability besides radar. It was a relatively compact area defended by thick belts of searchlights and anti-aircraft artillery backed by vast accumulations of ammunition. Heavy flak has the proven effect of causing bombers to drop their bomb loads short. Russian radar would not have needed to be technically advanced to provide alerts; against mass attacks nothing more was possible.

Later, in the period from January 1944 to the end of the war, Russian radar played a role in the tactical air battle along the front, which was by this time moving continuously westwards.

The battle fought in North Africa between German and Italian forces on the one hand and British later joined by American forces on the other was similar to the German-Russian struggle, in that it was waged over large land areas, with air power supporting mechanised armies over highly mobile front lines.

Radio communications were at a premium, signals intelligence was practised with success by both sides, and ground radar was extensively deployed. When the German-Italian position collapsed, large quantities of German radar equipment fell into British hands.

Strategic Area Defence

Radar's first and most famous epic was in defence of British airspace and the British homeland against German attack in 1940 and 1941. With this battle radar entered military history. What is important in military practice is not the theoretical refinement of a defensive system, but solely its effectiveness in combat.

Chain Home faced its only crucial test in the Battle of Britain. It proved entirely capable of detecting German aircraft over the North Sea or assembling in formation over northern France. It gave their approach courses and provided estimates of force strengths.

It could not discriminate individual aircraft, but the effect of a large group of aircraft was to cause the reflected pulse seen on the cathode ray screen to beat: the blip on the cathode ray tube went up and down.

Force strengths were estimated from the magnitude and rapidity of this beating. There was an operational tendency to under-estimate size of formations.

Chain Home operated best against aircraft at about 4,000 to 6,000 metres (15,000 to 20,000 feet); it was not effective against low altitude aircraft, at for example 1500 metres (5,000 feet). This was not a serious weakness in the Battle of Britain, because it was desirable for invading fighter and bomber formations to gain the advantage of height. But Chain Home's effectiveness was also low against targets above 6,000 metres, a weakness which was exploited by Germany in the last phase of daylight operations, sending in aircraft at or above 6850 metres (22,500 feet).

By itself Chain Home was able to give 20 or 30 minutes alert to the fighter defences. It eliminated the need for standing patrols. But it did not cover the inland region from the coast to London which was the actual arena of battle. There was no means of telling, by radar, whether this arena was clear of intruders. Here, as Churchill says, ground observers with binoculars, reporting over telephones, were the principal means of surveillance. To Churchill this was a contrast between the 20th century and the Stone Age.

Only in retrospect, after nearly half a century, did it become clear that radar's alerting function in the Battle of Britain was shared with signals intelligence from radio. German air communications were intercepted, principally at the British coastal location of Kingsdown in Kent, but also inland at Cheadle, Staffordshire. German fighters used telephony, and German bombers telegraphy, both on HF. German base communications preceding operations were also intercepted.

British interception of this traffic typically gave up to two hours warning time, plus detailed information about numbers, routes and identity of attacking formations.

The Effect of Secrecy

But because this was a long kept secret, a myth prospered about the unique role of radar in the Battle of Britain. It was fed by enthusiastic testimonials from high-ranking commanders and combatants on both sides. They did not know that the part played by signals intelligence had been protected by far tighter security than was applied to radar.[3]

The truth was that the British achievement in signals intelligence by radio during the Battle of Britain was at least as great as in area-defence radar. In signals intelligence the British repeated their naval successes of the First World War but in the new combat medium of the air.

Because of this, radar was generally waiting to register aircraft whose approach was already expected.

Of course, it would be absurd to belittle radar's role.

In the first place, the fear always existed that German measures might reduce the value of signals intelligence. Against this danger radar was the insurance.

In the second place, along Britain's eastern seaboard, which according to pre-war military thinking was the principal coast at risk, as in the First World War, radar did its intended job so effectively that it deterred attack.

This was shown dramatically by the events of 15 August 1940. It was always to be expected that German attacks in the south would be varied by flank attacks at various points along the east coast, and this development came on the third day of the main phase of the Battle of Britain. Large bomber formations from bases in Norway and Denmark converged on to targets in the Tyne Tees and Humber regions. Chain Home radar, working under its most favourable conditions, out over long stretches of water, was able to give ample warning for fighter squadrons to move into good defensive positions. As a result the raiders suffered heavy losses, just as in the British attack against Wilhelmshaven the previous December.

Germany drew the correct conclusions. She obviously understood the role of radar in making daylight attacks in this region excessively hazardous. They were not repeated. Instead she went over to night bombing – a precursor of the strategy which eventually prevailed everywhere when the transition from the Battle of the Britain to the Blitz was complete.

British success in anticipating German attacks was obvious to the Germans. The radar stations, if not in fact the only cause, were the apparent cause. There were two patterns of response. Firstly, radar countermeasures were born with German bombing attacks on the stations. Secondly, flank air raids exploited the fact that the south coast sector of the radar chain only extended for about half the British south coast.

This coverage would have been adequate if Germany had not gained bases on the Cherbourg peninsula.

The main achievement of the British investment in defensive preparations during the late 1930s was the construction of the long coastal radar chain backed by a defensive fighter force. This could be claimed, to the credit of British governments of the late 1930s, to be an impressively thorough preparation – but for one fact, namely that it did not take account of the possibility that France would fall under German control. This had not been foreseen. It caused crisis.

Germany took advantage of the limited south sector by mounting attacks along the coast west of where the radar chain terminated, or else routing attacks so that they passed over the coast west of the chain before turning back eastwards. In accordance with military logic, the strongest radar bombing attacks were launched against the western end stations, Ventnor and Poling, both of which were temporarily disabled.

Naval Double-Banking

Possibly the most vital target in this area was the naval base of Portsmouth. Here British naval radars had come into operation from June 1940. These were equipments contrasting strongly with Chain Home, rotatable arrays, horizontally flat, containing four dipoles, working on frequencies of either 43 or 90 megahertz, with power outputs up to or above 1 megawatt.

Consequently the temporary loss of the Ventnor and Poling Chain Home stations did not deprive Portsmouth of radar cover. At the opposite end of the radar chain, in the far north, naval radar also protected the British main fleet base at Scapa Flow, thanks to shipborne equipment working on 43 megahertz. This effectively double-banked the cover afforded by Chain Home. But the latter applied only to high-altitude aircraft which were hardly a threat to warships, while low-flying aircraft were.

Despite everything that electronic means could achieve, in daytime they yielded their role to ground observers once intruding aircraft were over land. This was far from satisfactory since visibility was dependent on cloud cover. But in practice the dice were so loaded against the daytime intruding bomber that it was never a crucial issue.

Once the light had gone it was a different matter. In darkness bombers were free to penetrate unhindered. Chain Home radar could detect their approach, but fighters had no way of finding them.

True, it was possible to set up searchlights near main target areas and attempt to catch and hold bombers in cones of light while they were attacked by day fighters – 'illuminated night fighting' – or brought under anti-aircraft fire. But this only offered chances to the defence in proximity to small specific areas. It did nothing to bring the penetrating bomber under threat during the longest part of its penetration.

This was a gap in the defences that only radar could close. The change in tactics from day to night penetration that came between the Battle of Britain and the Blitz brought a dramatic change in the challenge to radar. Radar needed to accomplish much more than it did in the Battle of Britain. It needed to accomplish airborne interception at night.

British radar rose to the challenge but as it started to obtain results, the contest departed from British skies. It reappeared over Germany, where German radar took up the challenge and fought it out on a titanic scale.

The conditions of fighting at night were totally different to those in the day. In daytime visual contact could be made at large distances, tens of kilometres. Radar gave early warning and left enemy aircraft to be found by the fighter. This was an adequate contribution. But at night visual contact range might be less than a few hundred metres. Radar had to help the fighter all the way into attack at this distance.

Not only was a bigger contribution from ground radar demanded, but a completely new contribution from hitherto non-existent airborne radar in the fighter. This had to take over at about five kilometres range, which was about the closest approach that instructions from ground radar could achieve. From this point on airborne radar had to complete the approach up to visual contact.

Chain Home Low

Britain began to tackle the problem of airborne interception at night during 1940. Chain Home radar could not provide an input; it was not sufficiently precise for the task of controlling individual fighters. But during this year a new ground-based early warning radar was introduced, Chain Home Low (CHL). This was an advance in the direction of Freya – though Freya's existence and technology were still almost totally unknown to the British.

Like Freya, its development began against a requirement for the detection of surface ships. Like Freya it was found applicable to other purposes. The most important of these was to provide coverage against low-altitude aircraft – hence the name. Chain Home Low covered at altitudes of about 1500 metres (5,000 feet). Chain Home had not proved capable of this. By the end of 1940 Chain Home Low stations had replaced Chain Home as the most numerous type of radar installation around the British coast.

Chain Home Low worked on a frequency of 200 megahertz. It used horizontal polarisation but the low altitude coverage was significantly better than with Chain Home, thanks to the higher frequency. The antenna was an array about 10 metres across, which, as with Freya, was rotated to scan the horizon. It was mounted in various ways, sometimes on clifftops, sometimes on top of a 185-foot tower, Depending on the mounting, it had a detection range of up to 40 miles against aircraft at 5,000 feet.

By virtue of its higher frequency it indicated aircraft positions more accurately than Chain Home. This, and its all-around scanning enabling greater directional accuracy, gave it the capability to support night interceptions. It was joined in this function by an important advance in the way the cathode ray tube screen was used to display the radar's information.

Formerly the screen showed a single horizontal baseline on which aircraft echoes appeared as blips. The blip's displacement to the right indicated range. There was no indication of direction, which was derived independently. As a result, the target's direction and range were not simultaneously apparent to the operator.

But using Chain Home Low for airborne interception, the screen was made to show a plan with the radar station at the centre. The scanning rotation of the antenna was followed on the screen, and the blip was registered as an intensified spot of light, nearer to or further from the centre according to range.

The screen therefore became a map with blips corresponding to the hunted and the hunting aircraft, in correct geographical relationship both to each other and to the radar station, all simultaneously apparent. This was the 'Plan Position Indicator' (PPI). It was a major advance which made it easy to give instructions for interception directly off the radar display.

The communications link to the fighter was no less vital. At this time British fighter aircraft had recently converted to radio telephony on VHF. The speed and accuracy of the radar operator's instructions were matched by radio's speed and clarity in conveying them to the interceptor pilot.

Another requirement became obvious at this point. The radar operator had to know which blip represented his fighter. The idea of 'Identification Friend or Foe' (IFF), that is to say, a means of identifying radar blips corresponding to friendly aircraft, had already been attempted with Chain Home radar. But with 'ground-controlled interception' (GCI) it became crucial.

Using the radio telephony link, the radar operator asked the fighter pilot to identify himself. This could in principle be done by making a turn, or even waggling the wings, either of which would show up on the screen. But with Identification Friend or Foe it was done more conveniently and effectively by switching on, briefly, an apparatus which responded to the radar pulse.

In effect it periodically intensified the returned echo, causing the fighter's blip on the screen to flicker. The system therefore gave positive identification of 'friends' and left non-responsive blips to be assumed as 'foes'. Occasionally of course the assumption could be dangerous, as it remains even today. With latest technology this limitation tends to be forgotten rather than overcome.

Secondary Radar

Identification Friend or Foe was the beginning of 'secondary radar'. Primary radar relies only on the metallic bodywork of the target to reflect the signal, without amplification; secondary 'reflects' the signal by picking it up with a radio receiver, amplifying it and retransmitting it. It is in some ways a technique half way between radar and radio.

The final ingredient of airborne interception was the most difficult of all to provide: a radar compact enough to be airborne. It needed only short-range performance, but the antenna array had to be mounted on the wings or the nose, and the frequency had to be as high as possible.

After a number of attempts a satisfactory set was produced in Britain and operationally deployed by October 1940 – 'AI Mark IV'. It was the smallest radar yet, a few hundred pounds in weight. Nevertheless it dictated the design of the night fighter. It eliminated the typical high-performance day fighter from the night-fighter role (unless for illuminated night fighting without radar). It increased not only weight, but drag, through its array of antennas. This made a bigger aircraft essential.

The night fighter's performance, so long as it was adequate to overtake a bomber, was not critical. The night fighter did not have to engage in combat with day fighters. Twin engines were convenient because they offered the option of nose-mounting the antennas. The Beaufighter was the first British aircraft used as a radar-equipped night fighter.

MAP 8.1 **United Kingdom Area Defence Radar, September 1939**

MAP 8.2 **United Kingdom Area Defence Radar, September 1941**

The two maps have been redrawn from those which appeared at the end of the Second World War in a British government publication. They were republished by Sir Robert Watson-Watt in 1957 in his book *Three Steps to Victory*. Sir Robert changed the detection height attributed to Chain Home Low (CHL) from 500 to 5,000 feet (without altering the range outline). This seems entirely realistic but indicates the earlier confusion regarding the role of CHL.

CHL was introduced urgently during 1940. It was a much more advanced radar, technically, than Chain Home, working on 200 MHz and mounted upon a rotating turntable to provide 360-degree scanning. It was the counterpart of the German Freya. But, despite its name, its performance against low-altitude aircraft left much to be desired and when its shortcomings were brought to attention by low-level German intrusions, the naval Type 271 radar was hurriedly adapted for ground-based surveillance. CHL's true historic significance lay in enabling ground-controlled interception of intruding bombers at night, for the first time.

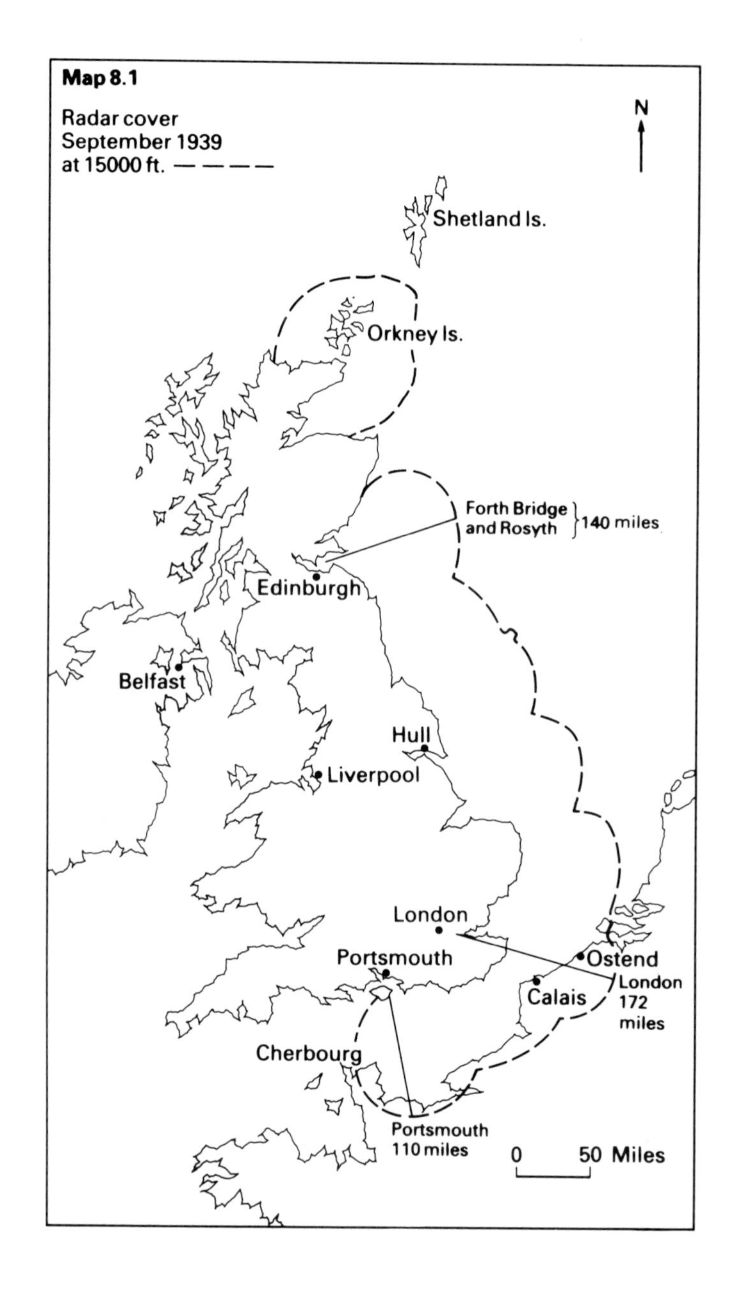
Map 8.1
Radar cover
September 1939
at 15000 ft.
N
Shetland Is.
Orkney Is.
Forth Bridge
and Rosyth
140 miles
Edinburgh
Belfast
Hull
Liverpool
London
Portsmouth
Ostend
Calais
London
172
miles
Cherbourg
Portsmouth
110 miles
0
50 Miles

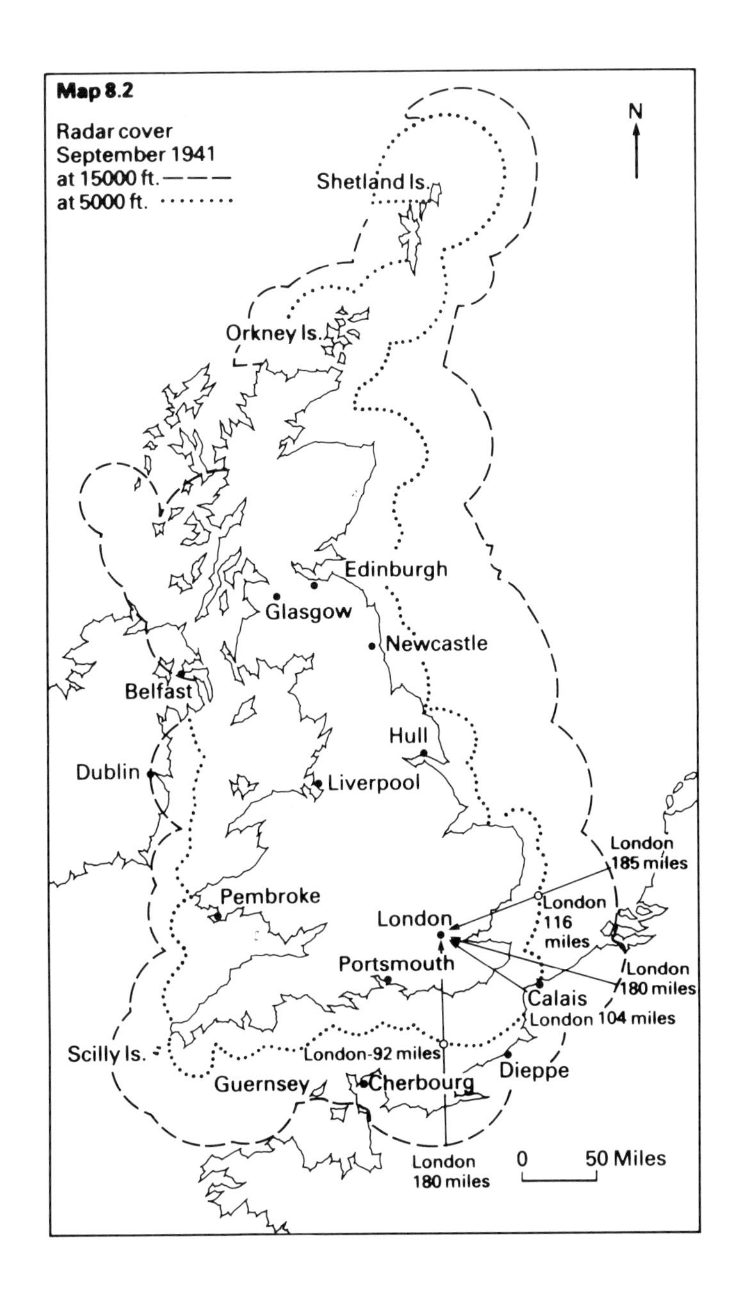
Map 8.2
Radar cover
September 1941
at 15000 ft. — — —
at 5000 ft. ....
N
Shetland Is.
Orkney Is.
Edinburgh
Glasgow
Newcastle
Belfast
Hull
Dublin
Liverpool
London
185 miles
Pembroke
London
London
116
miles
Portsmouth
London
180 miles
Calais
London 104 miles
Scilly Is.
London-92 miles
Dieppe
Guernsey
Cherbourg
London
180 miles
0
50 Miles

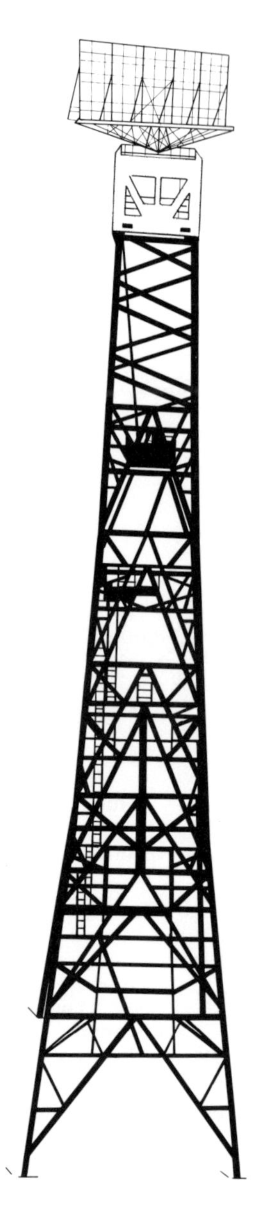

FIG. 8.1 **Chain Home Low** British radar technology leapt forward from Chain Home to Chain Home Low (CHL), which became the most numerous equipment during 1940. Working on the much higher frequency of 200 megahertz, it was compact and was mounted on rotating turntables to provide 360° scanning. It was mounted on 185-foot towers (as above) or cliff tops to improve performance against low-altitude intruders. Like Chain Home, CHL used horizontal polarisation, a good choice for long-range surveillance out to sea, but prone to ground clutter inland, and it remained chiefly a coastal radar. CHL was the first radar to make ground-controlled interception (GCI) possible at night.

The British AI Mark IV set worked, like Chain Home Law, on 200 MHz. It departed from previous British practice in using vertical polarisation. It gave adequate indication of the target's range and position to enable the night fighter to close from the rear until visual contact permitted gun aiming.

It had a range limitation in that it picked up a strong ground echo, the ground acting in effect as a target at a range equal to the aircraft's height. Only over ranges less than the aircraft's height was the screen clear to show the blip from a real target.

Using the ground-controlled interception variant of the Chain Home Low radar in conjunction with the AI Mk IV-equipped Beaufighter, the British obtained mounting success from October 1940 against night intruders over the south coast. This was a frequent penetration route employed by German bombers. It was destined to become the first battlezone of ground-controlled interception.

Success began for the British modestly. Small loss rates began to be inflicted. But often there was no effective interception even when it might have been expected. This was the case for example against bombers flying to Coventry on the night of 14 November 1940. The raid and its target and the path of the bombers, following navigational beams, had been anticipated since early afternoon of that day.

Of course, opportunity to intercept was limited to the vicinity of suitably-equipped ground radar sites. Sites could only handle on a one-at-a-time basis. These were some of the reasons why night interception could not impose loss rates on the same prohibitive scale as daytime interception. Moreover Chain Home Low was essentially a coast zone radar, sharing the same inland vulnerability to ground clutter as Chain Home.

Nevertheless by April 1941 there were eleven operational ground control interception stations and in this month Britain claimed 48 successful night interceptions, rising the following month to 96. It is fascinating to speculate where this rising tide of night conflict might have led, but at this time the German air force dismounted its bombing effort against Britain in order to redeploy eastwards for the impending invasion of Russia. For British ground defence radar the conflict was over.

Chain Home had fought the battle for which it had been preparing ever since 1935. In daytime fighting it had made its designed contribution. It had been pre-empted to some extent by radio signals intelligence, but this could neither have been foreseen nor relied on. In night fighting it had passed on its role to the technically more up-to-date Chain Home Low. The battle was never destined to be renewed on similar terms. Chain Home radar was not destined to make a further contribution to defence.

Later Threats

There were to be subsequent German attacks, but they did not come with massed bomber formations. They came with sporadic low-level fighter-bomber intrusions; with pilotless V-1 'flying bomb' cruise missiles; and with V-2 ballistic rockets. Against none of these was Chain Home effective. Chain Home radar was able to pick up V-2 ballistic missiles climbing after launch, but the impact point could not be predicted sufficiently accurately for anything to be done about it in the short remaining time. Interception was out of the question, attacking launch sites was not very effective.

While many V-1 cruise missiles were destroyed by radar-laid anti-air gunfire at the British coast, this was using a magnetron-based American radar, the SCR584, as described in Chapter 10.

The significance of Chain Home Low also declined. It continued to support a small number of night interceptions, but German incursions generally employed fighter-bombers flying at levels which were too low for it. By the early part of 1943 the failure of early warning radar caused embarrassment and hurried measures were taken to adapt and install the British naval type 271 centimetric radar for coastal early warning (see Chapter 9).

Thus the British Chain Home ground radar family largely reached the limit of its usefulness by mid-1941. There was no strong stimulus to continue improving it.

Undoubtedly the most creative part of the British home defensive effort was the development of air interception, particularly the radar plan position indicator and airborne radar.

Comparable efforts were soon being made in Germany. British bombing attacks during 1940, although not on the same scale as German attacks against Britain, convinced the Germans of the need for serious defensive measures, hitherto hardly regarded as necesssary. These began with the appointment of General Kammhuber to command a night-fighter force, and grew into the 'Kammhuber Line' (so-called by the British) by late 1941.

At this time Britain and Germany confronted each other as two nations far ahead of any other in the practice of electronic warfare. Nothing is more instructive and fascinating than to compare the systems they evolved to protect their civilian populations, exposed in the heart of their own homelands to the threat of attack from the air.

The Kammhuber Line did not arrive all at once. It continuously changed and grew. From the beginning it utilised the Freya radar for early warning. This was an excellent radar, effective inland as well as on the coast. Taking advantage of this fact, the line incorporated existing coastal installations and added others. By 1941 it began in

Denmark, bifurcated south of that country with a seaboard spur following the German and Dutch coasts, and a longer inland part curving back to pick up the German borders with Holland, Belgium, Luxembourg and France. This gave a double line of coverage, coastal and inland.

Conical Scanning

Initially, fighters took off on Freya's warning and waited in orbit around radio beacons until intruding aircraft were caught by searchlights. But Germany found, like Britain, that illuminated night fighting left a lot to be desired. During 1941 another radar arrived which complemented Freya and made a more effective system possible. This was Wurzburg, produced by Telefunken, again a radar which became a historic prototype.

Wurzburg was not designed, as Freya was, for around-the-horizon surveillance, but relied on Freya to give an approximate target bearing. It then searched this bearing and locked on to the target, giving precision figures for bearing, range and elevation. It could therefore be used to direct searchlights, anti-aircraft batteries, or airborne interception. Wurzburg is the classical prototype of the 'target-tracking radar', as opposed to general surveillance. The original Wurzburg was improved by increasing its parabola from about ten feet diameter to 25 during 1941 – 'Giant Wurzburg', with increased range and resolution.

Wurzburg combined the UHF band, at 570 megahertz, with a large parabolic antenna and 'conical scanning'. Thanks to the highly directional antenna and the intrinsically accurate resolution of its frequency, Wurzburg could determine the position of an aircraft in the sky with a precision hitherto impossible. Its scanning method further served this purpose.

Conical scanning has become a classic radar technique. It means that the beam rotates in a small cone around the central axis of the parabolic antenna. The level of the return signal 'wobbles' unless the target is in the centre of the cone. This enables the target to be rapidly centred and held.

Conical scanning is, like other radar techniques, vulnerable to countermeasures. If for example the target emits an artificially wobbling signal on the frequency of the radar, this renders the radar unable to centre the target. But in the days when Wurzburg was introduced, the British were far from thinking about radar countermeasures; they had still to be convinced that German radar existed at all.

In the beginning Wurzburg supported illuminated night fighting. A master searchlight, distinguished by its pale blue vertical beam, waited until coordinates fed from a Wurzburg radar enabled it to swing instantly on to the target. Normally three other searchlights followed, trapping the bomber in a cone of light from which escape was difficult. The searchlight belt was in depth; while the bomber continued on its course, passing out of range of the first searchlights, new searchlights were ready to take over.

Germany soon came to the decision that searchlights were better concentrated for the defence of cities, with anti-aircraft flak. The Kammhuber Line was devoted to airborne interception without their assistance. For this purpose two Giant Wurzburgs were combined with

Fig. 8.2 **Wurzburg** Wurzburg was primarily a target-tracking radar, combining a parabolic antenna with a central rotating dipole to obtain conical scanning. It provided accurate azimuth and elevation. Frequency was about 560 MHz. The vertical rods are secondary radar (identification friend or foe (IFF)) antennas.

a single Freya to defend an area of about 20 miles square – the '*Himmelbett*' (literally 'sky bed', the term corresponding to the English 'four-poster'). The Kammhuber line was divided into compartments of this size.

The positional accuracy given by Giant Wurzburg made a difference in technique possible as compared with the British system. It was possible to attempt night interception without airborne radar. One Giant Wurzburg was assigned to track the intruder aircraft and the other the night-fighter. Using their inputs the ground controller sought to bring the fighter into visual contact with the target.

This system did not call for a plan position indicator display on a cathode ray tube, such as the British had developed. The idea had occurred to the Germans but not been developed. It would have been harder to achieve in a system in which information was being fed by two separate radars.

The Seeburg Table

This information was combined in a different way. The action was plotted on a horizontal translucent screen about 1½ metres in diameter, much larger than a cathode ray tube screen. The position of the intruding bomber was shown as a red light, projected from below by an operator receiving the input from the appropriate Giant Wurzburg. The position of the fighter was similarly projected as a blue light. The controller watched the screen from above. This was the Seeburg plotting table.

The effectiveness of the Kammhuber line was increasingly apparent towards the end of 1941. True, British losses were high during the summer months, but this was when the number of sorties was high and daylight long, giving better opportunity for day fighter interception. They declined slightly as this opportunity passed, but then mounted again towards the end of the year, when, with the longer nights, the reason could only be effective night interception.

With losses amounting to hundreds a month, the British sought to maintain the level of their bombing attacks as the only immediate means of supporting the Russians, fighting in front of Moscow. The policy proved costly however. It climaxed on the night of 7 November 1941, when the British announced their biggest raid of the war to date but were obliged to acknowledge 37 aircraft missing. The German claim was 27 aircraft destroyed by their defences. Four hundred aircraft had been deployed in the raid, against Berlin, Mannheim, Cologne and other targets. The loss rate was not sustainable.

What was the British reaction? The existence of Freya had been realised by the British since February 1941, but by itself Freya did not explain the destruction of aircraft at night. This, as the British knew from their own experience, required accurate control of night fighters.

The pinpointing capabilities of Wurzburg would have made such losses understandable, but Wurzburg only became known to the British at the end of February 1942. At this time the celebrated British parachute raid on a Wurzburg site at Bruneval on the French coast succeeded in capturing the essential components.

Meanwhile the losses of 7 November 1941 were officially and publicly ascribed to the weather. Newspaper speculation at the time probably got nearer to the truth, rumouring strong German defences. A hidden debate over the *débâcle* continued, swiftly leading to the resignation of the British bomber force's commanding officer and to a rethink of strategy.

The comparison of British and German radar capabilities in 1940 and 1941 is instructive. The needs were early warning at all times and airborne interception at night. Both nations had the technology for both tasks, but were initially slow to reckon with the other's technology.

Ironically, the Germans had suspected a British defensive radar chain before the war began, but had failed to detect it despite a Zeppelin flight made off the British east coast in 1939 specifically for this purpose.[4] This was probably because they did not credit the possibility that the radar would operate in the HF band. But by the time of the Battle of Britain in 1940 they were evidently well aware of British radar.

By comparison, the British neglected to make a similar check, being sure no such thing as German radar existed. It took until early 1942 for them to realise the full extent of their mistake. As noted already, they had the opportunity to inspect a German radar in 1939 – the Seetakt naval fire control radar on the pocket battleship *Graf Spee* scuttled off Montevideo. They also had the Olso Report. But the implications were not realised. Not until February 1941 was it formally accepted that German radar existed and not for another year was its scale appreciated. Only then was it understood that this persistent underestimation of the opponent had undercut Britain's only striking power – the bomber force.

On both sides intelligence had been less effective than it might have been, but Britain made the more serious misjudgement and took longer to correct it. Insofar as ground-based defensive radar was concerned, the German Freya and Wurzburg were operationally superior to British equipment. Both could be operated coastally or inland and attained greater precision.

9

Reversal of Roles

1942 WAS THE pivotal year in the air war. Germany retired to the defence, undisturbed by such threats as Britain seemed capable of making. Her protective air cover had so far proved adequate. Britain swung into the attack, seeing bombing as the only aggressive option she had. She cherished the same hope as Germany before her, that bombing might force an end to the war.

The pivot was electronics. Britain was obliged to recognise two formidable problems: target-finding and the German night defences. Germany was obliged to recognise that her defensive system, good as it was, needed improvement in the face of stronger attack. For both countries the necessary developments were in radio and radar technology. Other technologies such as aviation and weaponry were marginal by comparison.

In 1942 Britain confronted the fact that the majority of her bombs were falling miles away from their targets: in 1941 90 per cent more than five miles away, out of some 45,000 tons dropped. So long as this statistical proportion governed, increased offensive effort was effort 90 per cent wasted. It only conceded mounting losses to ever-stronger anti-aircraft defence. Britain now strove to break out of this pattern, but with little success.

The problem of target-finding had been anticipated by Germany before the war. She had developed three electronic navigation and bombing aids. The German systems were Knickebein ('Bent Leg'), X-Gerät ('X-apparatus'), and Y-Gerät ('Y-apparatus').

It was thanks to these that her bombing offensive against Britain was able to switch from day to night operations in 1940, without any phase of blind floundering. In practice, there was no sharp cut-off of day operations in favour of night, instead a gradual phasing-in, with Knickebein in use from the start.

Knickebein utilised frequencies from 30 to 33.3 megahertz, that is in the lowest part of the VHF band. It relied on forming narrow beams at

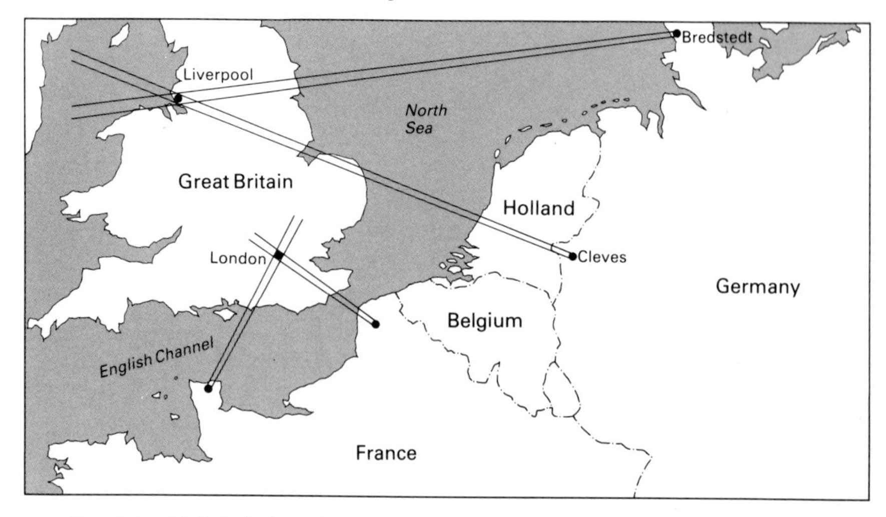

Fig. 9.1 **Knickebein** Germany's first navigational and targeting system used radio beams at about 30 megahertz, set up to intersect over the target, looking on a map like a 'bent leg'. As compared with the original base locations at Cleves and Bredstedt, the bases which later became available in Northern France were closer to British cities and offered better angle of cut, nevertheless Knickebein was at best a system for area bombing only. The beams were soon effectively jammed.

these frequencies by the use of large rotable antenna arrays. Two such beams, projected from different locations, were adjusted to intersect over the target – forming, when seen on a map, the 'bent leg'. The bomber equipped with Knickebein receivers flew along one beam until it detected the other, when it was assumed to be over the target.

Knickebein was an extension of a system developed in Germany during the 1930s by the Lorenz company to assist aircraft landing. The Lorenz system was widely used not only in Germany but elsewhere, including the British air force. It created a beam along which aircraft made their approach to an aerodrome. Developing it into Knickebein meant providing additional transmitter power and receiver sensitivity, enabling a tenfold increase of range, to the order of 300 miles.

The problem with such a system is to achieve sufficient accuracy. Although the frequency is high enough for a narrow beam to be defined, it is difficult for the receiver aboard the aircraft to detect, just on the basis of signal strength, when it is in the exact middle of the beam, which is where it needs to be.

To counter this problem Knickebein used a split beam. It was really two beams on the same frequency overlapping in the middle. The difference between the beams was that one was modulated with dots and the other with dashes. The receiver on the aircraft, picking up both, produced an audible output composed of dots and dashes.

Dots or dashes predominated in loudness according to which side of the centre line the aircraft was on, left or right. The dots and dashes were timed to fit together, so that in the middle where the beams were of equal strength they merged into a continuous note – the 'equisignal'.

In this way the directional accuracy was increased, and at the same time a simple navigational indication was given. If the pilot could hear dots, he knew he had to steer to the right, and if dashes, to the left. Split beam technique was not a novelty unique to Knickebein, but an example of a known method of obtaining higher precision with radio beams. Sometimes the dashes were on the left and the dots on the right.

Accuracy

Knickebein could identify the general target area, but its accuracy was limited to about one kilometre at best. Best in a theoretical sense. No electronic bombing aid, German or British, ever produced consistent practical results approaching theoretical maximum accuracy.

Precision was lost in many ways. One critical operational problem was determining the exact moment for bomb release. Every second of error was roughly equal to a 100 metres miss-distance. Knickebein gave little help with this.

X-Gerät represented a considerable improvement. Like Knickebein it provided a director beam for the bomber to follow with similar audible dots and dashes modulation. But the airborne equipment included an additional indicator giving a visual left/right signal. Total reliance on hearing, which given the high noise background in aircraft was undesirable, was avoided.

Moreover, as the target was approached, the director beam was intersected by no less than three beams in sequence, the first alerting the bomber crew, the second and third measuring groundspeed and determining the moment of bomb release.

X-Gerät's higher frequency, 65/75 megahertz, permitted more accurate beam formation. Coarse and fine beams were used in a complex combination, the total number of beams possible to be used being no less than seven.

A coarse director beam with a width of 4 degrees indicated the sector within which the fine director beam was to be found. This had a width of about 0.5 of a degree. A reserve fine director beam was projected alongside the other, within the coarse beam; either could be followed. This increased the security of the system against equipment failure and countermeasures.

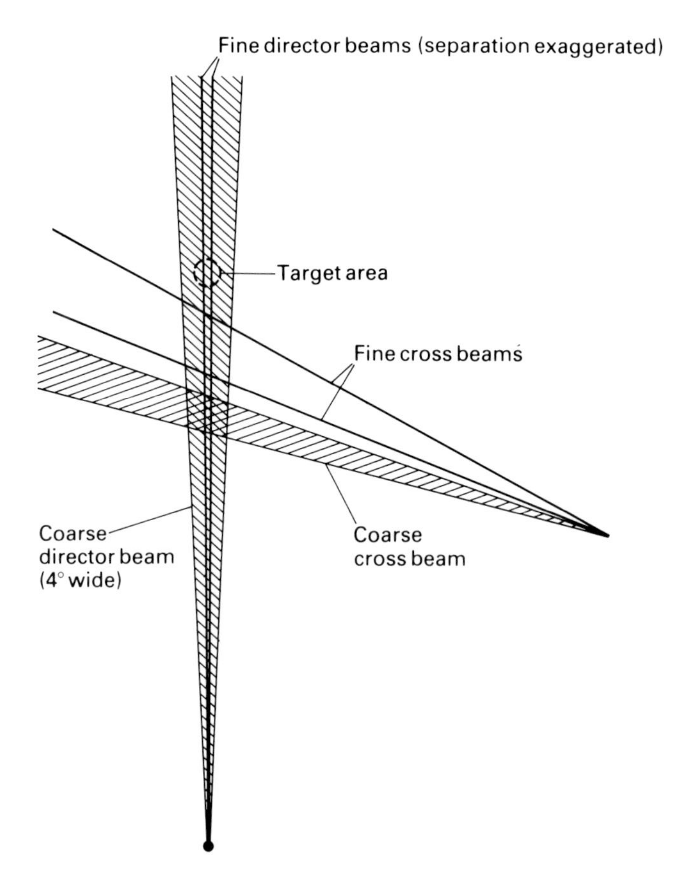

FIG. 9.2 **X-Gerät** X-Gerät was on the same principle as Knickebein but answered the need for more accurate beams and precision timing of bomb release, plus resistance to countermeasures. Working at about 75 megahertz, it used three approach beams: one broad, with two fine beams within it either serving for precision approach. The first cross beam was broad, serving to alert the crew. The second was fine, encountered normally 20 kilometres before the target. It was the signal to start a stop-watch with two hands, one moving faster than the other. The third beam, 15 kilometres further on and 5 kilometres before the target, was the signal to press the stop-watch knob again. This stopped the fast hand. When the slow hand caught up, an electrical contact caused bomb release. In other words the stop-watch measured the aircraft's time to cover 15 kilometres and allowed for another 5 kilometres to be traversed, assuming the same speed. To discount the forward distance the bombs would travel after release. Depending on height, an auxiliary hand, moving with the fast hand, was off-set backwards by an adjustable amount; this hand made the electrical contact. Jamming of X-Gerät was not very effective.

Beam formation of this accuracy testified to a high level of technology in constructing large antenna arrays. These were the common basis of both Germany's target-finding and ground radar systems.

X-Gerät's first, alerting crossbeam was coarse. The second and third were fine. The third actually comprised two fine beams close together. The second and third beams crossed the director beam at distances of 20 and 5 kilometres from the target. The time taken to cover the 15 kilometres between them was measured by pressing the knob of a mechanical computing device, an elaborate stopwatch, as the second beam was crossed and pressing it again at the third.

The device measured the true groundspeed, made allowance for it, and automatically determined the moment of bomb release.

In effect it assumed that the aircraft continued at its measured speed and held its course over the final five kilometres. Allowance had to be made for the height, which was fed in by the crew.

Altogether this was a sophisticated way of determining bomb release. It helped to give X-Gerät a claimed accuracy of some hundreds of metres. But the need to assume that the aircraft would stay at the same measured speed and on course over the last five kilometres inevitably introduced a factor of error.

Control

This source of inaccuracy was eliminated in the third system, *Y-Gerät*. It did not predict from past data when bombs should be released, but controlled the aircraft's flight to the correct point and ordered bomb release when the point was reached.

While Knickebein and X-Gerät were radio navigation systems, in which the bomber passively utilised the signals it received, Y-Gerät was a move in the direction of radar. It might be described as a form of secondary radar, in that it responded to a signal from base. It did not require the transmitter power characteristic of primary radar, nor pulsed operation. It was described in principle in the Oslo Report. Y-Gerät operated with one beam only, on frequencies near 45 megahertz. This beam was complex.

Equipment on the bomber analysed the signal received, gave a visual steering indication to the pilot, and could directly navigate the aircraft through the autopilot. This eliminated the 'weaving' which will occur with a human pilot reacting, always with slight delays, to visual indications.

The beam was modulated at 300 hertz. This was an audio frequency, but there was no need to listen to it. Instead the airborne equipment extracted this modulation and applied it to a new carrier wave at a slightly different frequency. This signal was rebroadcast back to the

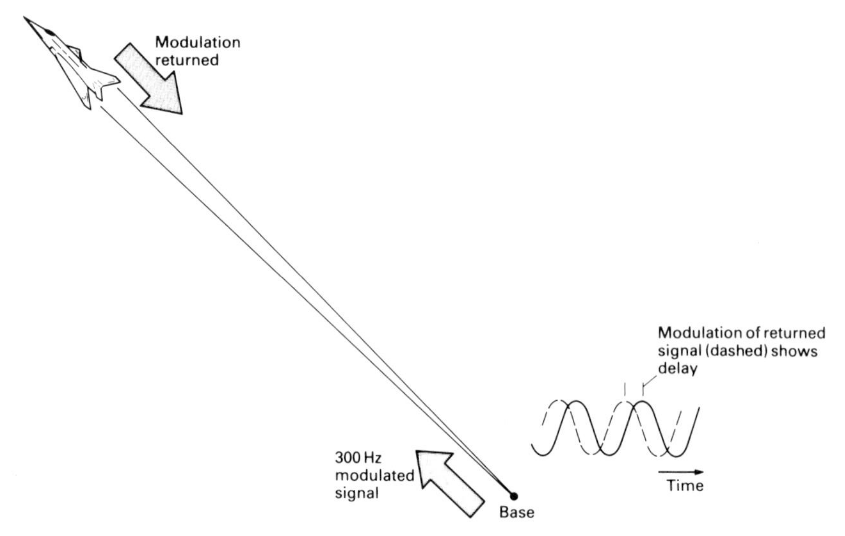

FIG. 9.3 **Y-Gerät** Y-Gerät attempted high precision by commanding bomb release when the bomber, flying along its beam, had reached an exactly determined range from the base station. The range was measured by transmitting to the bomber a 300 hertz signal, carried as a modulation on the radio beam at about 45 megahertz. The bomber returned the modulation on a slightly different carrier frequency, enabling the base to measure the phase shift due to the time taken to go out and back. This gave the range. The two-way communication proved easy to jam and Y-Gerät was not successful.

base transmitter. For example, in attacks on London the base station's signal was on 45 megahertz (modulated at 300 hertz) and the return signal from the aircraft was on 46.9 megahertz (similarly modulated).

Thus the 300 hertz modulation was returned to the base after completing a round trip to the aircraft and back. By this time it was out of correspondence, or 'phase', with the 300 hertz signal at the starting point.

In other words the waveforms no longer coincided; the peaks were displaced from each other. Measuring the difference indicated the time taken for the signal to travel and so gave the instantaneous position of the bomber along the beam. The instruction for bomb release was signalled to the bomber from the base, again through the beam, at the calculated moment.

In principle, Y-Gerät was more accurate than X-Gerät. Moreover it was easier to set up, requiring only a single beam. On the other hand it required individual control of each bomber. When a small group of bombers used the system, they waited near the target and took turns to enter the beam.

Accurate systems, such as X- and Y-Gerät. can mark a target for follow-on mass attack. This proved to be the practical path of development for both Germany and, later, Britain, when she had developed comparable systems. Elite pathfinding units were formed whose task was to find targets and mark them in one way or another. This might be by initial bombing to start fires, or by flares suspended on parachutes ('sky marking'), or, in later British practice, by coloured long-burning ground indicator bombs.

Even with these methods sources of error arose. The irreducible minimum of 'electronics error' was compounded by the error of target-marking and this in turn was compounded by the miss-distance of the follow-on bombing, aiming at the marking. Flares would of course sometimes permit direct visual observation, but this was less satisfactory than ground indication. The main use of flares became to sky-mark targets veiled in cloud.

By contrast with X- and Y-Gerät, Knickebein was general to all bombing aircraft. X- and Y-Gerät were always used by separate pathfinding groups. Possibly because of its fundamental versatility, possibly because of its purely navigational utility, Knickebein continued in use after the introduction of X- and Y-Gerät. All systems remained operational, in one way or another, for most of the war. An additional system, based on Freya radar, came into use in 1944.

Why Germany?

It was surprising foresight which led to the development of these systems in Germany before the war began. Surprising, because it was in Britain rather than in Germany that attention had been focused on the attack potential of the bomber as an independent deep penetration weapon. For this reason the strategic four-engined heavy bomber had appeared in Britain but not in Germany. In Germany attention had focused on the tactical bomber, supporting army operations. Britain, rather than Germany, should have addressed the problems of long-range strategic target-finding and bomb-aiming.

Probably it was German experience of long-range bombing with Zeppelins in the First World War that suggested the need for radio-navigational and target-finding methods. German long-range bombing was carried out later in that war with Gotha aircraft, but this was in daylight.

Britain on the other hand relied on traditional sea-faring methods of navigation by taking observations on stars, not allowing for the fact that aircraft represent a totally different operational environment.

Neither Britain nor Germany realised before the war that bombers on deep penetration missions would be confined to night operations, and that visual target-finding would be impossible. Except, of course, in conditions of bright moonlight combined with near-cloudless skies, which however were very rare and in any case stripped the bomber of its protection.

It was yet another unforeseen factor which created conditions in which the German systems could be applied so effectively. This was the geography of Europe following the French collapse in mid-1940, unexpected by either side. Britain was brought within easy striking range, by both aviation and electronic standards, from bases near the northern French coast.

Originally Knickebein was deployed from base stations at Cleves and Bredstedt, both in Germany. These were established by June 1940 – before the fall of France. They would not have given a very accurate angle of cut against most British targets. For maximum accuracy beams need to cut at about right angles.

Knickebein was chiefly directed at London, a large, diffuse target, easy enough to find approximately on account of the River Thames, but difficult to bomb with precision. Later, sites for the beam systems were put into the Cherbourg peninsula and elsewhere in northern France, giving better angle of cut and closer range against a variety of targets.

Britain had first of all to learn about the systems, then seek ways of countering them. Sources of information were signals intelligence; prisoner-of-war interrogations; retrieval of apparatus and written material from crashed aircraft. Initial attention focused on Knickebein. Expert reaction in Britain was to deny the possibility that radio beams at 30 megahertz would propagate far enough at flying altitudes.

A lesson in radio technology had to be absorbed. It was made more difficult by the general inferiority of British radio instrumentation at that time, for example for measuring frequency. But once the basic technology had been understood, it proved easier to degrade the performance of Knickebein than it had been to create the system in the first place. The countermeasure was the simple one of noise jamming.

Diathermy sets commandeered from hospitals were the somewhat unlikely first resource. Generating a broad band of radiation, normally to produce heat in the body for medical purposes, they would when positioned under the beams produce a noisy 'mush' in the receivers.

Another resource was a number of Lorenz blind-landing transmitters already in the possession of the British air force; these were adapted to produce interference. Later specially-made transmitters reproducing the Knickebein dashes were brought into service. They were not synchronised with German transmissions but made the genuine dashes impossible to discriminate.

Beam-bending

A legend sprang up about *'bending the beams'*, and picturesque stories began to circulate about bombings inexplicably directed at the open countryside, cratering fields and claiming chickens as occasional victims.

To bend the beams synchronised emissions would have been necessary, selectively intensifying the dashes and thereby displacing the equisignal towards the dot region. This would have been 'deception jamming', with the result of leading bombers to a false target. This was not done, despite the many assertions that it was which are still to be found in otherwise respectable textbooks.

But the result of straight jamming was in practice exactly the same, bombloads discharged over open countryside. Any circumstance which makes the work of a bomber crew more difficult tends to make it dump its bombs on any indication, however uncertain, or none at all. Knickebein's problems became apparent to Germany when X-Gerät was already being introduced. The British code name for Knickebein was 'Headache' and the countermeasure transmitters were 'Aspirin'. X-Gerät had a successful operational history from October 1940 onwards. It began to be jammed with some effect from January 1941, but it supported the German Blitz on Britain during its most intensive period.

The long nights, with fires burning for days at a time, made London an easy area target, but without X-Gerät the Blitz could not have been so effectively extended to provincial cities. The attack on Coventry in November 1940 was a remarkable success for X-Gerät. The raid was carried out in moonlight but this alone could not explain the accuracy of the attack.

X-Gerät was countered with jamming in the same way as Knickebein, using specially-made transmitters. It was code-named 'Ruffian' or 'River' and the countermeasure was 'Bromide'.

X-Gerät's long run of success was due to a number of factors. One was that it represented a practical level of electronics technology higher than that obtaining in Britain. It used several beams at frequencies which the British could not at first measure with sufficient precision. They could not therefore precisely 'spot-jam' them.

Spot-jamming means radiating a jamming signal on exactly the frequency in use by the enemy, as opposed to barrage jamming which covers an extended frequency band. Spot-jamming makes better use of the available jamming power. It is the most effective way of obliterating a signal on one particular frequency.

Another factor was the British oversight in failing to adapt the audio frequency carried on the jamming signal from 1500 hertz, as for

Knickebein, to 2000 hertz for X-Gerät. The audio frequency not only provided the tone heard by the system user listening to dots and dashes, but actuated the X-Gerät's visual indicator. It was therefore the ultimate target of the jamming.

The difference between 1500 hertz and 2000 hertz, the latter as used in X-Gerät in 1940/41, is about half a musical octave in the third octave above middle C. Although the jamming signal might be received, the false dashes would be at the wrong pitch.

It was not necessary for the ear to detect this: the airborne X-Gerät equipment included a filter which removed them before they reached either the headset or the visual indicator. Although the British discovered, from salvaged equipment, that X-Gerät was using the higher frequency, there was a costly delay in applying the information.

Ultrasonic Modulation

Change of modulation frequency was successful in defeating British countermeasures not once, but twice. The second time came when X-Gerät was used in early 1942 for the so-called Baedeker raids against British regional towns. This 'Taub' variant of X-Gerät used ultrasonic modulation, well above hearing range. But, in a finesse typical of electronic warfare, the functionless audio modulation was continued in the hope, which proved to be well-founded, that it would continue to be the object of such jamming attempts as were made.

The ultrasonic modulation operated a directional indicator. Although intelligence reports pointed to the use of this technique, it was not identified and effectively countered until after another costly delay. When the British at last introduced effective jamming, they saw the proportion of the bombs judged to be on target fall from 50 to 13 per cent.

X-Gerät, good as it was, was not ideal. It could not supply the need for a means of striking point targets. This lack was intended to be rectified by the introduction of Y-Gerät. For this reason Y-Gerät should have marked a significant escalation in the success of the German bombing attack. But Britain had plenty of time in which to learn about Y-Gerät in advance of its introduction, and preparations to jam it were ready.

The signal rebroadcast from the aircraft, which should have told the base station where the aircraft was, proved to be the vulnerable point. This signal was picked up in Britain. Its modulation was transferred back on to the same frequency as the base station. The new modulated carrier wave was transmitted as the jamming signal. It was accepted by the airborne receiver, being indistinguishable from the genuine signal from the base station.

But the modulation had now covered extra distance and had lost time in doing so. It was out of phase with the modulation in the genuine signal. Nevertheless it was instantly rebroadcast from the aircraft – the corrupt signal along with the genuine signal. Everything now happened all over again. The rebroadcast signal instantly became so degenerate that the base station could not work with it and the range indication failed.

Germany attempted to use Y-Gerät for the precision bombing of London, using a base station near Cassel in northern France. In the circumstances a public television transmitter, set up at Alexandra Palace in North London before the war to operate at 45 megahertz, proved ideally located for jamming purposes. Consequently Britain was able to frustrate the attempt from the outset.

This was a more important achievement for British countermeasures than has generally been realised. The diffuse area bombing to which London had chiefly been subjected had the hallmark of Knickebein. But London was a very large area and could absorb indiscriminate bombing without sustaining much damage to the numerous high-value point targets which were within its boundaries.

Successful precision bombing of London in the winter of 1940/41 would have made the British war position far more critical. This was evidently realised in Germany and was a major reason for the introduction of Y-Gerät. But London, like Berlin later in the war, was destined to remain out of the grasp of precision bombing.

Despite its sophistication, Y-Gerät proved more vulnerable than its predecessors. It exemplified the tendency of highly automated systems to lack the in-built resilience against countermeasures that a human operator can often provide. It was code-named 'Benito' and the countermeasure 'Domino'.

By February 1941 all the German systems were being countered. This did not stop the bombing assault nor did it make the systems futile, though this is the impression which many accounts create.

Starfish

Some important targets were ports approached from the sea, giving reduced opportunity to jam. Moreover the systems were being used by elite pathfinding crews which drew on their experience to offset the effects of jamming. It was often possible, for example, to continue through a region where jamming was strong, by using the autopilot to stay on the previous course until the jamming weakened.

Undoubtedly however jamming reduced the bombing effectiveness, causing greater reliance on such visual indications as might be obtainable. Under such circumstances visual countermeasures in the form of decoy fires became effective (code-named 'Starfish').

Even when a pathfinding group initially bombed a target correctly, the presence of more than one group of fires could mislead subsequent bombers, which would usually opt to bomb the most intensive conflagration they could see. The defensive need was therefore to bring the first fires under control as quickly as possible, while the decoy fires were kept burning strongly.

During the middle of 1940 Britain faced a difficult task: she was behind in electronics technology, and had to work out the technology being used against her from whatever indications she could obtain. She had to study all German electromagnetic emissions, and distinguish the bombing systems from German radar – not easy, because of official reluctance to accept the existence of the latter.

Besides, radar and bombing systems were similar in terms of ground hardware and frequency. They were mostly in the VHF band and utilised large scale antenna arrays mounted on turntables. Photographic reconnaissance did not find them easy to separate.

The irony of the situation was that much of the information Britain obtained came thanks to her own more modest use of electronics in warfare. Although her electronics technology was less advanced, it was concentrated in signals intelligence and countermeasures, and these were good enough to take a toll of the more highly developed electronic systems being used against her.

The nature of the German systems was revealed in many ways, sometimes by direct electromagnetic eavesdropping and measurement, sometimes by luring German aircraft to land in Britain. The latter was the result of simple electronic deception, applied to German navigation systems. Simple as it was, it reaped as harvest knowledge of the most advanced electronic developments.

In this way conflict lubricated the transfer of electronic technology. The principle is universal; later in the war the flow became two-way.

Navigational deception was accomplished by 'meaconing'. This was the simple technique of duplicating radio beacons in the Continental navigation system set up for the German air force. There were some eighty such beacons, working on medium or low frequency, transmitting omnidirectional signals with an identifying call-sign. Only a limited number worked at any one time.

Operational beacons and frequencies were changed daily. But British signals intelligence often intercepted the encoded order signals. Radio emissions from beacons were received and re-radiated from false 'meacons' which were hundreds of miles away from the true beacons. From time to time German aircraft fell victim to these lures, getting on to wrong courses, running out of fuel and being forced to land in Britain. X-Gerät fell into British hands this way.

Simplicity versus Sophistication

Thus simple tricks undid highly engineered systems. Small expenditures negated big investments. Electronic warfare has never outlived this vulnerability. For this reason it remains an area of obsessive secrecy. Fear persists that if the enemy learns basic details of what is being done, some easy way of confounding it will occur to him.

Moreover, there is not always a sure standard by which to recognise superior technology in the military sense – which in time of conflict is the only sense that matters. Undoubtedly Germany began the war with extensive reliance on her superior electronics technology, and did not realise the extent to which her superior systems would eventually give themselves away to her technically inferior opponent. The efficiency of her bombing systems was bound to decline. The need for continuous invention and investment in new systems became apparent as a general principle of electronic warfare.

This principle was already clear when, with the pivoting of the air battle in 1942, it became Britain's turn to introduce target-finding aids.

The first equipment was Gee. This was introduced as a radio-navigational system in the expectation that it would function as a target-finding aid sufficiently accurate for bombing. It provided a positional indication to a suitably equipped aircraft anywhere within range, which was about 600 kilometres. It was not a point-indicating, or course-indicating system, as the German bombing systems were.

Gee operated from three base stations in Britain, one master and two slaves. The operating frequency was approximately 30 megahertz.[1]

The master station periodically emitted brief radio pulses. The slaves received and reradiated them. The slave pulses came at different time intervals after the master – corresponding to the times necessary for the original pulse to reach the slaves.

But at any remote point the three pulses were heard at intervals which were different again. They depended on the location of the point. The intervals were changed by the different path lengths from each of the three stations to the point.

In principle, airborne equipment measuring the intervals enabled an aircrew to locate themselves. In practice, the navigator worked with a map covered by two sets of hyperbolic curves – any one curve representing a line along which the interval between the master and a particular slave was the same. The navigator found the curve he was on in each set, and the intersection point defined his position.

Unfortunately, such coordinates have a small angle of cut, except close to the base stations. Consequently the accuracy is not high, except near home. Towards Gee's maximum range its positional accuracy was not much better than about 10 kilometres.

Gee was admirable as a navigational system enabling aircraft to hold courses out to the approximate target area. They did not have to fly straight out and back, as with the German systems requiring beam-

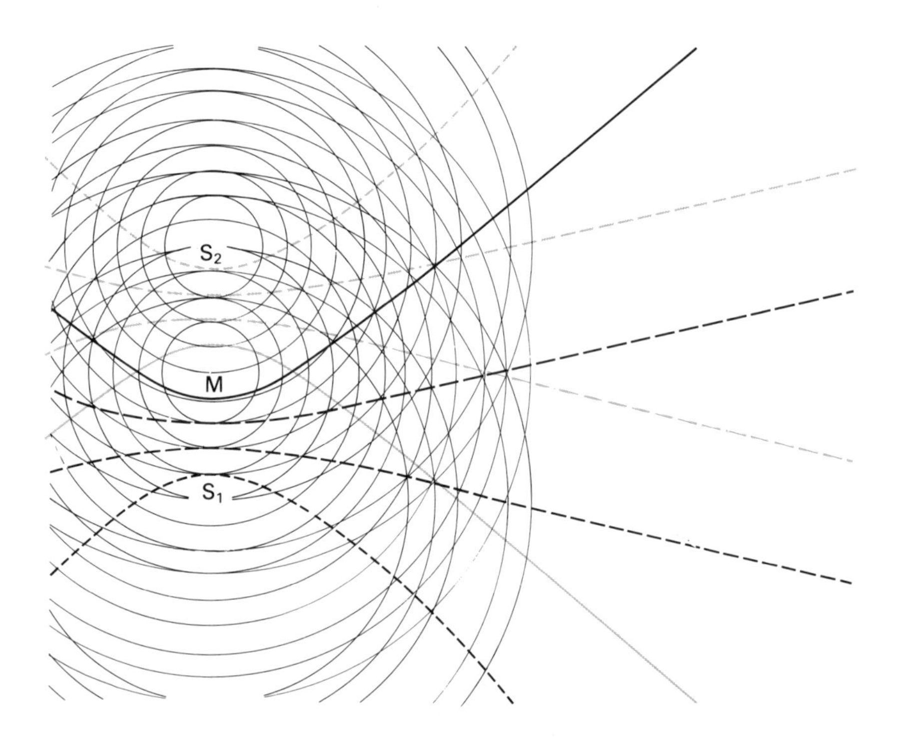

Fig. 9.4 **The Principle of Gee** Gee simplified the air navigator's task to timing intervals between signals from radio beacons. The base system comprised a master beacon M and two slave beacons S1 and S2. Pulses from M were received and simultaneously reradiated on slightly different frequencies by S1 and S2. At any distant point the pulses from M, S1 and S2 arrived at times depending on the total path lengths. Having noted the intervals MS1 and MS2 on a cathode ray tube display the navigator referred to a chart with coordinates joining points with given values and found the intersection. The coordinates are hyperbolic, as in the above illustration which shows a simple layout of M, S1 and S2. The intersections are sharp near the base stations but unavoidably, less so further away, for which reason Gee was not sufficiently accurate for bombing. Gee was developed in Britain using HF, and independently in the United States using MF as loran, a system still in use.

following. They could go by indirect routes. They could return to various airfields. The nearer to home, the more accurate Gee became. But this was the limit of Gee's capabilities. It did not fulfil other hopes.

Coordinated Attack

One practical advantage of introducing Gee was to enable the streaming of large bomber formations along pre-determined courses. It made coordinated bombing attacks possible, in contrast to the previous method of allowing bombers to find their way individually to designated targets, navigating by stars.

Hitherto bombers arrived at their target, if they did so at all, at widely separated intervals. A raid lasted many hours. Both in going out and in coming back bombers passed through the Kammhuber Line at different points and different times. This gave everything away to the strategy of the Kammhuber Line. Its individual cells were set up to deal with such a flow.

Gee enabled the appropriate counter-strategy, for by taking all the bombers through in one sector – in the absence of a beam, which sector it was could not be determined by the defence in advance – it overwhelmed local resources. It created the possibility of a concerted pattern of attack, bombers arriving in timed waves for specific purposes. It put a premium on attacking in large numbers and heralded 1,000-bomber raids. The introduction of these was the most spectacular British initiative in the air war in 1942.

But Gee did not solve the problem of bombing accuracy. While it took bombers to the general target area, unless visual identification was possible, the attack was no more precise than hitherto.

Gee can be compared with Knickebein in that it created a path to the target. It was more flexible than Knickebein in that the path was not confined to a single straight route. Moreover Gee gave navigational assistance wherever the bomber might find itself. But it was inferior to Knickebein in giving no worthwhile indication of the bomb release point. Knickebein was anything but accurate, but at least it was better in this respect than Gee. Like Knickebein, Gee could be jammed.

The development of Gee was remarkable in that trials were made over Germany from July 1941. The folly was only realised when a Gee-equipped aircraft was lost over Hanover. This approach was then discontinued.

Gee was introduced operationally in March 1942, when some 30 per cent of British bombers carried Gee sets. Jamming began from August 1942. Gee continued in use but its most dependable significance was as a navigational aid away from Germany. Despite jamming the bomber stream technique became permanent.

Gee launched the bomber stream technique with the first 1,000-bomber raid, on Cologne, 30 May 1942. This was highly successful both in reducing losses and inflicting heavy damage. Forty-one bombers were lost, 3.8 per cent of the attacking force. But subsequent attempts to repeat the success brought diminishing returns. Essen and Bremen were also attacked, the latter marking the end of the 1,000-bomber raids.

The problem was that, in the continuing absence of accurate electronic target-finding, visual identification was indispensable. If it was not obtainable, because of cloud or darkness, and this was generally the case, attacks had little effect. They were too dispersed. Essen, the most important single target in the Ruhr, enjoyed considerable immunity because it was featureless from the air and surrounded by several other similarly featureless towns, always semi-shrouded by industrial haze.

Essen's immunity was disrupted by the second British target-finding aid: Oboe. Oboe, like Y-Gerät, was a step in the direction of secondary radar, in that the aircraft re-radiated signals received from base transmitters, enabling range measurement to be made.

But, unlike Y-Gerät, it was a pulsed system. It worked on a frequency of 200 megahertz, unprecedentedly high for this purpose and capable of providing unprecedented accuracy, but placing a considerable restriction on range.

Attaining Ideals

Oboe's accuracy was enhanced because it was a triangulation system. It used two base transmitters – 'cat' and 'mouse'. The aircraft flew with 'cat' to its side. Oboe kept the range from 'cat' constant – in other words the aircraft flew around 'cat' in an arc, which was calculated to pass by the target. The aircraft followed this arc by receiving simple navigational indication, in the form of dots or dashes, or steered right or left, according to its measured radial range.

As it did so, its linear range from 'mouse' gradually changed. 'Mouse' measured this range independently until the correct point was reached, when bomb release was signalled.

Oboe attained many ideals. It gave simple navigational indication. It indicated precisely the moment of bomb release. It required the two base stations to measure only range, which could be done with extreme accuracy. Refinements of accuracy included allowing for the tangential effect of bombs dropping from an aircraft flying in a circle; for variation in the velocity of radiowaves with altitude; and for the fact that the earth's surface is not exactly spherical.

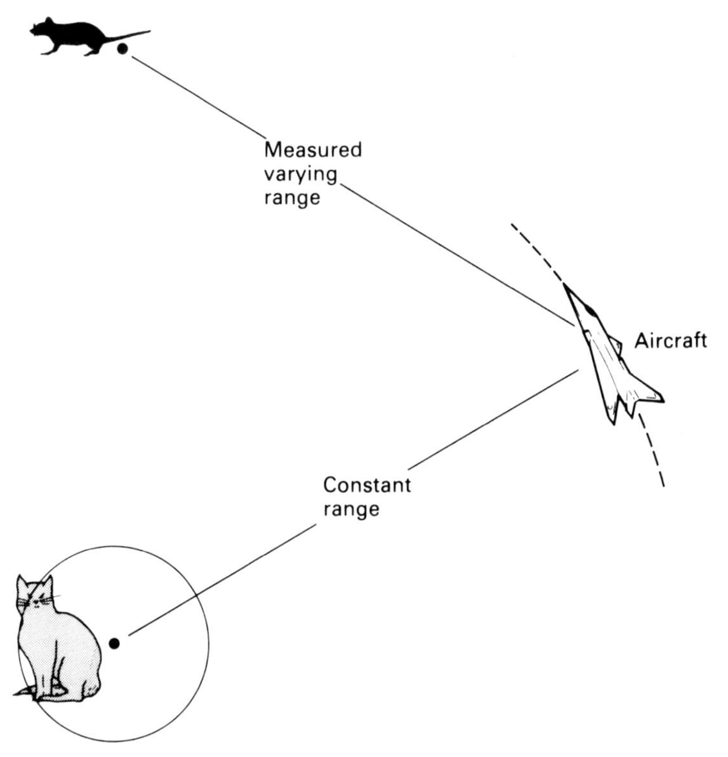

Fig. 9.5 **The Principle of Oboe** The bomber flew under the control of two base stations, 'Cat' and 'Mouse'. Cat kept the bomber to constant range, in other words it flew around Cat in a circular arc. Pulses emitted by Cat were received at the bomber, amplified and returned, enabling Cat to measure the range accurately and incorporate a navigational instruction into its signal, dots meaning steer inwards and dashes outwards, while a continuous tone indicated the bomber was on correct course. Mouse measured the range by similar means, but this was a changing range, and Mouse's role was to signal the correct moment for bomb release. The roles of Cat and Mouse were interchangeable. The United States developed a similar system under the name of Shoran. Oboe and Shoran enabled precision bombing. Oboe was used by the British against Essen and other Ruhr towns from late 1942 – Cat being near Dover, in Kent, and Mouse in Norfolk, near Cromer. Airborne equipment was mounted in Mosquitoes flying at 30,000 feet. Below this altitude, the Oboe frequency (200 megahertz) could not be received. The consequent necessity to drop marker bombs from such a height inevitably eroded Oboe's theoretical accuracy.

Theoretical precision was of the order of 100 metres. This was eroded by practical factors to more than 600 metres, even so it was exceptional by any previous standard.

But some ideals eluded Oboe. Range was severely restricted, for which reason practicable targets were confined to the nearest part of Germany to Britain – the Ruhr. Even the Ruhr could only be reached because Oboe was carried by Mosquito aircraft which flew at high altitude, 30,000 feet (9,150 metres), where the Oboe signals, which had very little tendency to refract around the earth, could be picked up.

Oboe was introduced operationally on 21 December 1942 with an attack on Essen. Eighteen months elapsed before it began to be jammed. A later version was based on frequencies made possible by the cavity magnetron, and this survived for the rest of the war.

While Gee was comparable with Knickebein, in that both were usable by an unlimited number of aircraft, Oboe was comparable with Y-Gerät in that both were limited in the number of aircraft they could control. Oboe was used chiefly for target marking by pathfinders, the Mosquitos which carried it dropping target indicator bombs or, in cloudy conditions, sky-marking flares. Accuracy inevitably varied with the chosen technique of target-marking.

The Oboe principle could be combined with Gee. Using Gee the aircraft could reach the general target area. Here its approximate coordinates, given by Gee, were refined by recourse to an accurate position check. For this purpose the aircraft, rather than the base stations, had to initiate the signals. By emitting signals which were returned from the base stations it obtained an accurate determination of its range from each, and therefore an accurate triangulation fix.

This combination was yet another form of secondary radar, similar to Identification Friend or Foe, from which it was derived. The system was known as G-H. It did not involve continuous monitoring of the aircraft. It enabled the aircraft to maintain radio silence for much of the time. It could be used by a much larger number of aircraft than Oboe. Its range was about the same.

Oboe was the most accurate bombing system used in the Second World War, but its limited range highlighted Britain's fundamental disadvantage in bombing Germany. That is, of having to operate at longer range than Germany did in bombing Britain, because of the German bases in northern France. This particularly affected electronic target-finding. Until this problem was resolved the British bombing attack could not range over all Germany.

'H_2S'

The solution came with H_2S, the best-known of all the equipments based on the British discovery of the cavity magnetron.

H_2S was said to stand for 'Home Sweet Home'. To bomber crews, the first portent of the new system was the space and connections being made available on newly-manufactured bombers for an as yet undelivered equipment. Faced with this challenge to the imagination, they dreamt up a homing navigation system and christened it appropriately.

Alternative but less plausible explanations were not lacking. As the chemical shorthand for sulphuretted hydrogen, the gas which emanates from rotten eggs, H_2S was supposed to symbolise 'it stinks'. This remark was attributed to someone at a high level, commenting that the idea was long overdue for exploitation.

The latter claim hardly stands up to examination, for until the SHF band became available to electronic warfare it would have been impossible to realise the idea of H_2S in airborne equipment. The antenna dimensions alone would have ruled it out. As it was, H_2S was the largest and weightiest electronic equipment yet carried by aircraft, about a metric ton.

Yet as soon as the SHF band did become available, H_2S was a top priority development. The development and production of H_2S was a major part of the national investment in Britain's bombing force, which in its turn is generally held to have absorbed a larger share of Britain's wartime production than any other sector of her armed forces.

H_2S made the earth itself the target. This was not entirely a novelty, for the radar altimeter which had made its appearance in the United States during the 1930s did the same thing. It measured the height of an aircraft by bouncing a signal off the earth's surface.

But the radar altimeter was a simple device. Unlike most radars it needed little power, for its target was enormous and returned a good echo. It came before pulsed radar, for it used continuous waves. It radiated continuous waves at a modulated frequency, and measured the time interval for echo return by noting the difference in the modulation. This was adequate for a radar device which could assume where the target was and only needed to measure range.

H_2S was at the opposite end of the scale. It was a conceptual leap. Thanks to the small wavelength, it made the rotating radar antenna, hitherto restricted to ground radar, compact enough to be airborne. It mounted the antenna beneath the aircraft, to look down instead of up. It shaped its narrow beam, not with an array of rods, but with a curved reflector. The microwave radiation was fed to the reflector's focal point. As the reflector rotated, the beam scanned the earth's surface.

The scanning rotation was followed on the radar display, using the same idea as the plan position indicator in ground controlled interception. With ground controlled interception the targets were few, and the radar returns showed up as isolated blips on an otherwise featureless map. But with H_2S every point of the earth gave a radar return. H_2S covered its whole display with echoes. Because different areas reflected at different strength, the screen became a map of the surface below.

Water areas absorbed the radar signal and appeared dark. Built-up areas, with many surfaces vertical to the ground and at right angles to each other, reflected strongly. Forests reflected more strongly than open country. Coastlines appeared clearly. Recognisability of individual towns varied. With towns on the coast, or where there were docks or lakes, or a distinctive river, recognisability was good.

True, the picture was often difficult to interpret and skill was essential. But H_2S was independent of range, independent of cloud cover, and exceedingly difficult to jam or deceive. From the time of its introduction in January 1943, the British air force acquired great effective range. It could roam all over Germany, finding targets with varying degrees of success, nevertheless finding them where they could not have been found before.

Combined Strength

In practice H_2S was used in conjunction with Gee, Oboe, and G-H. The whole was greater than the sum of the parts. Operating together, the new systems transformed British target-finding. Gee, for example, might take an aircraft into the target vicinity and H_2S did the rest.

The idea of using radar to obtain a picture of the ground did not spring into being as a result of the invention of the magnetron. The possibility had been considered earlier, using lower frequencies. Britain realised from early experience with airborne anti-surface vessel radar, working on 200 megahertz, that it detected coastlines extremely well. In practice, H_2S grew out of the application of the magnetron to airborne interception radar.

Airborne interception radar was initially seen as the most urgent priority for centimetric waves. The shorter wavelength enabled a far more compact and aerodynamic equipment, not needing external rod antennas, but fitting into a streamlined nose-mounted radome. This was accordingly produced and tested in late 1941 – a classic prototype in radar and aviation history. By the time it was produced however the need for it was no longer so urgent, the German Blitz on Britain having ceased. But in testing it, the marked propensity of SHF radiation to reflect from the ground became clear.

At 10 centimetres, the first SHF equipment employed a wavelength 15 times shorter than the wavelength used hitherto by the British for both airborne and ground controlled interception radar, 1.5 metres (the wavelength corresponding to 200 megahertz). The equipment became more compact in the same proportion.

H_2S was the most spectacular application of the magnetron. It marked the advent of a new radar era. This is with us to the present day, in that SHF remains the frequency band most often used in radar.

As already noted, at SHF rod antenna arrays were replaced by curved metallic reflectors, with the radiation brought to the focal point through waveguides from the transmitter. Waveguides are simply square or rectangular metallic conduits, which have the property of 'piping' radiation as if it was a fluid. The conduit's cross-sectional dimensions are determined by the wavelength.

With H_2S, Britain leapfrogged Germany in radar technology. The leapfrog was implicit from the time that the cavity magnetron was discovered, in 1939/40, but took time to become effective, that is about three years.

The leapfrog came not only from the magnetron itself, but from the creative stimulus which the magnetron provided. Much new electronic circuitry had to be devised. But in the interests of balanced judgement, it is important to note that the leapfrog was a limited one. It did not compromise Germany's strength in ground-based early warning radar – the form of radar which had mainly introduced the radar age.

Like other airborne equipments based on the magnetron, H_2S was not ready for service before the beginning of 1943. It was delayed to some extent by misgivings that magnetrons flown over Germany would sooner or later fall into German hands, and a corresponding search for alternatives which were never found.

Inevitably the secrets were lost. H_2S became known as the 'Rotterdam Gerät' in Germany after its recovery from an aircraft brought down in the vicinity of the city in early 1943. By July 1944 Germany had duplicated H_2S, in the 'Berlin Gerät', but this came too late in the war for aggressive use.

Lichtenstein BC

Britain's increased offensive pressure was already forcing Germany to improve her air defences in 1942, well before the new bombing aids, apart from Gee, could make their contribution.

Depth was added to the Kammhuber Line. It became an area system, so that incoming bombers were continuously overflying Himmelbett interception sectors instead of facing the hazard only once or twice. An airborne interception radar was introduced – Lichtenstein BC, working on 490 megahertz, mounted on the Ju-88 or Me-110, both twin-engined aircraft able to carry the nose-mounted radar antenna arrays.

Ground control could hand over the target to Lichtenstein – called 'Emil-Emil' in radiotelephony – at about two kilometres range, instead of trying to bring the fighter within visual range, a few hundred metres at best. German night interception technique began to parallel the British technique of early 1941. Emphasising this change, searchlights were withdrawn from May 1942, being redeployed to assist flak defences near cities.

The German improvements were challenged in 1942 by the first British attempts to disrupt German radar. Freya was jammed with airborne equipments. Straight jamming on the Freya frequencies was transmitted with 'Mandrel' with the aim of obliterating the genuine echo returns, at least from the direction of the jammer. The principle of radar deception jamming was introduced with 'Moonshine'.

Both Mandrel and Moonshine were mounted in aircraft dedicated to countermeasures, fighter types obsolete for armed combat (Defiants), which became the first examples of the breed of dedicated electronic warfare aircraft. The breed multiplied during the Second World War and eventually became prolific, including such classic examples as the 'Wild Weasels' of the Vietnam War.

Mandrel was employed to give cover to British bombers approaching and flying over Germany at night. It became a standard technique remaining in use throughout the war. Moonshine was briefly deployed in 1942 to create feint daytime attacks against northern France, generally as cover for real raiding aircraft.

The Moonshine-equipped aircraft returned not only its own echo to the radar, but numerous amplified pulses, simulating the effect of a considerable formation. The idea was only a short step away from Identification Friend or Foe, or secondary radar, 'illegitimate' pulses being returned instead of 'legitimate' ones.

Imagination is the only limit on what deception jamming may attempt. By adjusting the timing of the counterfeit echoes in relation to the regular pulse from the radar, it is possible to make a ghost formation seem nearer to the radar than the aircraft which is conjuring it up, and to approach at varying speeds.

By exploiting the fact that a rotating radar cannot limit signal reception entirely to the direction it is facing at any moment, which ideally is what it should do, it is also possible to make the echoes seem to come from a spread of directions. But in the pioneer days represented by Moonshine, simplicity was the keynote, and directional deception was not attempted.

With Moonshine it was necessary to try to deceive a number of Freya radars simultaneously, each working on a different frequency. One Moonshine-equipped aircraft had to be allotted to each Freya.

Diminishing Returns

The hope of raising a swarm of defensive fighters at the wrong time and place occasionally succeeded. But for obvious reasons the law of diminishing returns applied. Moonshine was discontinued in airborne use. Nevertheless it became the first and remains the classic example of radar deception jamming. The basic principle remains widely practised.

Once straight jamming was in regular use, it automatically became effective as a form of deception. For when straight jamming invariably preceded real heavy attacks, it sufficed to lay on straight jamming to force the assumption that a heavy attack impended. Conversely it was suspicious when early warning radar was apparently being allowed to track an approaching formation, unjammed.

Aircraft carrying Mandrel flew with the main bomber stream. To try and prevent the jammers serving as beacons for night fighters, they were intermittently switched on and off. This was the first recognition of the 'home on jam' principle, according to which defencers treat the source of jamming as their priority target.

Freya jamming was countered by widening the operational frequency band, from the original 118 to 128 megahertz to 107 to 158 megahertz. This brought an unexpected bonus: the higher-frequency Freya started triggering the Identification Friend or Foe equipment in British bombers, which gave themselves away to it as 'Flammen' (flames), a name possibly given from the enlarged, flickering trace on the cathode ray screen. In this way they invited and facilitated interception.

This was not realised at the time. Only much later, at the beginning of 1944, did Britain discover that use of Identification Friend or Foe over Germany was being heavily penalised. No reason ever existed to use it there, but a myth had become established amongst bomber crews that turning the equipment on caused searchlights to go out.

Probably this had no more foundation than another myth, that the same effect resulted from throwing empty beer bottles out. But Identification Friend or Foe sets had become objects of superstitious reverence to bomber crews. They were only persuaded to turn them off after Flammen had amassed an unknown but undoubtedly high tally of victims. When this became known, a British airborne device was introduced, 'Perfectos', to trigger the corresponding German Identification Friend or Foe equipment.

In 1942, Germany introduced new early warning radars, 'Mammut' and 'Wassermann'.

These radars looked ahead far to the future. Both of them utilised the principle of the planar array antenna, which scans by electronic means.

Strictly speaking every radar with a flat array of rods collectively forming an antenna can be said to have a 'planar array antenna', but in the early forms of such equipment, like Freya, the same signal was fed to all the individual radiating rods at the same time – that is, all the rods were radiating 'in phase'.

As the radiation from each rod was the same, the effect of the geometry was to reinforce the signal directly ahead of the antenna but to reduce or cancel it in other directions. In other words, the antenna always radiated a beam directly ahead and had to be rotated mechanically in order to scan.

Electronic Control

The name 'planar array antenna' is however usually reserved for the type of radar in which the individual radiating rods are fed with signals which are not in phase. The effect of the geometry in this case is to make the radiation reinforce, not in the straight ahead direction, but in some other direction which depends on the phase difference.

The phase difference can be varied by electronic means, therefore the radiation can be projected in any desired direction purely by electronic control. The principle works in reverse; the direction of an echo can be found.

In other words, mechanical rotation or tilting is no longer necessary in order to scan.

Mammut resembled Freya but did not rotate. It scanned its beam through a 100-degree sector electronically. It was about the same height as Freya, 10 metres, but the width was five times bigger, at a remarkable 30 metres, no doubt giving the radar its name. This large width was to enable the planar array antenna to form a vertical fan beam in an accurately controlled direction. Mammut did not find the target's elevation.

Wassermann on the other hand determined both azimuth and elevation. It had a tower-like antenna up to 57 metres high, while the width was from 6 to 12.4 metres. Wasserman demonstrated mechanical and electronic scanning in combination. It was rotated mechanically to scan around the compass, and at the same time the antenna was controlled electronically to determine the elevation of echoes reflected from the target.

Wassermann's directional accuracy in azimuth was plus or minus 0.25 of a degree, and in elevation plus or minus 0.75 of a degree. Mechanical scanning was through 360 degrees of azimuth. Elevation measurements were possible from 3 to 18 degrees above the horizon, which was as large an arc as necessary for long-range early warning. Range was from 35 kilometres against a target at 50 metres height to 210 kilometres against a target of 8,000 metres height, with an accuracy of plus or minus 300 metres.

The combination of mechanical and electronic scanning made Wassermann the first fully three-dimensional radar. It could simultaneously resolve the bearing, range and altitude of a target aircraft.

Only the introduction of electronic scanning made this possible; it would have been impracticable to rotate and tilt the antenna simultaneously by mechanical means.

The British Chain Home was a three-dimensional radar, but its goniometer-based method of finding both azimuth and elevation was a long way behind Wassermann's technology. Of course, the six- or seven- year difference in origination dates needs to be remembered.

Electronic scanning offers numerous advantages. It can be much more rapid than mechanical scanning, and is not tied to a steady rotation around the compass every six seconds or so, as is the case with mechanical scanning. It is not so predictable and this increases its immunity to deception and jamming.

Electronic scanning has become the desirable norm for military radars, either in combination with mechanical scanning as with Wassermann, or by itself. The radar antenna can be controlled electronically for both azimuth and elevation.

Today frequencies are higher than with Wassermann, and the radiating elements are correspondingly much smaller. They may be slots, which are the equivalent of rods, but thanks to the semiconductor revolution, they may now even be solid-state radiation emitters.

Either with slots or solid-state devices, an array with many more elements can be built than was possible to Wassermann. This in turn implies precision beam formation with more freedom from 'sidelobes'.

Sidelobes are unwanted parasitic beams projected in different directions to the main beam. They cannot be entirely avoided, and represent a weakness which radar countermeasures can exploit. A bogus pulse received through a sidelobe looks like a target in the direction of the main beam. Planar array antennas with a large number of array elements tend to be more immune to sidelobes than traditional reflector antennas.

Wassermann operated on three frequency bands, each offering continuous frequency change, covering between them the range from 75 to 250 megahertz. It therefore had considerable ability to defeat jamming by changing to a different frequency.

10

Climax

In keeping with its pivotal role, 1942 was not a decisive year in itself but rather one in which the stage was reset for the final act. The thunderous climax commenced in 1943. From the beginning of this year all the British bombing aids were operational.

It was soon found that they had a tendency to be target-specific, in that Oboe was specific to the Ruhr, while H_2S was attracted to Hamburg.

Oboe could always find Essen and the other Ruhr targets with good accuracy, but could not go much further. H_2S could easily identify Hamburg as a seaport with a characteristic plan of river and docks, but although it could go anywhere, it never found another target it could recognise quite so easily.

What made Hamburg even more vulnerable was that Gee could take bombers unjammed all the way over the North Sea, finally handing over to H_2S for Hamburg to be pinpointed.

The developing battle reflected these fundamentals of electronics capability. The British bomber force did what electronics enabled it to do, and could not do much else. Accordingly 1943 became the year of the Battle of the Ruhr, the Battle of Hamburg, and finally, the battle of Berlin. The first was fought mainly with Oboe, the second mainly with H_2S and in the third H_2S sought to achieve the same success against Berlin as it had achieved against Hamburg.

Initially, British persistence and resources were held in check by the intensity of the opposition. While severe damage was done to the Ruhr, bombing was less accurate and heavy than it would have been without the attentions of night fighters and the hazards of radar-directed searchlights and flak. Bomber loss rates were generally high.

This was a tribute to the efficiency of German radar, above all to ground-based Wurzburg and airborne Lichtenstein as the core of the defensive system. But the sudden introduction of 'window' to blind these brought disaster to Hamburg in a series of raids at the end of July and beginning of August 1943.

The idea of window, dropping huge numbers of metal strips cut to the correct length to reflect a given radar frequency, thereby overwhelming the radar with meaningless reflections, was not new, nor anybody's invention. Germany had tested it under the name 'Dueppel' (from the site of the experiments). Both Britain and Germany long shrank from using it in case, paradoxically, they were giving away something to the other side. But in mid-1943 it seemed to the British that they had far more to gain than they had to lose, given Germany's defensive posture.

Hamburg had been attacked from the beginning of 1943 with H_2S, though the results were not catastrophic. But the proportion of H_2S-equipped bombers grew steadily, reaching 90 per cent by the end of July. This was the background against which window was introduced in the heavy raids starting on the night of 24 July 1943.

Window returned the conditions of night interception to the pre-radar age. It took defensive pressure off the attackers, enabling them to fulfil their mission largely unhindered. At the same time, H_2S showed the target clearly and enabled methodical, area-concentrated attacks to be carried out, beginning with accurate target-marking and following up with high explosive and incendiary bombing.

As the combined result of all these effects, the attacks caused unprecedented damage. Eventually firestorms were started. In the course of nine days, including four heavy night attacks, some 50,000 people were killed. Yet in the first attack (24 July) the proportion of aircraft missing, out of 791 attacking, was no more than 1.5 per cent, when it might have been expected to be at least four times higher.

Had it been possible to apply the same technique of attack to other such targets, and achieve comparable results, the aim of strategic bombing might have been realised and Germany forced out of the war. Six Hamburgs, according to German judgement at the time, might have done this.

Stepping Stones

But not a single further target proved immediately vulnerable in the same way. Grave damage was done to at least four cities, Frankfurt, Kassel, Hanover, and Mannheim-Ludwigshaven. However these were seen by the attackers as merely stepping stones on the way to Berlin, which held out the promise of being the decisive arena.

Against all the preliminary indications, this next phase of the war, unfolding in the months after Hamburg's destruction with the ultimate aim of devastating Berlin, brought the British bomber force grievous losses, but no measurable advance towards any of the objectives which motivated it.

Berlin was not devastated; the German economy was not devastated; German morale was not devastated; no end to the war through Germany's internal collapse was brought into sight. At the end of March 1944, with the Allied invasion of France impending, the night bomber attacks on Germany temporarily ceased.

German air interception technique reacted swiftly to Hamburg, within days of the first window-using raid. The loss of radar was temporarily parried by the deployment of single-seater day fighters, looking for targets by the glare of fires below and reflected light from clouds above. This was the 'Wilde Sau' (Wild Boar) tactic, a variant of illuminated night fighting.

It was assisted by the fact that repeated attacks on the same target gave away the advantage of surprise and inevitably tended to improve the defenders' score. The missing rate rose from 1.5 per cent for the first window-using raid to 2.2, 3.5, and finally 4 per cent (24 July, 27 July, 29 July and 2 August 1943 respectively).

But even 4 per cent was still below previous levels. For the longer term, Germany needed to restore the effectiveness of radar, penalise the use of H_2S and other airborne electronic equipment, and find new tactics to combat the long bomber streams wending across her night skies.

The battle against window became the core of a programme to reduce radar's susceptibility to countermeasures. So long as Wurzburg and Lichtenstein remained unjammed, the attempts to jam Freya, begun late in 1942, were not excessively menacing. But window had changed this.

The survival of radar was suddenly a crucial issue. The night bomber attacks threatened Germany more immediately than the turn of the tide on the still-distant Eastern Front. Combating window meant diversifying radar wavelength. Because the frequencies used in German radar did not go higher than the lower part of the UHF band, diversification had to be in the downward direction.

The Lichtenstein air interception radar was the most critical single equipment. It appeared in a new variant, the SN2, working at lower frequencies, from 73 to 91 megahertz, and therefore immune to window in short lengths. Greater combat range than the previous version, about 4 kilometres against two, increased its effectiveness. It had a long operational life. Its frequency range was later widened to 37.5 to 118 megahertz. It was ironical that while the British transformed airborne interception radar by going up the frequency scale to SHF, Germany perserved it by dropping down the frequency scale from UHF to VHF.

FIG. 10.1 **Stag Antlers** The stag antler antennas of the Lichtenstein air interception radar (shown here on a Messerschmitt 110) enabled leading fighter aces to build up unsurpassed scores. Paradoxically, the antlers symbolised both an outdated technology and a highly effective system of night interception.

Despite the drawbacks of antenna that projected into the airstream, Lichtenstein SN2 performed extremely well. It never permitted the aerodynamic streamlining possible with British centimetric technology. It took about 10 per cent off top speed. But for all that it was amazingly successful. It claimed more victims than any other airborne interception radar in history.

Stag Antlers

Lichtenstein SN2's existence was suspected, but not until an equipped Ju-88 landed at a British airfield in July 1944 were its characteristics, including frequency, accurately known. From this time on, short-length window was replaced by longer ropes.

Even so, the effectiveness of Lichtenstein SN2 was never totally eroded. As late as February 1945 it was still culling the invading bomber streams. To the end of the war, the stag-antler-like antennas of Lichtenstein continued to symbolise two opposites: the seemingly outdated radar technology of Germany's night fighters, and their continuing high operational effectiveness. It is a provocative thought for all who meditate on the historical lessons of electronic warfare.

Similarly, although Wurzburg had been designed as a single frequency device (at 560 megahertz), it was modified to work over a range down to 490 megahertz. By itself this was a modest variation. Choice of frequency improved matters, but did not give the same rejection of window clutter as Lichtenstein obtained by going to much lower frequencies. It was necessary to try and distinguish the echoes returned by window from those returned by aircraft.

Being metal foil, or 'chaff', window floated with the prevailing wind. This distinguished it from aircraft, which were travelling at speeds of up to four hundred miles an hour or more.

In this difference radar confronted one of the biggest technical challenges it has ever had to face: the challenge of discriminating moving targets. It met the challenge, and in doing so opened up one of its most creative avenues of development.

Most targets important to radar, particularly aircraft targets, are of necessity moving in relation to their background. When it is possible to pick out moving targets selectively, radar acquires an enormous operational advantage. It can reject the majority of clutter that would otherwise make target discrimination difficult, uncertain, or impossible. 'Moving target indication' (MTI) is an inseparable part of modern radar technology. Without it, modern radar would be unthinkable.

It depends on the 'Doppler effect'. The standard example of this is always stated as an express train sounding its whistle going through a station. The pitch of the whistle, as heard by someone standing on the platform, suddenly drops as the train goes past.

The fact is that if the frequency of the whistle is, for the sake of example, 1000 hertz as heard when the train is stationary (the base frequency), then when the train is approaching it is heard higher, perhaps 1,100. Because of the approach, more wave cycles reach the ear in one second than they would if the source was static. Similarly, when the source is receding, fewer wave cycles reach the ear in one second and the frequency as heard drops.

The same happens with electromagnetic radiation. The size of the effect depends on the velocity of the aircraft or other source as compared with the velocity of electromagnetic radiation. It makes no difference whether the target is originating its own signal or reflecting a signal.

Because the velocity of electromagnetic radiation is very large compared with the velocity of most targets, the frequency change is relatively speaking small compared to the base frequency. The actual magnitude of the change is proportional to the base frequency; the higher the latter, the bigger the change.

'Wurzlass'

The challenge of discriminating moving targets comes down to detecting this frequency change. It was first tackled in Germany after the raids on Hamburg. The need was for additional electronic equipment to be combined with Wurzburg, enabling the slight change of frequency in the echo pulse from the genuine target to be recognised as compared with the virtually unchanged frequency of the clutter reflected by window.

The result was the 'Wurzlass' system. Understandably it was far from perfect but it is generally considered to have restored the defensive efficiency of Wurzburg to about 30 per cent of its value in the pre-window period. Today, radar, aided by massive advances in computer-processing of the returned echo, does very much better than this, but Wurzlass was an impressive start, considering the desperate conditions under which it had to be designed and produced.[1]

The technical battle against window was matched by a new defensive strategy against the bomber stream, gradually superseding the Kammhuber Line. Night fighters took off all over Germany, orbiting

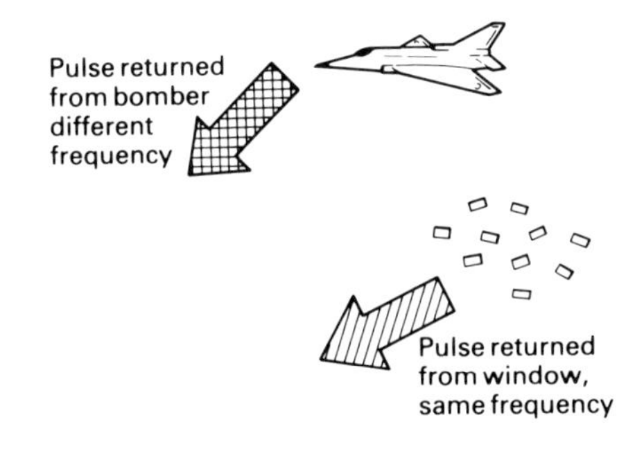

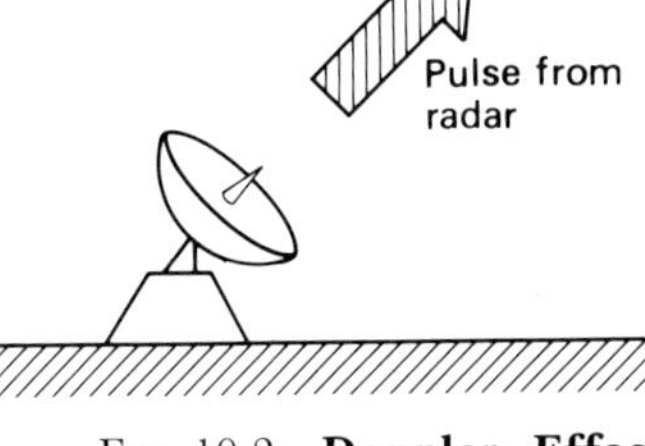

Fig. 10.2 **Doppler Effect** When radar pulses are returned off an approaching aircraft, the frequency is very slightly higher than that of the transmitted pulses. This is on account of the speed of the aircraft. By comparison reflections off window, or chaff, drifting with the wind, are virtually at the same frequency. Detecting the frequency difference enables the rapidly moving target to be distinguished from the window. If the aircraft is receding, there is again a frequency difference (the returned pulses are at a lower frequency than those transmitted).

radio beacons whilst awaiting instructions. When the target for the night became evident to the defence, the fighters were vectored towards the incoming bombers by a broadcast commentary.

This was the 'Zahme Sau' system ('Tame Boar'). It was open to deception and feint attacks, nevertheless it was an air defence strategy, based on radio and radar, that survived almost to the last days of the war and brought a continuing sequence of nightly victories.

From this time onwards new methods were used to track German night fighters from the ground. Formerly tracking was dependent on Wurzburg radar, and therefore liable to interference from window. One new method was a development of the Y-Gerät bombing system, generally referred to as Y-control.

As will be apparent from the description of Y-Gerät in Chapter 9, it was in essence a beam which tracked the direction and determined the range of an aircraft from a control base and passed navigational instructions. As such it was adaptable in principle to controlling the movement of fighters, so long as only simple manoeuvres were required. In practice it was used to transfer fighters from orbit around assembly beacons towards the bomber stream.

Even more significant was a new technique of tracking known as 'Egon', based on the German Identification Friend or Foe device 'Erstling'. This was an example of advanced 'secondary radar'.

In other words the primary ground radar no longer relied on evoking an identification friend or foe response by its normal pulsed transmission. Instead it was equipped to send special interrogatory pulses in addition to and in the same direction as its normally transmitted pulses. Erstling usually worked with Freya or Wurzburg radars, either of which sent interrogatory pulses at 125 megahertz. Erstling responded at 160 megahertz. The Egon system had a greater range than Y-control.

Both Egon and Y-control were immune to window. While window may scatter a radio signal, it does not prevent it from getting through to an aircraft. When the return signal is at a different frequency, it is not confused with the random echoes of window.

Electronic devices now began to proliferate on both sides. Great inventiveness was not required for this; the devices were in the main adaptations of existing radio, radar, and in particular secondary radar equipment. Secondary radar provides the pattern for many forms of airborne electronic warfare.

Rule of Four

The proliferation had begun even before the use of window over Hamburg initiated the sharp battle of countermeasures and counter-

countermeasures. It escalated afterwards. The basic principle was that the more electronic devices were used by the enemy, the more opportunity there was to use electronic devices against him.

A 'rule of four' might be said to dominate this proliferation. Devices do not come singly, but in fours. Any device introduced by one side provokes a counter-device by the other side. The other side also imitates the original device, which in turn provokes the first side to produce a counter-device. The operation of this rule needed to be watched for, but in practice it usually came as a surprise to the originator to find that his idea had been turned back against him.

The British impulse to proliferation was based chiefly on centimetric technology, of which H_2S was the prime example. German counter-proliferation was largely based on 'anti-centimetric' technology. This developed with rapidity once the British technology had been revealed.

Centimetric technology was aggressive and based on generating and transmitting centimetric radiation. For transmission considerable power was needed. Anti-centimetric technology was defensive, based on receiving the same radiation and detecting its origin. It had no need of similar power.

German receiver design was adequate to make a swift anti-centimetric response, which was in the main what Germany's defensive role required. The distinction between centimetric and anti-centimetric equipment can be alternatively stated as that between active and passive centimetric equipment.

It has been the fashion to claim that it took Germany eighteen months to catch up with British centimetric technology but bearing in mind that Germany needed to catch up for defensive purposes and had no use for offensive centimetric equipment, this timescale is unreasonably stated. In countermeasures she caught up more quickly, in half that time. The parallel is with the British swiftly finding countermeasures against German bombing systems even when they were two years away from introducing comparable bombing systems themselves.

German active centimetric equipment, on the other hand, in its only form as the Berlin airborne interception radar, did not begin to be operational until early 1945, at which time it was two years behind British developments.

H_2S was the first centimetric equipment to be deployed over Germany, and it was through the loss of H_2S that centimetric technology was given away. Countermeasures appeared in the form of both ground and airborne warning receivers. H_2S became highly self-revealing, especially since its use could not be dispensed with.

The 'Naxos' airborne radar warning receiver could detect H_2S from 65 kilometres range, and lead a night fighter into the vicinity of the user aircraft. The ground-based warning receiver, 'Korfu', could detect H_2S

before bombers had taken off. It warned of impending raids and enabled the bombers' course to be plotted.

The British proliferation included devices which were counters to non-centimetric German equipment. For example, Britain sent her own night fighters with the bombing stream equipped with 'Serrate' to home on to the early-type Lichtenstein emissions.

Serrate had a range of up to 150 kilometres, though it only indicated bearing. It fed its indication into the display of the airborne interception set, which was ready to take over at appropriate range. But Serrate was not successful.

No Effective Answer

The initial mistake was made of mounting Serrate in the Beaufighter, when the Beaufighter had already ceased to offer adequate aerodynamic performance. Later, in 1944, it was adapted against the Lichtenstein SN2, and mounted in the Mosquito, where it worked in conjunction with the Mark X airborne interception equipment. The latter was centimetric. But for some reason even this formidable combination of electronics and aircraft failed to provide an effective combat answer to the German night fighters.

In fact no such answer was ever found. The most effective measure against the German airborne radar appears to have been an active jammer called 'Piperack', carried for self-protection by bombers.

Despite giving away the approximate location of the bomber, Piperack prevented the night fighter from using the radar to close on its intended victim. In these circumstances, the night fighter's success would depend on the range needed for visual contact. Active jamming by Piperack and passive jamming by window were the most successful weapons against Lichtenstein SN2.

British bombers were equipped with a centimetric tail-mounted radar, 'Monica', to detect imminent attack. Monica gave an audible warning to the pilot, with increasing urgency as the attacker closed its range. But Monica did more harm than good. Apart from generating copious false warnings from other aircraft in the bomber stream, it was a beacon which night fighters could home on to. For this purpose the German anticentimetric equipment 'Flensburg' was introduced.

It is an axiom of electronic warfare that radar warning receivers enjoy greater range than the radar they are intended to detect. The value of the information the latter may obtain therefore has to be balanced against the value of the information it will certainly give away. Flensburg could find bombers from a range of about 80 kilometres.

In the second half of 1943, Flensburg, Naxos, and Korfu joined Flammen (operational against British Identification Friend or Foe since 1942) in demonstrating the dangers that come with the burgeoning use of electronic transmissions.

The virtues of radio silence, known in naval practice since the earliest days of electronic warfare, had been forgotten. Only gradually, in 1944, did the British air force rediscover them. Eventually transmissions were silenced completely, as with Monica, or reduced to the minimum usage, as with H_2S.

Electronic aggression escalated during 1943, particularly in the form of jamming. It was a counter to the radio communications of the German defensive systems, first the Kammhuber Line, later *Zahme Sau*. Noise jamming against German fighter radio telephony was initially generated from aircraft in the bomber stream, broadcasting noise from microphones in their engine bays. This was 'Tinsel', on HF.

But the single commentary introduced with *Zahme Sau*, still on HF, was far more difficult to jam than the many individual communications channels characteristic of the Kammhuber Line. It was higher-powered and carried by many transmitters.

A jammer 'Special Tinsel' was introduced. A monitoring receiver was set up on the British East Coast to detect the radio telephony frequencies in use by German fighters, so that instructions could be radioed to the Special Tinsel operators. This was 'Grocer'. Later 'Airborne Grocer' appeared. Germany introduced VHF radio telephony for fighters early in 1943. This was countered with 'Cigar' from the ground, later by 'Airborne Cigar'.

Both HF and VHF continued in German use for radio telephony to the end of the war. A series of ever more powerful, and massive, jamming devices on a wider range of frequencies was therefore carried over Germany, culminating in 'Jostle IV'.

Inevitably the special requirements of electronic warfare, the specialised command, the skills, the number, variety, and increasing weight of equipments, and the maintenance needs, all separated electronic warfare aircraft from bombers and led to the formation of a dedicated group within the British air force (100 Group).

Deception

Radio deception jamming is something of a rarity in electronic warfare, as compared with radar deception jamming, but its heyday arrived with Operation 'Corona'. Corona was probably more entertaining than effective although it undoubtedly had its occasional triumphs. The German fighter controller, giving *Zahme Sau* directions, acquired a double whose voice could not easily be distinguished but whose assistance was unwanted.

The first time Corona was used, 22 October 1943, the real controller and the bogus controller got locked into a conflict of authority. The real controller swore. The bogus controller commented 'the Englishman is now swearing'. The real controller insisted 'it is not the Englishman who is swearing, it is me'. A month later, during a raid over Ludwigshaven, the Corona voice persuaded most of the night fighters to land, and only one bomber was lost.

As a psychological variant of Corona, speeches by the German Führer and other texts were offered, as well as loud bell ringings and other distracting effects, some inspired apparently by the ghost trains at funfairs. Among the more successful expedients was the requesting of time-wasting test transmissions of the 'one, two, three, four . . .' kind.

To defeat the bogus controller, Germany switched to female controllers, believing that the bogus controller was airborne with the British bombers, and that the British would not draft women for this work. This was a reasonable belief, given that the Germans were using VHF for the broadcast commentary, with the expectation that the British could only intervene from line-of-sight range.

But the VHF frequency range in use was 38–42 MHz, at the lower end of the band. This bent sufficiently well around the earth for the British to join in, transmitting from the ground with powerful transmitters and directional antennas. The German commentary was intercepted at Kingsdown in Kent, where female German speakers were ready to play the requisite role.

The contest moved on to a competition in transmitter power, then took a musical turn. Germany introduced an 'Anne Marie' broadcast programme, ostensibly intended for the armed forces, but in practice indicating by the type of music the area in which night fighters were to assemble. Providing the fighter pilot was sufficiently musical to recognise the difference between for example a waltz and a foxtrot, even if only catching them in snatches, the communication was difficult to jam. Further instructions were passed in code by the announcer.

'Annie Marie' was used with little or no interference for a couple of months, but in February 1944 was superseded by telegraphic transmissions repeated on different frequencies, MF, HF, and VHF. Simultaneously radio telephony on VHF was continued. Radio communications jamming was obviously troublesome, as is witnessed by the measures adopted against it, but did not prevent communications getting through.

German night fighting technique steadily developed. The disruption caused by window proved to be brief. Despite window German radar remained operational. In the second half of 1943, British losses resumed an upward trend.

In August 1943, the first complete month after the introduction of window, German night fighters claimed an unprecedented 290 victims, as against 150 in July, and 223 in June, the last full month before window. Of the 290, about 50 were credited to the Himmelbett system, the rest to the new fighter deployment methods. This figure was eclipsed with 308 in January 1944.

'H_2X'

Berlin suffered from bombing but resisted massive onslaughts in much better style than Hamburg. This was partly because H_2S was less effective in finding Berlin. For this reason a higher frequency variant H_2X was introduced in November 1943, in the hope that it would improve the recognisability of Berlin's outlines.

H_2X has been produced in the United States. It worked on 10 gigahertz, with a wavelength of 3 centimetres. A still higher frequency variant, H_2K, at 20 gigahertz, with a wavelength of 1.5 centimetres was also produced in America, but not in time for wartime service. The capital letters S, X and K as in H_2S, H_2X and H_2K formed part of a system of frequency band designations, as in the table accompanying Chapter 7. These designations are still used today, though not with international consistency.

The H_2X variant of H_2S produced sharper and more recognisable outlines, but still did not solve the problem of attacking Berlin. Too many other factors were involved. Berlin was a big area target. It required deep penetration which reduced the bombload which bombers could carry. Bombers were exposed for a longer period to attack. Ever stronger flak defences had to be confronted. Flak tended to damage aircraft without causing loss while night fighters accounted for most of the aircraft actually shot down. Nevertheless flak had immense deterrent value.

Setting aside the larger scope of the battle, and concentrating on the immediate duel at night, when the combatants could only find each other by electronic means, Germany retained the upper hand. German night fighters were far from enjoying the high performance glamour of the day fighters, but shielded by invisibility against any aircraft not electronically equipped for detection, they inflicted heavy losses whilst suffering comparatively modest losses themselves.

As large aircraft, they carried effective weapons and enough ammunition to make several interceptions on a single sortie. Adept crews had the opportunity to build up remarkable 'kill' scores, approaching or even exceeding one hundred. With night fighting crews, quality was more important than quantity. When it eventually became necessary to restrict the number of fighters flying into engagement, a small number of highly proficient crews was able to keep up a high rate of kills. The German night fighters' battle with invading British bombers was destined to become the longest and most colourful chapter in the story of electronic warfare.

It is conventional to claim that the period from August 1943 to March 1944 was a period in which the night fighter reasserted its mastery over the bomber. In illustration of this, the lowest point of the bombers' fortunes is cited as being reached with the raid on Nuremburg on 30 March 1944 when out of 795 bombers a total of 94 failed to return and a further 71 were damaged, some irreparably. Only a few bombs fell on Nuremburg.

However this is only a conditional truth. The heavy penalties did not deter the attack. The fact of the matter was that the economic strength of the attackers was such that instead of becoming demoralised they continued to escalate the attack. They compared their own losses, not with the losses they were actually inflicting, but with the losses they thought they were inflicting.

An Endemic Problem

This is an endemic problem of air warfare. It applies not only to bomb damage versus aircraft losses, which is not a comparison of like with like, but to air fighting which should be a straightforward count of aircraft lost on each side. But the historical lesson is that while one's own losses are accurately known, the other side's losses are invariably estimated too high, therefore it is easily possible for both sides to think they are winning.

Those who directed the night bomber force attacking Germany attempted to offer an economic balance sheet of destruction. But they had no real means at the time of reckoning the value of the damage they were causing, whether in monetary or military terms, against the value of the losses they were sustaining.

They did not even know with any accuracy how their own losses were being caused. They generally overrated the role of flak and underrated the role of the night fighters. But they persisted in the faith that the attack was worthwhile. Not for many years did it become fashionable to question this faith. The questions that were asked at the time were generally of a moral nature.

While the attackers carried on, the defenders, for all their considerable achievement, could never feel that the attack was being parried. Like the attackers, they lacked any means of comparing values. They could only see the destruction wrought in their homeland by bombing, and reflect that however many bombers they were shooting down, it was evidently not enough to stop them coming over.

For these reasons no conclusive significance can be attached to the night air battle over Germany.

What can be said is that as a gladiatorial contest in electronic warfare, it demonstrated the immense resilience of German electronics under highly unfavourable circumstances. This is shown up by the comparison with the daytime battle.

While the German night fighters were increasing their grip on the attackers, the daytime battle went the other way. Both Germany and Britain had early come to the conclusion that in daytime bombers could not survive against fighters. But the war had been joined by a new combatant, the United States, prepared to test the conclusion again, thanks to confidence in the heavy self-protective armament of her Flying Fortresses. American air forces operated from Britain from late 1942, aiming to use daylight to make precision attacks against strategic targets and industries, such as the ball-bearing plants at Schweinfurt.

At first German day fighters demonstrated that, in conditions of good visibility, nothing had happened to diminish the bomber's vulnerability. They inflicted appalling losses. The United States air force was briefly sustained by the optimistic belief that it was inflicting equally appalling losses on the fighters. But this did not last. In fact the day fighters' supremacy was only checked when it became possible to send long-range escort fighters over Germany with better performance than the defenders.

This was an aerodynamic breakthrough. It came with the Mustang, aerodynamically more refined and able to make more effective use of drop-tanks than previously possible. By mid-1944 the Mustang wrested air superiority away from German day fighters. In this daytime battle which never pivoted on electronics, Germany was the loser well before the war's end, whereas in the night battle which did pivot on electronics she fought to the last.

'Overlord'

At the point of lowest ebb for the bombers' success the British night attack on Germany was temporarily discontinued. This was to allow the Allied air forces to concentrate, from the end of March 1944, on precision targets in Northern France, in anticipation of operation 'Overlord', the invasion of France launched on 6 June 1944.

The period immediately before and during Overlord saw a high level of air activity over France, both by day and night. Targets were typically point targets such as rail junctions, marshalling yards, viaducts and coastal defence installations especially radar stations. As in the celebrated raids against the Eder and Mohne dams in 1943, the bombing techniques owed little to electronic means, which were not sufficiently precise, but were chiefly visual. Oboe however was used, Northern France being within its range.

The Allied powers were able to exert a considerable degree of air superiority over France, particularly by day. Indeed this was a prerequisite for successful invasion. Nevertheless there was still abundant hunting for the German night fighters which were able to operate with continuing success.

But the turn of the tide was evident when the British bomber force made its return to Germany's night skies after the liberation of France, in September 1944. The early warning radar defences had now been outflanked and the bombers could be routed in over France to take advantage of this fact. At the same time loss of territory in the East and damage to refineries was causing increasing shortage of aviation fuel.

These factors undercut the German night fighters. The terminal phase had set in. Only at this time did their ability to resist bomber attacks begin to decline. Their monthly scores fell away to under a hundred, although the bombers were coming over Germany in practically double the previous strength. Nevertheless their battle, a battle of electronics, had outlasted the battle of the day fighters, a battle of aircraft performance.

Purely from the technical standpoint, the advance of German defensive electronics did not stop even then. German industry demonstrated that its potential, in theory at least, had caught up with the centimetric revolution. But opportunity no longer existed to make effective use of it. Numerous new electronic devices appeared in this final period of the war, but by virtue of the circumstances none of them could make much difference.

In the middle of 1944 Germany introduced another ground-based early warning radar, 'Jagdschloss', expressly designed to work in a severe jamming environment. Jagdschloss gave a plan position indicator display, designed not for ground-controlled interception of individual aircraft, but for the *Zahme Sau* type interception of bomber streams. Probably because vertical polarisation had been general German practice and British jamming was directed against this, Jagdschloss switched to horizontal polarisation.

Jagdschloss operated on numerous alternative frequencies between 136 and 250 megahertz, whichever gave the most satisfactory results under particular conditions. It demonstrated better than any radar hitherto the principle of 'frequency agility', destined to play an all-important part in electronic warfare.

With Jagdschloss following on the planar-array Wassermann, Germany confirmed that in the technology of ground-based early warning radar, she was ending the war as she had begun it, in the technical lead, for there were no radars in the Allied inventory designed to operate under equivalent conditions.

'Neptun' was a family of radars, both for airborne interception and tail warning, of which the most important example was Neptun G/R, in which these functions were combined. With six frequencies for click-stop selection, between 158 and 187 megahertz, it introduced frequency agility in airborne equipment.

'Burn-Through'

Neptun also marks the beginning of another concept: 'burn-through'. This is the escalation of radar power to defeat jamming. Whereas Lichtenstein air interception radar had started at 1.5 kilowatts of power and progressed to 2.5 kilowatts in the SN2 set, Neptun operated at 30 kilowatts and would have gone to 100 kilowatts if the war had not ended. It attracted British countermeasures in the form of jamming and homing-on, but came too late for any serious assessment of its combat performance to emerge.

The German 'Bernhard' and 'Bernhardine' provided a new means of transmitting information from the ground to night fighters. Bernhard was the ground equipment, a transmitter tower which swept a high-powered directional beam around the compass. Bernhardine was the airborne receiver. Directional beams are inherently more difficult to jam. The modulation was telegraphic, and Bernhardine provided a simple print-out of basic information.

Another German initiative was 'Klein Heidelberg', a passive system which depended upon receiving the emissions from British Chain Home radar. It was intended to operate over the waters of the North Sea.

When an aircraft was present between the Chain Home transmitter and Klein Heidelberg, the latter could detect both the radar's original pulse and, after a slight delay, its reflection off the aircraft. The amount of the delay depended on the extra path length. With the aid of a radio bearing, the aircraft could be located. Klein Heidelberg's significance was entirely symbolic, as a pointer to a future time when passive devices might come to play a large role in electronic war.

While electronics was of declining value to the defenders in the war's final phase, it played its part well for the attackers, who could use all their devices with little hindrance. The worst of the bomb damage to Germany was done during the war's last few months. This was particularly true of Berlin. Even at this late stage the night fighters claimed monthly scores between one and two hundred, but this was against roughly double the number of bomber sorties typical of late 1943 and early 1944, about 10,000 a month against 5,000.

There was however considerable month to month variation and against this background January 1945 makes an interesting comparison with March 1944, the culminating month of the Battle of Berlin. The number of bomber sorties was nearly the same, 9,032 in March 1944, 9,603 in January 1945, but the night fighters, which shot down 269 in March 1944, could only shoot down 117 in January 1945.

While the most intensive air battle raged in the sky over Germany, other air battles continued elsewhere.

Some resulted from corresponding German invasions of British skies. The main German blitz on Britain had been discontinued in May 1941, but German fighter bombers came back for limited periods in 1942 – the 'Baedeker raids', in 1943, and again in early 1944 – the 'baby blitz'. Far more serious than attacks by piloted aircraft however were the attacks by pilotless V-1 and V-2 missiles in the middle of 1944.

In terms of electronic warfare there was technical symmetry. Dueppel, the German window, was used from October 1943. It reduced the effectiveness of British defences, particularly in ground-controlled interception.

This outcome had been feared. The British decision to use window had only been taken in the belief that the new Mark X centimetric airborne interception radar would be effective against it if Germany replied in kind.

The Mark X was adapted from an American equipment, the SCR720, which could lock on to the target and disregard clutter. It had a second display, an enlarged view of part of the primary display. On this the target could be selected, providing it had been identified in the first place, and held when window was 'bloomed'.

But introduction of the Mark X was delayed long beyond the expected time, well into 1944. This opened a gap of vulnerability to Dueppel. Had Germany been in a position to press home a strong attack, this might have become serious. In fact the use of Deuppel was of little consequence.

Low-level fighter-bomber incursions in 1943 against British regional cities provided a renewed test for the Chain Home Low radar which it did not sustain. It proved unable to detect them. German fighter-bombers were seldom attacked until they were on the way back, and often air raid warning sirens were not sounded until bombs were dropping.

S-Band

At this time British naval radar came to the assistance of the early warning network. The Type 271 radar, a naval surface centimetric equipment, was urgently adapted to coastal surveillance, giving coverage at heights below 500 feet. This was historic as being the world's first ground surveillance radar working in S-band, which subsequently became the most-used frequency band for this purpose.

It heralded a generation of ground surveillance radars destined to sweep away the antenna arrays composed of rods, characteristic of the Second World War. It replaced them with horn-fed reflector antennas. This generation is still in use for civil aviation and many military purposes. Only in the 1970s and 1980s did it begin to give way in military applications to a new generation of radars working on the planar–array principle which had been introduced by the German Mammut and Wassermann. But the frequencies remained high, in S-band or L-band, just below it, and the earlier rods were, as described in Chapter 9, replaced by slots in waveguides or by semiconductor radiators.

The 'baby blitz' made use of the German bombing guidance systems, notably the secondary radar system Egon. The bomber's course was followed by Egon and guidance information was transmitted by radio telephony. In practice Egon was countered with a device call 'Cigarette', jamming the fighters' radio telephony channels.

It was as a result of Egon that the British Perfectos device was introduced to activate Erstling, the German Identification Friend or Foe equipment which was the airborne component of Egon. Perfectos was intended to compel the bombers to stop using Identification Friend or Foe so rendering Egon ineffective, but the raids were discontinued before this tactic could operate. Nevertheless the advent of Perfectos put an end to the use of Erstling by German night fighters. It undoubtedly claimed some victims, though not very many.

Germany exploited British Gee by utilising sets retrieved from crashed bombers ('Hyperbel'), as well as Gee sets of her own manufacture ('Truhe'). Flying over Britain with these equipments, German aircraft enjoyed the advantage that Gee provided highest accuracy near the base transmitters.

German navigational facilities were expanded with the interrelated 'Elektra' and 'Sonne' systems. Elektra was a system of beams on MF, originating in late 1940. Sonne was a development which appeared during 1943. It was well understood by the Allies who were able to use it themselves. As with the earlier German navigational beacons, it was vulnerable to meaconing.

From May 1941 onwards German piloted attacks were never intensive. Vastly more threatening was the German bombardment of London by V-1 cruise missiles and V-2 ballistic missiles in 1944 and 1945.

The V-1 'flying bomb' was a 7.7 metre long pilotless aircraft with an approximate one ton warhead. It flew at about 400 mph at heights from

1,000 to 4,000 feet. The engine cut out after a certain range had been covered, measured by rotations of a small nose propeller.

In the history of weapons development the V-1 must count as a formidable offensive project. It exploited London's vulnerability over a wide arc of directions from the relatively close French coast. But what was most lacking to its success was specifically electronics.

Electronics challenge

The V-1 lacked electronics guidance and control and for this reason could not achieve more than a highly dispersed area attack. Range measurement would have been better with radio. Radio was fitted on some examples as a check on range. It correctly indicated that the missiles were generally falling short. It was disbelieved. Without more accurate control by electronics the weapon could not realise its potential.

At the same time, the V-1 highlighted the powerful defensive capability of three Allied electronic equipments, all American-developed. The first was the SCR584 centimetric target-tracking radar. The second was the M9 director which took the coordinates provided by the radar and predicted optimum aim for anti-aircraft fire. Predictor devices had always been necessary with anti-aircraft guns, to allow for the movement of the target, but were 'mechanical analogue computers', that is worked on the same principle as a slide rule. The M9 was an 'electronic analogue computer'.

Finally there was the proximity fuse. Screwed into the nose of the anti-aircraft shell, it detonated at close approach, making impact, which was rare, unnecessary. It comprised a miniaturised radio transmitter and receiver about 7 centimentres in length. The transmitted signal was reflected off the target with a considerable Doppler frequency shift on account of the high relative velocity, and this was detected by the receiver.

This triple combination of electronic techniques made ground gunfire a consistently effective defence against the straight-flying V-1, which although non-evasive was a dangerous target for fighters because of warhead explosion. Maximum score was on 28 August 1944 when 94 missiles approached Britain, of which 65 were destroyed by gunfire compared with 23 by fighters and by two barrage balloon wires, leaving four which penetrated.

The V-2 ballistic rocket delivered an approximate one ton warhead over a slightly longer range of about 200 miles. It was totally reliant on electronics control at the time of launching. But although it was unstoppable, it was incapable of precision targeting.

In the Second World War the V-weapons were ahead of their time and could make no difference to the outcome. Eventually all launch sites were overrun by ground armies. The solution of the challenge posed to electronics to make this type of weapon, under the new name of strategic missiles, one of the most important military assets, became a major part of electronics in warfare from 1955 onwards.

Paralleling her two embryonic strategic missiles, Germany developed numerous tactical missiles, few of which were used operationally and none of which had any serious military significance apart from the remarkable way in which they foreshadowed the future.

The biggest operational success was achieved by the SD1400 Fritz X, a free-falling 1.4-tonne bomb capable of being steered to some extent by its operator through a radio link. It had stubby wings, and 'spoilers' on the tail surfaces were actuated to adjust the trajectory. After Italy had withdrawn from the Axis alliance in 1943, the Italian battleship *Roma* was sunk by three hits obtained in this way.

More ambitious but less successful was the Henschel 293, a small rocket-powered aircraft with a 550-kilogram warhead. It was designed to be carried, typically by a Heinkell 111 bomber, and released at up to 20 kilometres from its target. It reached a speed, in diving flight, of up to 950 kilometres per hour, implying a flight time on the order of a minute or more.

The requirement for an operator in the launch aircraft to control the missile over this time and distance was a severe test for the radio link. The 27 and 60 megahertz frequencies used were highly vulnerable to jamming, which increasingly limited the weapon after some initial naval attacks in the Bay of Biscay. Possible counters to jamming, never in fact deployed, were switching to the UHF band with a directional beam, and control through fine wires paid out from bobbins attached to the wingtips.

Another operational difficulty was for the operator, following the missile's flight by a red flare in the tail, to lay it accurately on to a target at other than short ranges. This problem brought forth the daring solution of a miniature nose-mounted television camera. Its signal was intended to be beamed back on a UHF carrier wave (411 megahertz) to a television receiver on the launch aircraft.

But the system, imaginatively anticipating the 'smart' missiles of the 1970s and 1980s, was never operational in the Second World War. Other imaginative developments never deployed were the Rheintochter and Wasserfall ground-to-air anti-aircraft missiles, both intended to be radio-controlled.

Apart from the air conflict of Western Europe with its sophisticated electronic equipment, another air battle raged along the eastern front between Germany and Russia. This was a battle in support of ground armies. Tactical ground attack and bombing were the primary functions. Day fighting had an important role, night fighting a much smaller one. This front did not see the vast elaboration of electronic warfare which happened in the west.

In the first phase of the war, Germany's rapid *blitzkrieg* advance, radio had more to contribute than radar. Thereafter Wurzburg and Freya appeared, sometimes mounted on trains for mobility, itself a significant initiative. They were able to provide a Himmelbett system. However the scope for conventional night fighting was extremely limited. Russian avionics was simple and restricted to radio communications. The only call for countermeasures might have been jamming, but there is little evidence for this.

Radar later developed in Russian hands. This came after the fall of Stalingrad, when the German armies had begun to fight a long defensive retreat, relieved, so far as possible, by daytime air harassment of the attackers.

Until the beginning of 1944, Russia depended on visual observations for the detection and interception of German bombers. These observations were relayed to fighter command posts. For this purpose it was necessary to fly standing observation patrols on 2½ or three-hour duty tours at a height of six to seven thousand metres. The advent of mobile truck-mounted Redut radar relieved the strain of maintaining patrols.

Radar stations were located about 10 to 15 kilometres behind the front and gave 12 to 15 minutes warning of approaching German aircraft. Fighter pilots, scrambled against this warning, continued to receive information by radio, enabling them to take up tactically favourable positions. Ground radar is claimed to have contributed to the shooting down of more than two thousand German aircraft on the eastern front.

Assessment

The significance of the air war over Germany can be studied from many standpoints. From the standpoint of electronics it shows Germany initially ahead, then reeling from the introduction of window and centimetric radar, finally regaining parity in technological terms, even if this parity was limited in value by being restricted to defence.

This assessment is a particular one relating to the electronic war. But it has all too often been assumed that, because the war in general went against Germany, the electronic war must have gone against her also. This is a false deduction. It is linked with the idea that undue neglect of electronics was a failing of the German wartime government.

Certainly there was a time when Germany was forced to increase her efforts in electronics, because her results had ceased to be good enough in comparison with her opponents results. But the same happened in other military technologies.

Germany found herself outclassed in tank technology almost from the outset of her war against Russia, nevertheless it has never been the fashion to accuse Germany of neglecting tank warfare. On the contrary it is known that she pioneered it, always attached great significance to it, and reacted vigorously after encountering Russian developments, putting radically new designs into large-scale production.

The pattern was similar in electronics. Moreover there is no evidence to suggest that if Germany had put still more effort into electronics than she did she might have crucially changed the outcome. Electronics did not have the potential to deliver such a result. Germany did not lose the war through neglect of electronics. Germany lost the war by becoming committed to a strategically unsustainable position.

The fact is that Germany made a powerful and many-sided effort in electronics. This began as part of an offensive drive to introduce new technology in war and continued in the defensive development of systems to respond to her opponents' use of electronics.

Defensive developments could never win the war, but altogether Germany's technology drive, including the development of the V-1, V-2, various guided missiles, new types of submarine, and a range of jet aircraft, was arguably wider than that made by her opponents, except for the development of atomic weapons.

Bearing in mind that technological advance rests at least partly on the random pattern of scientific discovery, there were almost certain to be areas where Germany's opponents would at some time gain a technological lead. When this happened German technology showed resilience. Centimetric radar is the prime example.

Germany went into the Second World War with a technological momentum stronger than that of any other European country. This momentum was part of her general cultural pattern. It was an outgrowth of her economic, industrial and scientific advance over a long period, speeding up in the second half of the 19th century and early years of the 20th.

Nevertheless social changes in Germany in the 1930s had begun to slow the country's pace of advance, by reducing the numbers of students and driving abroad many teachers. Despite this the traditions of excellence were far from dissipated and in specifically war-directed areas the German government conserved and encouraged them. This was as true of electronics as of other militarily valuable technologies.

What happened to German electronics during the Second World War is one of the most fascinating issues in the history of electronic warfare. Electronic warfare is a contest between national technological capabilities just as much as between national armed forces, and it is necessary to study how these technological capabilities wax and wane.

There is no lack of examples of German politicians, during the war, placing blame in various quarters for the country's real or imaginary electronics failings. Equally, there is no lack of examples of German politicians being retrospectively blamed themselves, after the war, for these same failings. Naturally many historians have been glad to quote both sides of this debate. But both are fundamentally useless to a real understanding of what happened and why.

German electronics had an impressive record before and during the war, right up to the end. It may be favourably compared with Germany's aviation industry, which, despite many talented designers and despite its acknowledged importance, left the country without an answer to aircraft such as the Mustang and the Mosquito until just too late.

The basic deduction is the same in each case: no single nation can establish leads in all technologies, nor keeping renewing the leads it does possess. Hiatuses and reversals will occur.

11

Sonar Versus Radar and Radio

SEA WARFARE in the Second World War contrasted with warfare on and over land particularly in respect of the role played by electronics. In this war, electronics gained the same importance in land warfare that it had gained at sea in the First World War, which at first sight may simply seem to mean that the two branches were at last on an equal footing.

But what was distinctive of the Second World War was massive new investment in electronic warfare on and over land. By comparison the investment in electronic warfare at sea was neither so new nor so massive. Instead, it was often derivative and secondary. Yet in spite of this, at sea the achievements of electronic warfare were greater and it made a more decisive contribution to the outcome of the entire war.

Consequently, the priority given to electronic warfare over land may be claimed to have been a misjudgement, and there were those who were sufficiently farsighted to make this claim at the time.

Military imagination probably fixated on electronic warfare over land because it was a new gladiatorial arena. There was failure to understand that sea electronic warfare was confronting an even more dramatic expansion of possibilities. These arose not so much in purely surface engagements, as in meeting the challenge of the more complex, multi-dimensional battlezone created by submarines and aviation.

To appreciate the significance of electronic warfare at sea, it helps to regard the Second World War as four sub-wars, two of which are sea conflicts, the Battle of the Atlantic and the Battle of the Pacific, and two land conflicts, the Battles of Eastern and Western Europe.[1]

The Battle of the Atlantic hinged on Germany's attempt to cut the lines of supply from the United States to Britain and Russia. It began at the outbreak of war in September 1939. True, the United States was not formally a warring party until December 1941, but it was in practice actively committed to the battle long before.

The German offensive depended mainly on submarines. Its success mounted spectacularly but from its highest peak plunged abruptly in one month of 1943 to irretrievable defeat. This German naval disaster opened the way to the Allied land victory in the battle of Western Europe two years later. Its strategic significance was therefore immense.

The Battle of the Pacific embraced the entire sub-war between the United States and Japan. From beginning to end this was maritime conflict. The contested land was amidst ocean. Ground battles were for relatively small islands. Sea communications and control of ocean areas were the decisive factors. Without these, troops occupying islands were merely stranded outposts. Japanese forces never reached the United States, and when United States forces landed on the mainland of Japan it was after the latter's surrender.

Thus the battlezone of electronic warfare at sea was global, whereas electronic warfare on and over land was mainly a feature of the Battle of Western Europe. In the Battle of Eastern Europe its role was much smaller. This begins to put the Second World War's sea and land electronic warfare into realistic perspective. But there are further considerations.

The sea is a two-dimensional surface, featureless and vast. Access to it is open to most nations and there are no geographic barriers. It is an excellent hiding place and any of the warring parties may conceivably turn up anywhere. The potential for surprise is unlimited.

For these reasons the premium on communications, early warning, navigation and target finding is much greater. Electronic warfare is called upon to respond to a much more formidable challenge. Moreover it is on duty all around the clock. On and over land, electronics is more important at night than during the day. At sea, electronics is important during both day and night. Distance and weather shroud enemies no less than darkness.

On top of this comes another factor. The surface of the sea not only constitutes an arena of warfare in its own two dimensions, but forms the boundary between two three-dimensional spaces – the realm of the aircraft and the realm of the submarine, both of which react upon it whilst having totally different military characteristics.

Contrasts

To match this extra challenge, electronic warfare at sea fortunately enjoys extra potential. Expanses of water provide a favourable background for electronics. Electromagnetic waves propagate well. Both radio and radar have particular significance.

To take radar first. The surface of the sea is a more uniform background than the land against which to pick out targets. Indeed, at sea the contrast between the target and its background is often better for radar than it is for the eye.

Submarines and ships represent hundreds or thousands of tons of metal, highly reflective to radar, set against a background of sea and sky which, to radar, is relatively dark. On the other hand, to see the low profile of a surfaced submarine against the greyness of the ocean may be not at all easy, and fog or other atmospheric precipitation may reduce visual range to little more than nil, even against massive targets.

Naval surface radar benefits greatly from these facts. But they are more important still to airborne radar at sea. The radar horizon for an aircraft is much more distant than for a warship. In the Second World War, the range of naval surface radar depended on the height of the antenna and the massiveness of the target, and was generally a few tens of kilometres against battleships, while against surfaced submarines it was less than ten kilometres. Even from the beginning, airborne radar improved on these figures.

The development of airborne anti-surface vessel radar (ASV radar) was a uniquely British initiative in the late 1930s. It ran in parallel with the attempt to create airborne interception radar and was on the same frequency, about 200 megahertz. Like early airborne interception radar, it utilised rod antennas, but unlike airborne interception radar, which had to look forward and required nose- or wing-mounting, anti-surface-vessel antennas could be mounted along the side of the fuselage to look sideways. This was advantageous, both aerodynamically and in that a larger area could be scanned.

This equipment was mounted in a variety of maritime aircraft, both carrier-borne and ground-based (including Flying Boats), thus combining the vantage point of higher altitude with higher speed and range in seaching for targets. Its war contribution was immediate, though against surface warships rather than submarines. It was less effective against the latter partly because it was countered with radar warning receivers, and unlike surface warships submarines had an instant escape route. When centimetric anti-surface-vessel radar was introduced early in 1943, it not only provided a more revealing means of search, but gave no indication to warning receivers. It created a turning point in the sea warfare comparable with the turning point of Stalingrad on land.

A Combination of Facts

Radio's particular significance in warfare at sea lies in a combination of facts: the non-availability of any other form of long-distance communication; the correspondingly heightened opportunity for signals intelligence in all its forms from simple direction-finding to cryptanalysis; and the high tactical premium on the results of signals intelligence.

Intelligence lost to the enemy is often paid for in sunken ships, a more prompt and drastic penalty than is usually exacted on land. On land, the most serious loss to signals intelligence is usually strategic or diplomatic, which is an evil of the insidious kind.

Despite weather variations the sea environment is uniform and predictable. Consequently the strategy and tactics of sea warfare lend themselves well to logical analysis, in other words to what has become known as 'operational research'. The capabilities of radar, radio and aviation can be exploited to the maximum.

Air power played major roles in the Second World War over land and at sea. But despite the alliance between air power and electronics over land, it was a factor in sea warfare that air power allied with electronics exerted greatest influence on the course of the war.

Without electronics, air power over land might have achieved something, though only by day and at great cost; but at sea, air power without electronics would have achieved much less, either by night or day.

Submarine power also rests on electronics, but while all other forms of electronics in warfare depend on the electromagnetic spectrum, the underwater world shuts the electromagnetic spectrum out. Except, that is, for the lowest frequencies. Instead, the carrier of signals becomes sound in water, both at frequencies that can be heard (audio frequencies), and frequencies above the audible range (ultrasonic or supersonic frequencies).

The submariner has come to rely on the information that is borne to him by sound through his surrounding medium. He depends on it even more than the airman and the surface sailor do on radar and radio. Their visual world is rich compared with the submariner's vision through the periscope. The submariner's perception is changed in ways that are strange, in keeping with the propagation of sound through water.

An analogy can be drawn with radio and radar, in which underwater sound takes the place of electromagnetic radiation. According to this analogy, the main difference is that the signal travels at about 1,438 kilometres a second instead of 300,000 (0.893 miles per second against 186,000).

True, this is much slower, which may seem to make the comparison an unfavourable one. But such a view is far from correct.

In the first place, the speed of sound in water is more than four times faster than the speed of sound in air. In the second, this speed needs to be compared with the speed at which physical objects such as vehicles and weapons can travel under water, which is much less than in air. Water speeds up the passage of sound but is highly resistant to the passage of physical objects. This puts a more favourable aspect on the comparison.

A military aircraft may travel at 1,000, 2,000 or 3,000 kilometres an hour, and a missile even faster. But under water some tens of knots is the practical limiting speed for physical objects to maintain over any distance. Strangely, large vessels like submarines may travel faster than small objects like torpedoes, particularly if nuclear-powered, which torpedoes cannot be. Even so the fastest nuclear-powered submarine does not exceed about 50 knots (93 kilometres per hour).

Surface craft are better off, but only in proportion to the degree that they are surface skimmers, vehicles travelling in air rather than water. To this degree they are not really part of the underwater environment, and are not in good communication with it. All the same, their speeds come nowhere near the speed of sound in water; to do so they would need to exceed 5,000 kilometres an hour (3,200 miles an hour).

The analogy contains an important difference. Aircraft or ships do not automatically give their presence away through radio waves. Their presence is given away only if they make radio transmissions or if they are detected by radar. But physical objects moving in water, such as ships, submarines and torpedoes, cannot help originating sounds.

Passive means

They do this as they overcome the resistance of the water and as their propellers turn in it. Correspondingly there is much more scope in the underwater war for passive means of detection and tracking, as opposed to active means. Radar detects targets by the echoes they return. Underwater, the need to obtain echoes is less important.

Paradoxically, the use of underwater echoes to locate objects – underwater 'radar' – predates orthodox electromagnetic radar. It was introduced as 'asdics' in the First World War in the British Navy, a name which persisted in use into the Second World War, and only disappeared afterwards.

In the Second World War, the word 'sonar' was coined in the United States to parallel 'radar'; both are words of American origin. Sonar means in practice the totality of underwater listening technology, whether active or passive. It is a wider concept than asdics. Asdics was simply active sonar. For the purposes of this book it is convenient to apply the term 'sonar' universally and retrospectively.

Passive sonar was sufficiently effective by itself for the German navy to rely on it almost exclusively, making little recourse to active techniques (with some exceptions such as mine detection). This judgement has much to recommend it, for active sonar is self-revealing.

Of course self-revelation by active sonar does not greatly matter if the hunter craft using it is simultaneously revealing its presence in other ways. Broadly speaking the British were the submarine hunters while the Germans were the submarine operators, and this strategic pattern explains why the British pioneered active sonar and the Germans passive.

As in other areas of electronic warfare, particularly those connected with the sea, the British and the Germans were the first to confront each other using sonar technology in conflict. But other countries such as the United States and France contributed to it more than generously.

By comparison with radio and radar, sonar had a long gestation period before becoming militarily effective. This went back to the First World War, and was still far from complete in the Battle of the Atlantic in the Second World War. Sonar came of age in American use in the Battle of the Pacific, with emphasis on passive means, and was developed thereafter especially with the advent of nuclear-powered submarines. This development took advantage of the wartime legacy from German passive sonar, but it is no accident that sonar is an American word.

Today the predominance of passive techniques is a general fact of underwater electronic warfare, though not to the total exclusion of active techniques.

The analogy contains yet other differences. Radio waves generated on or above the surface of the earth either escape into the infinity of space, or die away at great distances.

They die away instantly. They do not reverberate. Echoes which return, such as those exploited in radar, do so in a minute fraction of a second.

By contrast underwater sound is trapped beneath the surface. It does not escape to any large extent into the air above. It does not necessarily die away at great distances or quickly. The submariner is in a reverberant box containing many natural and man-made sounds. The sounds he hears may have remote origins both in space and time.

Radio waves whether in air or space travel in predictable ways, at accurately known speed, with the strength of the signal falling off according to known law, that is in proportion to the square of the distance. At twice the distance the signal strength will be reduced to a quarter. Consequently at great distances all signals become weak.

True, there are slight variations, and anomalous propagation may sometimes occur. But with underwater sound, variations are the rule. The speed of sound in water varies with temperature, density and salinity, and these in turn vary not only from one part of the world to another, but at various depths in the same place. Acoustically, the sea is in layers.

Confinement

It follows that the opportunities for anomalous propagation of underwater sound are immense, through refraction, reflection, or confinement of sound to particular layers of water. The confinement of sound to particular layers of water means that the signal strength does not fall off in the same way as with radio.

Underwater sound may travel enormous distances, thousands of kilometres, with relatively small loss of strength – without, that is, much attenuation. As a result, a nuclear submarine proceeding in mid-Atlantic may be audible at a certain depth on both sides of the ocean – and the sound picked up from it will have been emitted perhaps 30 minutes previously.

Frequency plays a role. Frequencies used in sonar range from a few kilohertz up to about 300 kilohertz, but whereas in radio it is the higher frequencies that offer most opportunity, in sonar the premium is on the lower ones. Higher frequencies tend to be absorbed in the medium, not only by the water but by the small objects always present, and only lower frequencies propagate over long distances.

The effect of all this is that sonar, as the underwater equivalent of both radar and radio, is more necessary but less dependable. It is more of a black art. The factors of uncertainty are much larger. Range, which with radar is the value that can be determined most accurately, is more problematic.

In addition sonar is open to all the techniques of electronic warfare, such as noise and deception jamming, signals intelligence, and 'stealth'. The latter is also known as signature reduction – deliberate measures to suppress echoes or self-originated signals in order to avoid giving away the presence, location and even identity of a target. Above water, identifying a target by its primary radar return tends to be a theoretical ideal, but underwater, the sounds generated by a target often yield highly specific information.

The equivalent of chaff or window underwater is freely available: air bubbles. This is a consequence of the same fact that traps sound under water – namely, that sound reflects off a water–air surface. This was exploited in the Second World War by the German 'Pillenwerfer', a bubble generator which returned false echoes.

In practice it is necessary to listen to underwater sound with underwater devices. The sea surface, as a water-air surface, makes a remarkably complete separation between the world above it and the world below. The two systems of communication, based on electromagnetic waves above and sound waves below, do not interpenetrate. If this were not so, target-finding against submarines would be much simpler.

Magnetism

Because sound does not pass from water to air, the only means of directly sensing the presence of submarines from the space above the water must rely on effects which do pass from water to air. Magnetism is the most suitable candidate. But the airborne magnetic anomaly detector, sensing the disturbance to the earth's magnetic field caused by the presence of a submarine's steel hull, is too acutely range-limited to make an adequate substitute for sonar.

Magnetism only comes into its own when the range is short, as with the magnetic mine introduced by Germany in 1939. This was devised for use against shipping in the estuaries leading to many of Britain's ports. The mine rested on the bottom where it was invulnerable to conventional minesweeping. Thanks to shallow water it could detect the passage of a ship by the temporary disturbance to the earth's magnetic field.

The magnetic mine bred active and passive countermeasures. The obvious active countermeasure was to sweep shipping channels using ships fitted with powerful magnets in order to detonate mines at maximum possible range. But not even a 400-ton bundle of railway lines could make the range large enough and the idea was abandoned in favour of magnetic coils mounted on aircraft.

The coils were led around the extremities of the wings and fuselage in aerodynamic fairings and were supplied with current from a generator, thereby creating a magnetic field projecting vertically down from the aircraft. Nevertheless the detonation range was still small, perhaps one to two hundred feet, and it was necessary to fly at low level over the water surface. At best this technique, like the ship-mounted magnet, swept a narrow channel, and both were nerve-wracking.

An effective countermeasure was eventually found by taking advantage of the conductivity of seawater. By generating a circular pattern of electric current over a wide area in the sea surface, a vertical magnetic field was produced in direct proximity to mines.

In practice, two wooden (non-magnetic) ships, moving on parallel courses about 300 yards apart, towed cables which enclosed between them a rectangular area. Current was allowed to enter (or leave) the water a hundred yards or more behind the sterns. The sea absorbed some 3,000 amperes. A constant current was unnecessary; it was enough to switch on briefly to detonate all magnetic mines over about 10 acres. The minesweepers moved on to bring a fresh area between the cables.

A passive countermeasure was also desirable. This was called 'degaussing', the gauss being the scientific unit of magnetic field.

There were varieties of the method but basically it was to neutralise the inherent magnetism of steel ships by running an electric cable carrying direct current around the periphery of the hull, initially outside, later inside for better protection from rough weather. Ships had different magnetic properties depending on where and how they were built, consequently the current necessary to create a magnetic field exactly cancelling the ship's own magnetism had to be found by careful measurement.

The counter-countermeasure was to increase the sensitivity of the detonation device. Meanwhile ship-board power failure meant instant peril, and a new grimly humorous figure entered the realm of nautical legend. This was the captain whose last order, sailing into harbour after surmounting the dangers of an ocean crossing, had been to switch off the generator.

The magnetic mine was not unknown before the German variant introduced in 1939, but this type marks the solitary example of magnetism's effective military use. It well illustrates the short-range nature of magnetic warfare at sea, its simultaneous strength and weakness.

As a means of detonating mines, magnetism may be compared with sound. By contrast with magnetic mines, the problem with simple acoustic mines is that sound travels so well that they are easily swept; a road drill operating in a bulkhead tank has long-range effectiveness. In the Second World War Germany introduced acoustic torpedoes homing on the sound of ship propellers; they proved easily decoyed. Premature at the time, this weapon type came into its own decades later, when sophisticated electronics enabled different sounds to be discriminated.

Access to Underwater Sound

Both the submariner and the surface sailor have access to the world of underwater sound. But the sea surface and the warship are inherently noisy and the submariner, able to listen from quieter depths, has a superior vantage point. Moreover the surface water layer tends to be anomalous. For these reasons, active echo-ranging sonar tends to be best suited to surface craft, and passive sonar to submarines.

The range of passive sonar is much greater than that of active. It is difficult to give precise figures but typical distances today are suggested as 160 kilometres for passive sonar against 8 for active.[2] Consequently, the most effective way of stalking a submarine is with another submarine.

Aircraft have access to underwater sound through the Sonobuoy. This is an expendable buoy, dropped to float on the surface. It lowers an underwater microphone, or hydrophone, on the end of a cable. It radios a signal back to the aircraft. Alternatively, a hovering helicopter can lower an equivalent apparatus to some depth on the end of a cable – a dipping or dunking sonar.

Sonobuoys and dunking sonar can be active or passive. Aircraft, especially helicopters, are inherently noisy, like surface ships, but the low coupling between sound in air above the sea and sound in water below the surface gives considerable acoustic insulation and prevents the sonar performance from being unduly degraded.

The surface ship may lower listening equipment, but operationally it is usually more convenient to tow it in the form of an array at as a great a distance as possible, generally some kilometres. This permits considerable depth as well. Submarines may also tow arrays. Arrays of listening elements correspond in principle to array radar. But they do not actively scan with a beam. Instead they listen passively and, thanks to the array, are able to determine the direction from which a sound comes. This has become a vital aspect of sonar technology.

Already in the First World War, both the air and underwater dimensions were adding their characteristics to sea warfare. The airship contributed more than aircraft, chiefly in the form of airborne reconnaissance but occasionally as a means of attack. The submarine began to make good the threat of surprise attack (which was the original motive for its invention as far back as 1776). Radio, as the overwater means of communication, was important to the operation of both airships and submarines. Coordination through radio was developed mainly in the German forces.

The communications possibilities of the underwater medium were on the other hand hardly exploited. At that time the underwater medium was important only as the submarine's hiding place. As such it was two-dimensional. The submarine hid just beneath the surface; it did not exploit depth.

Attempts were made to use sonar as a means of target finding, but whether the target was a ship to be sunk by a submarine or a submarine to be hunted by destroyers, the technology was too limited to bring much success. The range of active sonar was about 450 metres – not very useful. The submarine's hydrophone had rather better prospects; it might pick up potential targets within a range up to about 18 kilometres.

In this respect, the war's main significance was as an impetus to research into the best ways of sensing underwater sound. The microphone is the well-known electronic means of sensing sound in air. Initially carbon microphones were adapted as hydrophones, but the need for a more sophisticated device was soon realised, for the requirements were much more demanding.

The quest focused on piezoelectric crystals, such as quartz. When compressed, piezoelectric crystals develop a voltage across their faces. When vibrating mechanically, that is experiencing alternate compression and expansion, they produce an electric signal at the same frequency as the vibration. The mechanical vibration is very stable and stabilises the electronic frequency. This effect is used in many ways in military electronics.

Rochelle Salt

Long before the quartz clock became popular, thin slices of quartz, with a natural mechanical rate of vibration measured in megahertz, were inserted in electronic circuits to control transmission and reception frequencies, typically for VHF radio. This was technology of the Second World War. In the First World War, quartz served in asdics.

Quartz is relatively easy to work with, being durable, but other crystals show the piezoelectric effect more usefully for sonar, notably Rochelle salt. However there is nothing Rochelle salt does better than dissolve in water, so it requires special encapsulation. It played an important part in the development of sonar, but has now been discarded in favour of other crystals.

The beginnings of sonar during the First World War came as the electron tube, with its ability to amplify, was ending the era of the spark transmitter and breeding a new generation of radio apparatus. At this time radio was ready with the means to amplify sonar signals from quartz or other crystals, making it no longer necessary to listen to underwater sounds with the unaided ear. The first application of radio apparatus to the amplification of underwater sound was a German contribution.

From this time on the hydrophone, as a sensor device, was coupled to electronic circuits which amplified, analysed and presented its signals, just as the antenna of a radar system is coupled to electronic circuits for the same purpose. The analogy between the hydrophone and the radar antenna is more apt than between the hydrophone and the microphone, for the hydrophone is a larger, more complex device, often formed into arrays as already noted.

The Second World War saw a vast expansion of submarine warfare. The submarine began to explore the three-dimensional possibilities of its hiding place, down to a couple of hundred metres below the surface.

Variable depth immensely increased the difficulties of locating submarines. It increased the likely miss-distance of depth charges or other anti-submarine weapons. The lethal range of these devices was in any case quite small, from about 3 to 10 metres. Relatively small differences of depth could negate their effectiveness.

The attempt to locate submarines became more intensive. Despite technology improvements, sonar remained hardly equal to the challenge. Active sonar had a range not much more than about 1.2 kilometres. It could not remotely compare with the degree of success achieved by radar above the surface.

Sonar 'contacts' were often made, that is the detection of echoes off submarines. But it was difficult to develop these into successful attacks, because it was difficult for a surface vessel to drop its depth charges at the precise location on the surface beneath which the submarine's presence had been indicated. The difficulty was just as great with other anti-submarine weapons such as 'hedgehogs'. Hedgehogs fired a number of projectiles simultaneously to drop in a pattern at some distance away from the attacking warship.

As the warship closed the distance to the sonar contact, it was not possible to maintain the position indication right up to the instant of attack. Therefore there was an error factor. Ten seconds might be enough for a submarine to be gone from the lethal zone. To add to the problem, depth determination was primitive.

Typical victims

For the first time the submarine seriously asserted a claim to dominate the naval future. Submarines had tried to send battleships to the bottom in the First World War, but had not succeeded; they left the task to be performed by aircraft carriers in the Second. Instead the submarine's typical victim in both wars became the merchant ship or passenger liner.

This was bad enough however, for surface warships could do little to protect them. Even when merchant shipping was in convoy with naval escorts, submarines could not always be prevented from building up disastrous scores, generally without serious loss to themselves.

In fact, the convoy system invited the response of grouping submarines into 'wolf packs'. These were strategically directed from land headquarters where intelligence about convoy movements was gathered and assessed. Attacks were carefully coordinated. For these reasons, submarines in wolf packs sank more merchant ships than they could have done if operating individually and opportunistically.

Attacks on convoys brought submarines into battle with naval escort vessels, but even though the battle was as often on the surface as underneath it, the submarine proved a tough opponent. It was robustly built and, lying low in the water, presented a small target for shelling.

Like the aircraft carrier, the submarine emerged a winner at the expense of traditional gun-mounting surface warships. It did not sink all that many escorts, but neither did escorts sink all that many submarines, nor could they keep submarines from sinking their intended victims in large numbers.

A Contest of Elimination

The Second World War set the scene for an elimination contest between the new powers at sea below and above the surface – submarines and aviation. The contest was played out in the Battle of the Atlantic. Aviation defeated submarines. What determined this outcome was basic realities of electronic warfare; aviation exploited electronics more effectively than submarines. In the Battle of the Pacific, the contest was not played out. Japanese aviation left the arena to the American submarine, which exploited both sonar and radar and sank the Japanese merchant fleet.

The primary problem of surface anti-submarine forces was target-finding. British, and later American, naval ships were seemingly fortunate in having two ways of finding the target. As we have seen, these were sonar against the submerged submarine, and radar against the surfaced submarine. But neither was adequate.

This was true even though centimetric radar had its first operational application in the shipborne anti-submarine role at the end of 1941 Surface use of centimetric radar made no difference.

Surface vessels did not pose a sufficient threat to the submarine. When it was surfaced, they could not find it at sufficient range, despite using radar. Nor could they close to attack sufficiently swiftly. When it was submerged, sonar only enabled them to chase and attack it over very short ranges. This meant a practical limitation to when its presence had been realised, typically in the vicinity of a convoy.

In short, even when surface escorts found a target, surfaced or submerged, their means of attack through shelling or depth charges were insufficiently effective.

By contrast aircraft with anti-surface-vessel radar had only one way of detecting submarines, effective only when they were on the surface. But thanks to high operating altitude – typically up to 2,000 feet –

aircraft could detect submarines from much greater ranges. They could then move in to attack very swiftly. Operational research refined this procedure.

The Need for Precision

Operational research determined that it was necessary to bomb or depth charge a submarine whilst it was still on the surface or only just submerging, using a shallow setting. In other words, knowledge of its exact location was the crucial factor. It had to be attacked while it could be pinpointed; once it had been submerged for a few seconds the uncertainties about location, including depth, mounted so rapidly that it was not worthwhile persisting with the attack.

While the introduction of centimetric radar on surface escorts in late 1941 did not achieve anything, neither did it give anything away. Germany discounted the potential of SHF radar. She was not aware of its use in that year, and at the time it did not matter. The French-made Metox radar warning receiver used by German submarines from the last few months of 1942 did not cover the centimetric band. Consequently, when it was introduced on aircraft in early 1943, it came as a surprise, cutting out the submarine's first line of defence, the warning receiver.

Airborne radar gained effectiveness by its integration into a unique night target-finding system which had no real parallel in land warfare. It was combined with airborne searchlights – 'Leigh Lights' – mounted under the wings and throwing a fan-shaped beam coordinated with the radar. An aircraft moving in to attack a submarine already located by radar would suddenly switch on the Leigh Lights and illuminate it. This enabled optically-aimed precision bombing.

Thus radar and optical bombing achieved at sea a solution to a tactical problem which was never solved on land. That is of finding a small target and delivering an instant pinpoint attack. Radar could make its contribution to this system because of its better capability to resolve a target on the sea surface. But at sea, as on land, optical aiming was required for final destructive accuracy.

The main anti-submarine warfare aircraft in the battle fought out over the Atlantic was the four-engined B-24 Liberator. It was of American manufacture but was used by both the British and American air forces. It was classed as a medium bomber. As a high-wing monoplane it was well suited to carry Leigh Lights and give its crew good downward visibility. It also carried a relatively large bomb load and had good endurance.

First operational in 1941, it came into use in increasing numbers during 1943 from shore bases on both sides of the Atlantic. It was too large to deploy from carriers but it had sufficient range to extend patrolling into the ocean's middle. Thousands of Liberators were produced, and although the majority were deployed as bombers, many more aircraft were dedicated to ocean patrol than before. Carrier-based aircraft and flying boats ('Sunderlands' and 'Catalinas') operated alongside Liberators, but it was the latter which had the unique combination of advantages.

A Reversal of Fortunes

The sheer numbers of the hunters, the larger search area achieved by the height of the radar, plus the speed of aircraft into attack, and the lethality of precision bombing, turned the tide of battle against Germany's submarines. Given the propulsive technology of the mid-1940s, submarines required a sanctuary area where they could safely surface to recharge electric batteries, or else to rendezvous with supply submarines. The safety of darkness was also needed. All this was suddenly denied.

An amazing reversal of fortunes ensued. In the first ten days of March 1943, 41 ships had been sunk by German submarines, and another 44 followed in the second ten days, altogether over half a million tons, two-thirds of it sunk when in convoy. These figures were appalling for the Allies. But in May 1943, 41 submarines were sunk, even more appalling for Germany. In this month the German navy was compelled to withdraw submarines from the Atlantic. The initiative was never regained.

This was radar's most decisive single contribution in the Second World War – a one-way contribution, effected remarkably swiftly.

Airborne Centimetric Radar and H_2S

It is sometimes suggested that the British, allegedly fixated on bombing the German homeland, failed to foresee the importance of airborne centimetric radar in anti-submarine warfare and gave it second priority in relation to H_2S. This, it is alleged, was a failure of judgement; the Battle of the Atlantic could have been won by the Allies earlier.

But the argument, although it has received eminent support, hardly stands up. Airborne centimetric radar was a variant of H_2S and the development effort which produced the latter also produced the former and brought it into operation at about the same time. Anti-surface-vessel centimetric radar then brought about the collapse of the German submarine offensive before H_2S brought about the destruction of Hamburg.

There was an operational difference, in that H_2S was a geographical variable, more efffective against some town targets than others, while airborne centimetric radar over sea was a geographical constant. It was equally effective everywhere at finding point targets. These were highly reflecting metal masses seen against a relatively uniform background. The sea surface was capable of producing clutter on the cathode ray tube screen but the task of interpretation was easier than with H_2S.

The German Reaction

At first, the Germans did not believe that airborne centimetric radar was the fundamental cause of the disastrous reversal to their submarine offensive. By early 1943 they knew it was available to the British, centimetric technology having fallen by then into their hands on land. But it was not easy to assess its capabilities, either over land or sea, and they did not rate them very highly. Instead, the Metox radar warning receiver was suspected of emitting radiations which were being picked up and passively homed upon by British and American aircraft. Such radiations existed – it is not always easy to prevent any receiver from emitting some radiation – and Metox was withdrawn, to be replaced later by the non-radiating 'Hagenuk'.

Germany also suspected infra-red technology, a myth encouraged by the British. But by September 1943 the truth was realised. A version of the Naxos warning receiver introduced against H_2S was produced for submarine deployment, later to be replaced by the more sensitive 'Fliege'. Submarines began to be equipped with their own radar for use when surfaced, the 'Hohentwiel'. Meanwhile, paralleling the advance from H_2S to H_2X, Allied anti-surface vessel radar was supplemented with sets working on 3 centimetres wavelength (10 gigahertz). Germany countered with the 'Muecke' warning receiver.

The battle moved from the mid-North Atlantic to peripheral zones where submarines still hoped to find sanctuary, for example towards the Azores, where aircraft patrols could only be mounted from carriers (until the eventual occupation of the Azores by the Allies).

Under these circumstances anti-submarine warfare was concentrated on submarines attempting to transit through the Bay of Biscay. But the ubiquity of searching radars put the surfaced submarine at constant risk. To avoid the necessity of diving whenever a warning signal was heard, German submarines did not dive until the signal strength increased, indicating the search aircraft's approach. This tactic was countered by gradually reducing the radar power, simulating a search aircraft at constant distance.

The instruction finally given to German submarines to surface by day rather than by night underlined the success of the Leigh Light combination with radar. It was an attempt to avoid surprise illumination and attack at all costs. Instead, submarines were to surface in groups and fight it out with attacking aircraft using guns. This was not in any sense a hopeful strategy. The attackers could easily call up air and surface reinforcements.

The Role of Radio

Radar was not alone in anti-submarine warfare, but supported by radio. Radio sustained both the offensive and the defensive: centralised control over German submarines was exercised from headquarters at Lorient on the French coast, concentrating them for convoy attack. Inevitably there was a two-way flow of radio communications in frequencies from 1 megahertz in the MF band to 20 megahertz in the HF band. This was a target for both signals intelligence backed by cryptanalysis, and for direction-finding.

Before the breakthrough provided by airborne centimetric radar, signals intelligence had in fact dominated the Atlantic battlezone. Initially German signals intelligence had the upper hand, but the battle swung the other way during 1941. This was realised by the Germans, who combated the declining effectiveness of the submarine offensive by introducing improved security on codes and finally, from February 1942, an extra rotor for submarine Enigma machines.

This improved cryptography underpinned new successes. Eventually British cryptanalysis began to recover the ground it had lost. But the penetration of Enigma never produced results to compare with the drastic impact of airborne centimetric radar. Immediately before this impact, the balance of success in naval signals intelligence was still in Germany's favour. The main role played by penetration of Enigma was to help prevent German recovery after the radar impact.

German submarines aimed to minimise exposure to direction-finding by abbreviating their transmissions to short periods measured in seconds. But the Anglo-American system for HF direction finding, HF DF or 'huff-duff', incorporated a device which enabled it to record the bearings of such signals.

Huff-duff was based on a directional antenna array. This eliminated the usual 180-degree ambiguity about the direction of a signal. It also gave fairly accurate readings despite 'night effect'. This was not fundamentally new technology, but an application of an existing direction-finding antenna system (known as the Adcock system).

What enabled brief transmissions to be captured for direction-finding purposes was a device used in conjunction with huff-duff, the cathode ray tube direction finder, developed in Britain in the 1930s. It put a compass ring around a cathode ray tube display, and any signal was shown as a line pointing to the appropriate azimuth. It could resolve two signals simultaneously. There was an afterglow, sufficiently long for the azimuth to be read however brief the signal might be. It undercut the submariners' faith that a transmitted signal of 5 to 9 seconds duration was too short to give anything away. It also negated the masking jamming generated from Germany at pre-arranged transmission times.[3]

Huff-duff was operated both from shore sites and on warships at sea. Working out locations from which transmissions had been made was not instantaneous. It required comparison of times, signal frequencies and bearings collected from many interception points. It did not usually lead to immediate tactical action, as with radar, but produced a flow of strategically valuable information about submarine positions and courses.

There was a tactical aspect, in that escort vessels at sea could instantaneously identify the direction of a transmission and make an estimate of range. Long range would be revealed by the effects associated with HF when it is reflected from the ionosphere, such as fading and frequency smearing. Shorter range would be indicated by the absence of these effects and very short range would be apparent from signal strength.

German submarines did not always refrain from radio signalling when in the vicinity of convoys they were preparing to attack. Such nearby signals were often recognisable to escort vessels, which could make pre-emptive sorties in the indicated direction. This was largely a preventive measure but no less valuable for that.

Summary

The Battle of the Atlantic, as described so far, might be summarised as follows. The primary electronic antagonists were Britain and Germany. Radio began in Germany's favour. British naval codes were extensively broken by the Germans. In the early stages of the war, which saw heavy attacks on British shipping, and the German invasion of Norway, Britain lost heavily on this account.

Britain's break into German submarine Enigma did not come until 1941. Among its results was realisation of German penetration of British naval codes. The advantage began to swing from Germany to Britain, and this was reflected in declining merchant shipping losses.

But by 1942, Germany had sealed the intelligence leak and her submarine offensive resumed its success. This pattern was not broken despite America's entry into the war, which at first only gave Germany the opportunity for unchecked destruction of shipping off America's east coast. Neither intensified Anglo-American cooperation in protecting convoys, nor renewed penetration of German codes, broke the pattern. It was only broken at last by airborne centimetric radar, used by both Britain and the United States, in May 1943. This decided the Battle of the Atlantic.

In relation to signals intelligence from radio, radar came out of the Battle of the Atlantic with a greater and more exclusive achievement than it did out of the Battle of Britain.

The Battle between Surface Forces – the Bismarck *Saga*

The Battle of the Atlantic was primarily a battle of surface naval forces and aviation against submarines. It was not concentrated at specific points and times, rather it was dispersed and continuous over a wide area. But there was a secondary aspect in the form of British actions against German surface forces. In these localised conflicts, radar and radio and sonar revealed themselves in fascinatingly different light.

The most significant of all these actions was the seven-day saga of pursuit that ensued after the German battleship *Bismarck* put to sea for her first and last operational voyage on 20 May 1941.

The intention was that she should reach the middle Atlantic, with the heavy cruiser *Prinz Eugen* as escort, to destroy merchant shipping. This was to be Operation *Rheinuebung*.It needed to begin in secrecy, for confrontation had to be avoided with the superior surface forces which the British navy could assemble if the location of the German warships became known.

But in spite of the overcast weather, which from start to finish gave cover to the German warships, their outward sailing via Bergen in Norway was detected visually by aircraft reconnaissance. This triggered a British interception plan.

The squadron passed through the Denmark Strait between Greenland and Iceland, where a small British naval force made visual and radar contact. The cruiser *Suffolk* held the contact using naval gunnery control radar working in UHF at 600 megahertz, remarkably high by the standards of any previous operational British radar, and higher than German practice. It had a maximum range of about 10 miles.

Suffolk radar-tracked whilst hiding so far as possible in mist banks. *Bismarck*'s radar would have allowed her to open fire (as she did against *Suffolk's* Sister Ship *Norfolk*), but delaying for an engagement was counter to her objectives. As it was, *Suffolk*'s tracking enabled the British capital ships *Prince of Wales* and *Hood* to converge for an engagement on the morning of 24 May west of the Denmark Strait.

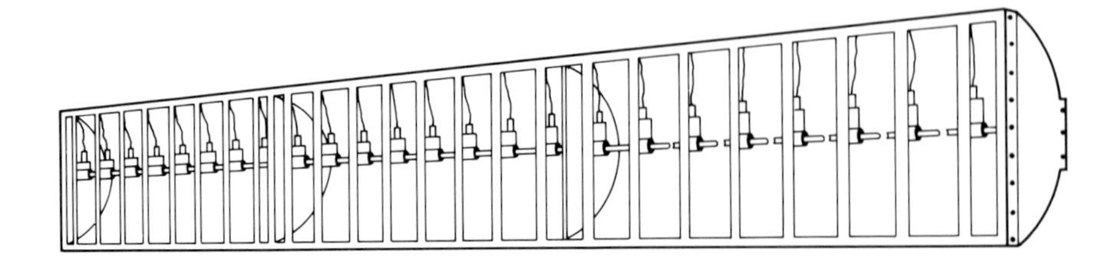

Fig. 11.1 **Type 284 Radar on HMS *Suffolk*** The Type 284 radar which enabled HMS *Suffolk* to track the *Bismarck* in May 1941 was considerably more sophisticated than the first British naval radars. Working on 600 megahertz, it had a pair of antennas each with 24 horizontal dipoles, backed by curved reflectors (one shown above). This gave a beam which was narrow horizontally, for accurate target location, but fanned out in the vertical plane, so that the ship's rolling would not affect the radar's ability to hold the target. Compare with early British naval radars illustrated in Figs. 7.4, 7.5 and 7.6.

German Advanced Sonar

It is well known that the *Hood* blew up, but no universally-accepted account of how this happened exists. The remarkable claim was made by the crew of the *Prinz Eugen* that it was her salvos not those of *Bismarck* which destroyed *Hood*. Even more remarkable, that they had sonar-tracked *Hood* from beyond the horizon with their passive hydrophone arrays and had their gunnery control set up in readiness when the decision to open fire was made.

Whatever the truth of the matter, the claim highlights the fact that German passive sonar was far ahead of any other sonar technology at that time, and its most advanced installation was on the *Prinz Eugen*. This comprised 120 Rochelle salt hydrophones, fitted in an elliptical array on the bows, 60 on each side. Whether or not they helped to sink *Hood*, they may well have saved *Prinz Eugen* on occasion by enabling her to avoid torpedoes.

Prinz Eugen survived the war and her passive sonar contributed enormously to post-war developments. German submarines had a comparable though smaller equipment, with 48 hydrophones in a horseshoe-shaped bow fairing called 'The Balcony'. German sonar was more an aid to survival, by evasion of anti-submarine attack, than a target-finding system, and for this reason its role in the Second World War is generally overlooked.

After the engagement with *Prince of Wales* and *Hood*, the German squadron continued on its course, still aiming to fulfil plans for a destructive descent on mid-Atlantic shipping in conjunction with support vessels already deployed for this purpose.

But *Bismarck*'s command had to reckon with the consequences of shell hits from the *Prince of Wales*. The battleship was slowed and losing oil. The intention to continue with the raid on commerce soon had to be abandoned in favour of a return to port for repairs. It had to be recognised that the chances of doing so without fighting another interception were not high whichever course was set. In the circumstances, the German command preferred to try and ensure the safety of *Prinz Eugen* at least.

The decision was taken for the ships to part company and make separate journeys back to Brest in France, travelling southwards through the mid-Atlantic and then eastwards. On the information

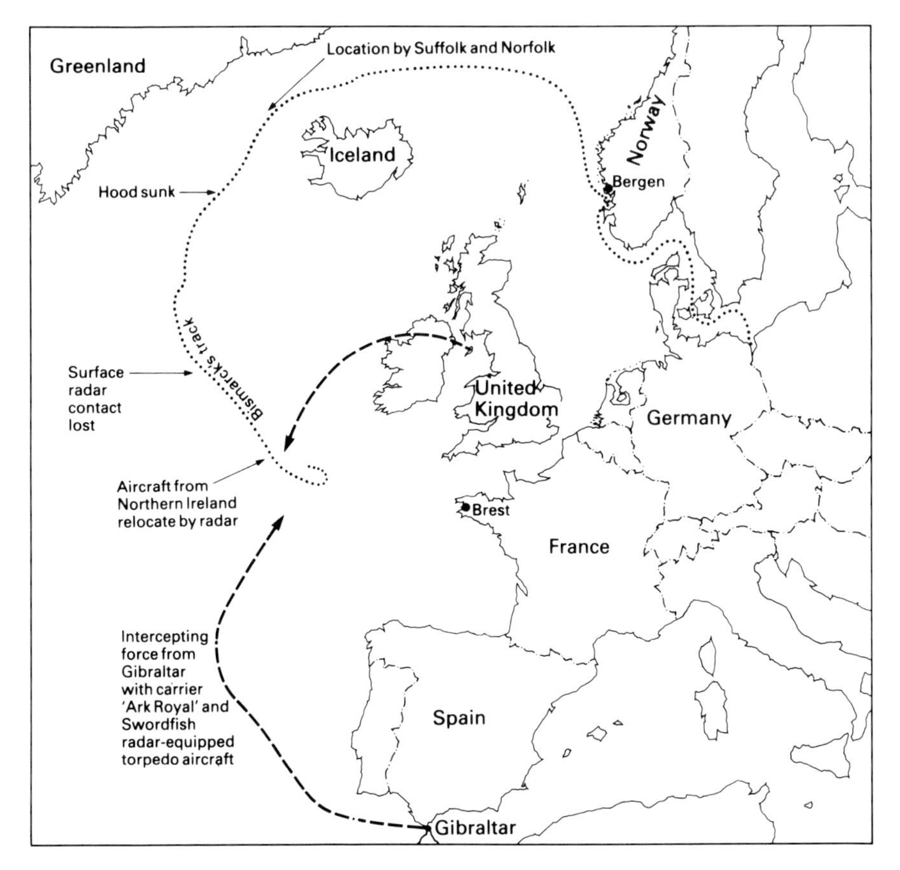

MAP 11.1 **The Pursuit of the *Bismarck*, May 1941** The general course of the seven-day pursuit which ended on 27 May.

available to the German command, this maximised the chances of avoiding further encounters. The decision seems realistic, though by splitting the force it highlighted the fact that an emergency existed. It was probably the joint strength of *Bismarck* and *Prinz Eugen* which had prevailed over *Prince of Wales* and *Hood*; individually they were weaker.

The decision was implemented about 12 hours after the engagement in which *Hood* had been sunk, that is the evening of the same day, 24 May. *Bismarck* turned and engaged the pursuers while *Prinz Eugen* slipped away. Its correctness was underlined a few hours later, when aircraft from the carrier *Victorious*, using anti-surface vessel radar, obtained a torpedo hit on the battleship.

The hit added only marginally to the existing damage, but the role of airborne radar was ominous. It meant that, for the first time in naval history, the ocean spaces were no longer the easy hiding place they had always been. This was still the time of pre-centimetric anti-surface vessel radar, but a warship as large as *Bismarck* made an ideal target.

Zig-zag

Following this incident *Bismarck* continued to be tracked by *Suffolk* using radar. *Suffolk* had to zig-zag because of the possibility of submarine attack and intermittently lost contact. Early on the morning of 25 May, contact by surface radar was completely lost. Much attention has been paid to this turn of events. It has been coupled with the fact that *Bismarck* continued to use her radio. Had she at this juncture observed radio silence, it is argued, she might well have given her pursuers the slip.

This argument overlooks the capability of airborne anti-surface vessel radar to find *Bismarck* – a capability repeatedly demonstrated in the action, despite the cloud and rough weather which offered her best hope.

The argument also overlooks the operational difficulty for a naval commander to take the decision to observe radio silence when there is a need to use radio and when it is obvious that the warship's presence and approximate geographical position are known to the enemy.

Bismarck had undoubtedly become aware, through her Metox radar warning receiver, that she was being tracked. She might have realised that radar contact had been lost without knowing the exact time this happened. The Metox would have continued to pick up the pulses even when *Bismarck* was no longer within the ten-mile range capability of *Suffolk*'s equipment. But at 600 megahertz the signal strength would have declined rapidly, due to horizon effect. This might well have indicated the increasing distance of the searchers and suggested that they had lost their quarry.

Bismarck probably considered that her pursuers were in possession of her approximate location at all times, and that radio direction-finding would not enable them to add much precision. This was a reasonable assessment, entirely borne out by events on the British side.

What her pursuers did not have, after losing radar contact, was the ability to follow changes of course unless and until these became evident through direction finding. Her radio transmissions were not read by British signals intelligence, but it was possible to recognise signals that came from her. This was done by the techniques of 'radio finger printing' (RFP) and TINA – not an acronym, but meaning the recognition of the morse characteristics of individual operators.

However, British errors in plotting the bearings obtained by direction finding completely negated their value. Thus failures in surface radar and signals intelligence compounded each other.

Eventually *Bismarck*'s radio did fall silent. But her approximate position was still known and, given all the circumstances, there was only one plausible option for the pursuit to consider, namely that she was making for France and aiming to get under German air cover. What was needed was confirmation.

This came through two discoveries of signals intelligence. The first was that control for *Bismarck*'s radio frequency switched from Wilhelmshaven to Paris. The second was the statement radioed by the German air force to Greece, for the information of its commander, that *Bismarck* was making for France.

In all, the positional uncertainty, beginning with the loss of radar contact, lasted for about 15 hours on 25 May. Its main effect was to oblige the British to guard against the possibility that *Bismarck* intended to double back on her tracks. By late on 25 May it was clear what course she was taking and where she would need to be searched for.

The following day, 26 May, *Bismarck* was found repeatedly thanks to anti-surface vessel radar, firstly by aircraft from British bases in Ireland, later by carrier-borne aircraft. This was under conditions in which visual search could well have failed, and when the search range of naval surface radar was proving inadequate, as *Suffolk*'s experience had shown.

Climax

The climax came on the evening of 26 May with torpedo attacks by radar-equipped *Swordfish* aircraft from the carrier *Ark Royal*, converging to intercept from Gibraltar.

The first attack was a classsic radar mistake: when the *Swordfish* went in through cloud against their radar target, it turned out to be the British cruiser *Sheffield*. This dramatically highlighted the need for positive visual identification to be coupled with radar.

The error was avoided – with help from the undamaged *Sheffield* – on the second strike, which was accurately aimed against *Bismarck*'s stern. This effectively settled the matter, leaving the battleship without steering. Indeed, when the wreck was found and photographed on the bottom of the Atlantic forty-eight years later, the stern was seen to have completely broken away, although the main deck was remarkably intact.

Bismarck sank on 27 May 1941 after being bombarded by battleships, but controversy persists as to whether she was scuttled. This may well have seemed a necessity to the German Admiral Luetjens in order to prevent the unmanoeuvrable hull falling into British hands. A torpedo from the cruiser *Dorsetshire* caused *Bismarck*, already settled low in the water, to capsize.

The action first made clear the obsolescence of the battleship in face of attacking aircraft, whether land- or carrier-based. Land-based Japanese aircraft emphasised the point by disposing of *Prince of Wales* and *Repulse* in the same way seven months later. This, however, was under good conditions for visual target finding, while the *Bismarck* episode was not only impossible without radar, but signalised the superior search effectiveness of airborne to surface radar at sea. It was two years later that nemesis overtook the German submarine fleet for exactly the same reason, combined with the special effectiveness of centimetric radar against smaller naval targets.

Strangely, the rich strategic significance of the *Bismarck* pursuit has generally been overlooked. The many writers who have been attracted to the subject have seen it as a nostalgic epic of battleship warfare.

Prinz Eugen succeeded in getting back to Brest. But a substantial number of tankers and supply ships had gone into the Atlantic in preparation for the German naval force's sortie, and these were now at hazard. The British had captured the June naval Enigma keys and intercepted communications.

From the beginning of June the British were in a position to sink all these ships. They considered that a total round-up might give penetration of Enigma away. But some which were intended to be allowed to survive were lost by inadvertent encounters with British warships.

So it was that the whole *Rheinuebung* operation ended as a total disaster, which could only arouse the Germans' suspicions. Nevertheless when their inquest questioned the security of Enigma, it came to the conclusion it had not been compromised.

The 'Channel Dash'

At Brest *Prinz Eugen* joined the battleships *Scharnhorst* and *Gneisenau*, which had previously completed a similar sortie unscathed. On 12 February 1942, the three warships joined in the greatest naval insult offered to Britain in the Second World War by sailing through the English Channel back to Germany. Radar was at the centre of the subsequent controversy.

The strategic value of relocating the ships further away from the threat of British attack was unquestioned. Correspondingly, Britain was waiting and watching for the attempt. Signals intelligence built up many indications of impending movement, but failed during the few crucial days beforehand because of a delay in reading Enigma messages.

Germany understood the crucial role of radar in watching the waters through which the warships had to pass. A careful plan was formed for radar deception, progressively building up the level of interference for some days before the bid was made. The actual choice of day was probably made spontaneously on the basis of good cloud cover.

In the event, British radar surveillance is generally considered to have fallen short of its expected performance. The anti-surface vessel radar equipment (pre-centimetric) failed in the reconnaissance aircraft which should have detected the German squadron's departure.

British Chain Home Low coastal radars detected aircraft circling over the German squadron, without detecting the squadron itself. The inference from the circling aircraft was not promptly drawn. Only later, as the squadron drew near the Straits of Dover, which was too late for effective intervention, was the range sufficiently short for the warships themselves to be detected.

With hindsight, Chain Home Low gave the performance which might have been reasonably expected from it. But this was not among the points which emerged from the massive inquest held.

Such inquests seldom justify the time and effort spent on them, a classic example being the post-war inquest in the United States on the disaster at Pearl Harbor, which radar should have averted. What emerges but what is not usually acknowledged is that radar has not been given the respect it warranted.

A Contrast – the End of the Scharnhorst

The 'channel dash' of the three warships is to be seen as part of the Battle of the Atlantic, as also is the engagement which ended with the sinking of the *Scharnhorst* at the end of 1943, even though this took place off northern Norway.

It contrasts with the sinking of *Bismarck* in several ways. If the latter was an epic of anti-surface vessel radar, without which the battleship might well have eluded her doom, the sinking of *Scharnhorst* was an epic of naval surface radar. It took place in waters hundred of miles north of the Arctic Circle, in severe weather and the perpetual gloom of Arctic mid-winter. Aircraft could play no part. Moreover visual ranges were short. In these circumstances surface radar dominated target-finding and gunnery control on both sides.

German naval radar had a lead on its British counterpart up to and for some time after the outbreak of the Second World War. But British naval radar, which unlike British area-defence radar matched the German frequency range almost from the beginning, was ultimately destined to excel its German competitor, something that British area-defence radar never did. In practice, British and German naval surface radar proved about equally capable when they were pitted against each other.

Plans for *Scharnhorst*'s impending sortie against a Russia-bound convoys off North Cape became known to the British through signals intelligence, and she was intercepted by the battleship *Duke of York* and a supporting force of cruisers and destroyers. Initial contact was made by the cruiser *Belfast*'s radar at 32 kilometres range at 8.40 on 26 December 1943.

An intermittent running battle ensued, additional British ships coming into action as *Scharnhorst* sought to withdraw. At 16.17 the *Duke of York* made radar contact at over 41 kilometres, and the engagement between the two battleships began at 16.45. Damaged by shells and torpedoes, *Scharnhorst* exploded and sank at 19.45.

Finale – Operation Overlord

The Battle of the Atlantic merged into the Battle of Western Europe with a final sea action, namely Operation 'Overlord', the invasion of Europe across the English Channel on 6 June 1944.

Electronic warfare played a prominent role. Germany anticipated the invasion and studded the French coast with a variety of coastal defence radars, including Freya and land-deployed Seetakt. Stations were at intervals of only a few kilometres. The military necessity was to obtain advance warning and to identify the main landing sector.

In practice, the main issue was whether the Allied landing was coming to the east or west of the Seine (in the Pas de Calais or the Caen area). Getting this wrong meant a potentially disastrous loss of time in redeploying defensive forces across the river.

Electronic warfare planning on the Allied side provided for intensive advance bombing of the German radar stations, deliberately leaving a minimal number operational. During the invasion, aircraft continuously dropped window according to a pattern intended to create the impression of a massive fleet approaching the east of the Seine, whilst the actual fleet approached to the west. Radar reflectors were used on decoy boats.

This was an interesting example of window used for deception jamming rather than straight jamming. At the same time, airborne Mandrel jammers were operated to cover the approach on the west.

Because of the seriously depleted number of coastal defence radars remaining operational, the Germans were unable to pierce the confusion and decide where the real invasion was taking place, until a delay of more than 24 hours had occurred.

The radar feint was backed up by radio transmissions intended to reinforce the deception. Undoubtedly however radar was the crucial intelligence-gatherer and the priority target for Allied countermeasures.

Germany's defensive problem was compounded by the loss of air superiority over northern France, which exposed her fixed radar stations to air attack. A military disadvantage of the large Mammut and Wassermann installations was vulnerability to bombing. In the circumstances, German's defensive preparations would have been better served by smaller, mobile radar stations. It would have been more difficult for the Allies to ensure that the majority had been destroyed in advance. The larger the number operational, the smaller the chance of maintaining a successful deception for any length of time.

Two Further Classics

Two other instances of sea conflict in the western hemisphere in the Second World War, without being part of the Battle of the Atlantic, provide classic demonstrations of the roles of radio and radar. These were the sinking of the British aircraft carrier *Glorious* by the German battlecruisers *Scharnhorst* and *Gneisenau* in June 1940 and the battle between British and Italian naval forces off Cape Matapan in Greece in March 1941.

The aircraft carrier *Glorious* was sunk at a time when German signals intelligence enjoyed the upper hand. The sinking occurred as the carrier withdrew from an operation conducted by the British in great secrecy, namely the evacuation of Narvik in Norway. Thanks to penetration of British codes, what was happening was better known on the German side than to most members of Britain's own naval staff.

The British obtained indications of the departure of *Scharnhorst* and *Gneisenau* from Kiel on 4 June 1940, northerly bound. Despite what should have been an obvious threat, no warnings were passed on.

Perhaps this was in the hope that the German battleships' departure was co-incidental and unconnected with the aircraft carrier's presence, presumed to be unknown. Four days later the carrier and its two attendant destroyers were caught by surprise. The British Admiralty learnt of the loss and details of the action from German news broadcasts. The event caused a considerable reorganisation in the handling of British naval intelligence.

Nothing in the whole of the Second World War ever symbolised the superiority of one side's naval radar over the other side's relative lack of it so dramatically as the culminating stroke of the Battle of Cape Matapan (south west Greece) on the night of 28 March 1941. Curiously, this happened against a background of Italian dominance in naval signals intelligence. Italian penetration of British naval codes did not permit the tactical disaster threatened by radar to be recognised, let alone averted.

The radar story was simple. The British flagship *Warspite*, with a powerful accompanying squadron, including a number of radar-equipped vessels, found two Italian cruisers, *Zara* and *Fiume* under cover of darkness. The battleships in the British squadron were given target coordinates and advanced to about 2.5 kilometres range, training their armament.

Zara and *Fiume* were suddenly illuminated with searchlights. Their guns were seen to be trained fore-and-aft, indicating unawareness, and they were annihilated with broadsides, together with their two accompanying destroyers. All four ships sank during the night. Radar had written the epitaph on Italy's bid to contest naval supremacy in the Mediterranean.

War in the Pacific

As already noted, the Battle of the Pacific embraced the entire sub-war between the United States and Japan. It invites an interesting comparison with the Battle of the Atlantic.

A principal feature of the Battle of the Pacific was the same as that in the Battle of the Atlantic: an attempt to deny freedom of navigation to the ships of one side. In the Pacific this side was Japan. As an island power, Japan was totally dependent on shipping. Once freedom of navigation was extinguished, so was Japan. Once her oil stocks were exhausted, she could not even move her navy, far less support the many outposts of her military empire.

In the Pacific, submarines and aircraft which fought each other in the Atlantic whilst respectively attacking and defending ships, joined forces in American hands to attack ships – both warships and merchant ships.

Warships were mainly targeted by carrier-borne aircraft. Carriers dominated surface fleets and naval actions. On the other hand Japan's merchant shipping fell prey mainly to American submarines.

Sinkings in the Pacific never approached the massive tonnages recorded in the Atlantic. Neither was there the same local intensity of conflict, with wolf-packs of submarines in pitched battles with convoys and escorts. But this was the proportionate effect of Japan's smaller economy. Across the Atlantic, America had to supply both Britain and Russia, no small task.

Moreover, the Pacific was a larger ocean and the action was more spread. The battle was a gradual process, without the same switchback ride of advances and setbacks for each side as the Battle of the Atlantic. But it was equally decisive. In a sense it was more decisive, in that the Battle of the Atlantic set the scene for the land Battle of Western Europe, while the Battle of the Pacific was final in itself.

America was unready for the battle when it was precipitated by the Japanese attack on Pearl Harbor in December 1941. But as a benefit from the fact that the Battle of the Atlantic had already been raging two years and had forced the development of airborne anti-surface vessel radar, aircraft such as the B-24 Liberator became operational in various versions much sooner than they would have otherwise done.

American merchant ships were not vulnerable to the Japanese to anything like the extent that Japanese ships were vulnerable to the Americans. Japanese submarines had neither the opportunity nor the capability to destroy shipping off America's west coast in the same way as German submarines did off their east coast.

American submarines were luxurious craft by comparison with those of any other country. Their contribution to the war was delayed initially by non-detonating torpedoes and inadequate tactics, but eventually such operational problems were resolved and they began the gradual elimination of Japanese merchant ships. Japan did not have the economic strength to make good the losses.

The target-finding task for American submarines in the Pacific can be compared with that for German submarines in the Atlantic. While signals intelligence played a role, this was not comparable either with its role in the Atlantic, or with its role in Pacific surface engagements. Correspondingly there was little central intelligence gathering and direction by MF and HF radio. In consequence, American submarines were chiefly thrown on their own resources of visual sighting (either when surfaced or through the periscope), passive sonar, and radar.

The climatic benevolence of the Pacific Ocean, as compared with the Atlantic, undoubtedly made visual target finding easier – a fact which is constantly reflected in all aspects of the Pacific battle, not only submarine warfare. Radar came to the assistance of visual sighting with X-band sets mounted on the conning tower. Initially, these were for use when surfaced. Later, sets usable when submerged to periscope depth were fitted. But in terms of range, radar hardly improved on visual sighting: a few kilometres, for example, when submerged. Potentially, sonar offered more.

Both Germany and the United States were driven towards passive sonar, in contrast to Britain's preference for active (asdic). But while Germany used it primarily for evading attack, the United States had to tackle the more formidable challenge of using passive sonar aggressively. This demanded exploiting the Doppler effect to distinguish moving targets and ship speed; ranging with hydrophones located at either end of the submarine to enable triangulation; and execution of an attack including torpedo launch all by sonar without visual observation through the periscope. This was looking far ahead to the future, and it would be too much to claim that this technology became operationally routine. But there is no doubt that American submarines enjoyed a high standard of sonar equipment, and that this contributed materially to their achievement as the principal destroyers of Japanese shipping.

Naval Battles

The celebrated naval battles of the Pacific war, Coral Sea, Midway, and Leyte Gulf, are climactic episodes superimposed on the general pattern much as the sinking of the *Bismarck* is superimposed on the general pattern of the Battle of the Atlantic.

In both oceans, these episodes destroyed surface naval strength which could have changed the course of the main struggle. The magnitude of this task was far greater for America in the Pacific than it was for Britain in the Atlantic.

MAP 11.2 **The Pacific Theatre, 1941–45** The Battle of the Pacific was fought at enormous ranges over vast stretches of water. The action was on, over and under the surface. Three great naval battles established the dominance of the aircraft carrier in surface naval warfare. Strategic air warfare reached an apocalyptic finale with the dropping of two atomic bombs. But the submarine, which had lost in the Battle of the Atlantic, was the real victor. Although its operations are unseen on the map, they conclusively severed Japan's maritime links. When American bombers smashed Japanese oil refineries, they were already long since dry. Interception of radio was America's greatest advantage in electronic warfare, chiefly in surface engagements. Both sides had radar and radar warning receivers, but the conditions often favoured visual target finding, except for the submarine. Sonar at last began to assert its importance against radio and radar.

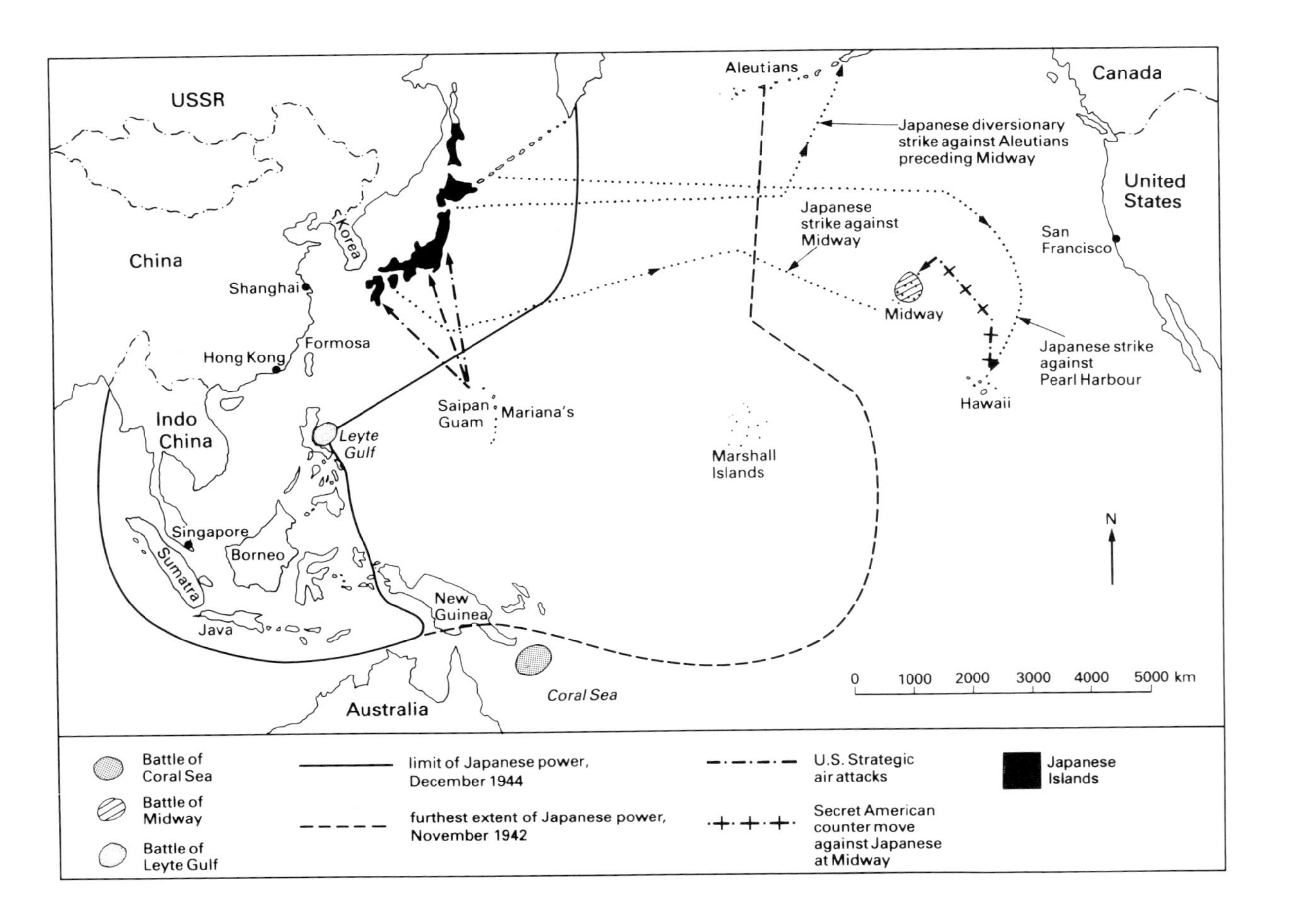

USSR
Aleutians
Canada
Japanese diversionary strike against Aleutians preceding Midway
United States
Japanese strike against Midway
San Francisco
China
Korea
Shanghai
Midway
Formosa
Hong Kong
Japanese strike against Pearl Harbour
Saipan
Guam
Mariana's
Hawaii
Indo China
Leyte Gulf
Marshall Islands
N
Singapore
Borneo
Sumatra
New Guinea
Java
0 1000 2000 3000 4000 5000 km
Coral Sea
Australia
Battle of Coral Sea
Battle of Midway
Battle of Leyte Gulf
limit of Japanese power, December 1944
furthest extent of Japanese power, November 1942
U.S. Strategic air attacks
Secret American counter move against Japanese at Midway
Japanese Islands

The Battle of Coral Sea in May 1942 was the first such episode. Although inconclusive it checked Japan's southwards expansion towards Australia.

Only a month later again, the Battle of Midway in the Central Pacific was a disaster for Japan. Heavily superior Japanese naval forces concentrating for descent on Midway Island were resoundingly defeated.

Midway goes down in history in the same relation to signals intelligence as Matapan does to radar. The battle was extended, with a diversionary attack in the Aleutians 1500 miles north. The complex Japanese preparations for it began with radio signalling from early May 1942. Ironically there was a delay in introducing intended new codes. Thanks to this failure, American signals intelligence was able to uncover the Japanese plan. That a Japanese stroke impended could not be in doubt; the central cryptoanalytic problem was to discover and confirm that the geographic grid designation 'AF' signified Midway (done with a bogus radio message reporting breakdown of the water distillation plant on Midway, which duly reappeared in Japanese traffic but with the location as 'AF').

Consequently, the American command did not fall into the diversionary trap prepared for it, but secretly positioned an American naval force with three aircraft carriers a few hundred miles north east of the threatened island. As a result, when the battle began with the diversionary attack on 2 June and the main attack on 3 June 1942, it was the Japanese who were the victims of surprise. It is well known how long-range air strikes caught the Japanese carriers with cluttered decks. Four were lost against the loss of one American carrier, while battleships, Japan's chief numerical strength, were shown to be little better than useless in such warfare.

Thus it was that signals intelligence wrote the epitaph on Japanese naval supremacy. The following year it added an ironic postscript. In April 1943 American signals intelligence decrypted plans for an airborne inspection tour in the Solomon Islands by Japan's most prestigious and talented commander, Admiral Yamamoto, the planner of Midway and Pearl Harbor. A strong force of P-38 long-range fighters intercepted his plane and shot it down into jungle.

In the last analysis, the Battle of the Atlantic was a triumph for radar rather than signals intelligence. Of course signals intelligence made an important contribution, but radar made the supreme contribution. Taken together these two contributions were decisive in the fullest meaning of the word. Asdics' contribution was small.

By contrast, in the Battle of the Pacific the outcome was the same but the contributions were otherwise. Signals intelligence made the supreme contribution, sonar contended for second place.

All across the Pacific, radar was deployed on ships, aircraft, and island bases by both sides. Japan was aware of American radar, used radar warning receivers, and occasionally used window as a countermeasure, though ineffectively. Japanese radar was behind American radar in operational quality and quantity, and was subjected to the full gamut of countermeasures.

Exactly what role the inferiority of Japanese radar played in successive Japanese setbacks is not clear. All aspects of conflict between American and Japanese forces tended to reflect greater American efficiency. Casualty ratios in set land battles were in American favour by a large multiple margin. It is possible that in this general discount of military competence, whatever usefulness Japanese radar possessed could make no perceptible showing. In the circumstances, it probably gave away more to American radar warning receivers than anything it gained. In American use in the Pacific, for example on submarines, the radar warning receiver tended to become an aggressive rather than an evasive device, in much the same way as passive sonar became aggressive.

Midway left the Americans as the Pacific naval victors. The next major sea battle, the Battle of Leyte Gulf, did not come until October 1944, by which time the pendulum was well into its counterswing and the Americans were undoing Japanese conquests throughout the south east Pacific. The largest naval battle in history, set in the context of the American invasion of the Philippines, Leyte Gulf was the culminating defeat for the Japanese navy, though there were many individual disasters still to come, such as the loss of the giant battleship *Yamato* to air attack.

With many island bases falling into their hands, the Americans extended their attack on Japanese merchant shipping into the most vital areas around China and south east Asia. Japan's oil supply vanished completely. When the *Yamato* was sunk in April 1945 it was, for lack of oil, on a one-way voyage to the defence of Okinawa, where it was to have been beached.

Opening the Strategic Air Offensive

Unique military significance attached to the Marianas Islands captured by the Americans in mid-1944: Saipan, Tinian and Guam. About 1500 miles south of Tokyo, without intermediate land, they opened the prospect of a strategic air offensive against the hitherto invulnerable Japanese mainland.

Even so, the striking distance was out of scale with all previous strategic bombing, and could only be bridged because of the arrival of a successor aircraft to the B-17 Flying Fortress used by the Americans in

Europe. This was the B-29 Superfortress with a range of over 3000 miles. The American drive to construct five huge airbases for it on the Marianas in short order remain one of the most astonishing feats of the Second World War.

From the European theatre of overland war the Americans brought a mass of strategic bombing experience. They had preferred daylight operations with visual target recognition, scheduling precision strikes against specific economic targets. This was a philosophy in marked contrast to the British and the Germans. In American practice, the role of radar bombing scopes of H_2X type only arose when cloud cover was found over the target. While the Americans had used jamming against defensive radar ('Carpet'), electronic warfare was far less important than in night-fighting. Instead, the most significant means of reducing their bomber losses had proved to be the long-range day-superiority escort fighter.

In strategic bombing across the Pacific, the Americans began with the same intention to mount precision visual strikes against economic targets, but the different circumstances led to its abandonment.

Japanese weather was expected to be much more favourable to visual bombing than the typical European overcast, but this was hardly borne out. On the other hand, there was a tendency for the cloud to thin at night which helped visual recognition despite darkness, especially with attacks at low altitude. The fact that the target cities were mainly coastal, with characteristic outlines, including rivers and canals, helped both visual and radar recognition. Long flights over water put a premium on the Loran navigation system which, operating on the same principle as the British Gee but at lower frequency, was called upon to work at extreme range, which it did better at night. The range precluded the precision Shoran system, analogous to British Oboe.

In the circumstances, both day and night bombing were tried, with radar assistance as necessary. Opposition was slight, more from flak than fighters, even so precision bombing was difficult and the results were modest. But in March 1945 a new and more effective formula was found: intensive area incendiary bombing. This did not demand precision targeting. Japanese cities were constructed of easily inflammable materials and densely congested. The technique began with a low-altitude raid against Tokyo, carried out by over 300 bombers at night making individual runs in little cloud and good visibility. Its results transcended the British attacks on Hamburg in July 1943: some 85,000 dead, 41,000 wounded, a million homeless, an area of 15.8 square miles burnt out.

The strategic air offensive continued with versatility as its keynote, both as between night and day operations and radar and visual target finding, but it was always area rather than precision bombing. Given the low altitudes (varying from a few to several thousand feet) radar was often needed to pierce smoke rather than cloud.

So far from carrying the panoply of electronic warfare equipment with which British bombers had tried to defend themselves against German night fighters, the B-29s increasingly discarded even their ammunition and cannon. True, Japanese fighters were seen. Initially they were fought off by the bombers, later they were countered with long-range escorts, but the bomber losses came generally when B-29s damaged by flak were obliged to ditch in the sea on the long homeward run.

The two atomic bomb raids, against Hiroshima and Nagasaki, were daylight missions. Nagasaki was overcast; radar found the target, but dropping the bomb by means of radar only had been countermanded. It was a small break in the cloud cover that doomed the city. This was characteristic of the way in which the Americans operated radar and visual recognition in conjunction.

It may be argued that the strategic air offensive against Japan at last vindicated the belief that air attack alone could compel a nation to surrender – the belief that had motivated the German Blitz on Britain and the British bombing assault on Germany, without producing in either case the hoped-for result. But Japan was different in that she had lost the war even without the strategic air attack, and the attack's primary function was to thrust that fact irrefutably before the people and the government.

Electronics played a significantly smaller role than in the European air conflict, but was vital for navigation and target finding, especially in view of the long striking ranges over water. That it did not play a larger role mainly reflected the vast military disparity between the opponents. True, Japan was highly vulnerable in that her cities were coastal. There was no defence in depth as bombers overflew land. In Europe, Hamburg had already exemplified the coastal combination of exposure to attack and easy recognisability to radar, and in the light of Hamburg Japan's defence problem can only be assessed as severe. The first electronic essential should have been a seawards-looking surveillance radar network. In its absence radar picket ships and standing air patrols were needed.

12

Transformation

It is sometimes held that with the end of the Second World War in 1945, electronic warfare became something for which there was no further use or prospect, and that this remained so until the Korean War broke out unexpectedly in June 1950, finding the combatants ill-prepared.

This judgement misses many things.

It misses the changed aspect of the world from 1945 onwards. It misses the significance of the years from 1945 to the early 1950s, as a period in which the Soviet Union had to reckon with areas of military technology in which it was behind its recent allies, and strive to catch up.

Nuclear weapons were an obvious priority. In practice electronics and aviation were of equivalent importance. So far as electronics was concerned, radar was the key area. One basic theme of electronic warfare between 1945 and the early 1950s became the Soviet attempt to match the United States capability in radar. The first requirement was ground surveillance radar, and the second airborne interception radar.

Both were as necessary to the Soviet Union after 1945 as they had been to Germany up to 1945. The Soviet Union considered itself as inheriting Germany's air defence problem. The United States had never experienced this problem acutely; nor did Britain after 1941. Neither needed to consider an air threat after 1945, until nuclear weapons were in Soviet hands.

1945 – A Watershed

In view of these facts, 1945 was the greatest single watershed in the history of electronic warfare. Through the century up to this time, electronic warfare had been dominated in practice by Britain and Germany. Not even the entry of the United States into the Second

World War greatly changed this, for America left the night air battle over Germany to Britain, and Japan did not have the same ability to put up an electronic fight as Germany.

But from 1945 on, the opposite poles of electronic warfare were the United States and the Soviet Union. They were the countries which undertook the massive developments, and when other countries got into conflicts in which electronic warfare featured, they were mostly using technology derived from or pioneered by these principals.

This is only one of the special aspects missed. Others must be returned to later. What is missed above all however is the general aspect. From 1945 to the outbreak of the Korean War in June 1950 is not so much a period by itself, as the beginning of a longer period, which forms a coherent whole in that during it historical forces completed a recognisable transformation. This is the period from 1945 to 1960.

It was a period of restructuring, a resetting of the historical stage. It saw a polarisation of global power between West and East, leaving the rest of the world non-aligned and in most military respects insignificant. Military transformation accompanied and underpinned political transformation. Electronic warfare was one of the largest factors in the military transformation.

The period began, as already noted, with the Soviet Union's post-war efforts to catch up in military technology. It saw these efforts measured in the Korean War. It saw a massive acceleration in military preparations on both sides as a direct result of the Korean War. Finally it saw a new balance of power.

It began with one unquestionable post-war Superpower, the United States; unique in possessing the atomic bomb; a long way ahead in two other key military technologies, aviation and electronics; with unchallenged global naval strength; and massive economic superiority.

It ended with much less to choose, militarily, between the United States and the Sovient Union. Not too much difference in terms of nuclear weapons and aviation. Nor in the new category of missiles. American naval strength was countered by a Soviet submarine threat.

A Question Mark

The pre-eminence of the United States had come to rest chiefly on more advanced electronics. If anything gave a qualitative edge to American weapon systems, it was electronics. Put the other way around, quality of electronics posed a question mark over Soviet achievements, especially in missiles and submarines. Both were highly dependent upon electronic warfare. Did they fully match American capabilities? If not, would the time come when they would?

These issues were already apparent by the end of the Korean War. America's economic superiority was unassailed, but much of the production power was committed to serving the affluent civilian sector. The Soviet Union had held back its civilian economy in order to divert a proportionately larger part of its resources to military requirements. The military comparison between the United States and the Soviet Union was less unfavourable to the Soviets than a direct comparison of economies might suggest; in fact in some respects it favoured them.

Soviet Achievements

The Soviet Union proved able not only to produce competitive weapon systems, but to do so in considerable quantities. This became clear with ground-based surveillance radar.

The Soviets had received radar technology from the West in the form of wartime supplies. These included centimetric radar. By 1951 the Soviets had developed their own 'Token' microwave surveillance radar. Technically it left the wartime Allied equipment behind. It reflected the up-to-date American CPS-6 radar. By 1952 Token radars were identified around the Black Sea, in Central Europe, and in the Far East, amounting in all to far more equipments than there were CPS-6 radars in American inventory.

Even more convincing, was the example provided in the course of the Korean War by the Mig-15 fighter. By 1951 it was evident that this was a modern jet aircraft, in some ways in advance of anything the United States or her allies possessed, and had been manufactured in far greater quantity than any American warplane. This was a remarkable achievement by the Soviet Union.

However, the achievement lay in aviation engineering, and lacked an electronics dimension. There was no airborne interception radar for the Mig-15, or for any other aircraft deployed by the Communist Bloc. The Mig-15 was in the tradition of the day superiority fighters of the Second World War. A corresponding night-fighting capability was absent. This proved a shortcoming.

In the American arsenal, the Mig-15 was matched by the F-86 Sabre, similar in concept. Neither aircraft was designed with the needs of airborne radar as a prime requirement. But the Americans had dedicated night fighters in the F-94 Starfire and the F3D-2 Skynight, both designed to carry airborne interception radar.

As the Korean War came to its end, in 1953, existence of the first Soviet airborne interception radar was verified – 'Scan Odd'. It was never operational in the war. Not until the late 1950s did the Soviets introduce aircraft dedicated, in the full sense of the word, to the use of airborne radar.

At this time the value of aircraft as a platform for radar had been borne in upon the Soviets, not only for airborne interception, but for search, surveillance and targeting. A variety of radars was carried by 'Badger', 'Bear' and 'Fiddler' aircraft, in under-fuselage or nose radomes. It had become a vital complement to their air-to-ground or air-to-sea missiles. Airborne radar came in, for the Soviets, largely with the missile age.

By 1960 it was plausible to claim that there were two Superpowers. In the popular view they were evenly matched. This was undoubtedly due to the impression created by the Soviet Union's space achievements. The reality was different. The Soviet Union still had a long way to go. This was particularly true in electronics; Soviet space achievements, however impressive, paradoxically highlighted electronic inadequacies.

Nevertheless in 15 years an enormous change had occurred in the US–Soviet balance.

'Solid State'

With the end of the Second World War, electronics in the West reverted to civilian motivation. The military urgency and investment of the wartime years slackened off. This was in contrast to the Soviet Union. But while the Soviet Union attempted to catch up in military electronics, in the West the basic technology of electronics moved ahead. This was the time when 'solid-state' electronics was born.

Solid-state electronics is associated above all with the American invention of the transistor in 1947. What it meant in practice was a vast simplification and miniaturisation. The electron tube ceased to be necessary for many purposes. Along with the tube were banished its appetite for electric power (to heat a filament, rather as in an electric bulb), and its need for high-tension voltage supplies.

Instead of controlling the flow of electrons inside the tube's evacuated envelope, generally glass, the new technology controlled the flow inside a small piece of crystalline solid. Natural crystals had been used in the early days of radio, but the electron tube had largely swept them away. Now the artificial crystal swept the tube away.

What was left were mainly specialist tubes. Such as for example the cathode ray tube, providing an irreplaceable visual function, and the magnetron, klystron and travelling wave tube. Like the magnetron, the klystron and travelling wave tube could provide high power at SHF. These tubes remained unique in their ability to handle the power requirements of transmission. They also handled the higher frequencies; solid-state electronics progressed only gradually up the frequency spectrum.

The transistor did not bring in any fundamental new principle. It simplified the design of electronic circuits, and hastened the trend towards miniaturisation. This was assisted by other techniques of the same era, such as printed circuit boards. Instead of assembling electronic equipment on substantial metal chassis, with multi-coloured wires linking the components, the industry began to use plastic bases with the requisite connections already plated on in metal, as if 'printed', saving materials and labour.

These developments could be described as a revolution in themselves, but only a revolution in the way basic electronic components were made and assembled, not in concepts.

Militarily, the question is whether these changes made it harder for the Soviet Union to catch up, or easier. The logic may be that from the purely electronic standpoint it should have become easier, for the new technology was simpler and more productive. The main hurdles were the chemical and physical processes needed to manufacture solid-state components, which required research and investment. The question is how quickly the Soviet Union recognised the need for this.

But from there on the main effect was to enable much more sophisticated electronic equipment to be created – containing more transistors than it could have contained electron tubes. It could perform more complex functions yet be packaged into smaller space. It was physically more robust.

These developments underlaid the advance of missiles in the later 1950s, because these were the exact demands that missiles made of electronics. The Soviet Union emerged as a serious concurrent competitor to the United States in missiles, and it cannot have done this without beginning to draw on the new generation of electronic components and construction methods.

At the time when the Korean War broke out these developments had been started, but only just, and their application was still well in the future. The war's level of applied military electronic technology was that of the end of the Second World War. Moreover this level was largely the monopoly of the United States.

New Demands

The electronic interest of the war was high. Korea revived air warfare but in military and geographical conditions quite different from those in which air warfare ended over Germany in 1945. How would electronics adapt to the new demands?

Korea's division along the 38th parallel was an agreement of convenience dating from the need to liquidate Japanese occupation in 1945. By 1950 Soviet and United States forces had been withdrawn.

The North Korean invasion of the South in June 1950 was primarily a local initiative to reunify the country – on North Korean terms.

It was a campaign of rapid movement. In the first few weeks it almost succeeded. But then United Nations forces, mainly contributed by the United States, turned the tables. By the end of September, North Korean forces had been driven from South Korea. The United Nations forces crossed the 38th parallel and in another month occupied almost the whole of North Korea.

At this point, reached in October 1950, Chinese 'Volunteers' intervened, crossing the Yalu river along Korea's northwest border with Manchuria. They drove the United Nations forces back below the 38th parallel.

After a United Nations counter-attack at the beginning of 1951, the line stabilised once again near the 38th parallel. Peace negotiations began in June 1951 but dragged on, with intermittent breaks and against a largely static ground position, for two further years, until the Korean Armistice was signed in July 1953.

The significant fact is that air power fought a constantly changing battle throughout the three years of war, in contrast to land power which after the first year was deadlocked.

Conflict continued in both spheres, but the air conflict was fluid and ranged over the whole territory of North Korea, whereas land power simply maintained the integrity of a geographical line across the Korean peninsula. Air power had the main political importance as a lever in negotiations. Electronic warfare was a vital ingredient of air power.

There was an air dimension to the fighting from the beginning. This came in the form of tactical ground support, by a surprising variety of aricraft representing a mixture of jet- and piston-engined technology. Piston-engined B-29 Superfortress bombers dating from the Second World War were among those used to attack troop concentrations. Later strategic bombing was applied against targets in North Korea.

When South Korean forces were in swift retreat, in the first few weeks of the war, only air power could do anything to stem the North Korean onrush, by counter-attacking ground targets. The Second World War saw similar fighting, though under offensive rather than defensive conditions. At that time, ground targets of opportunity was usually easily identified.

Korean terrain was completely different to the European countryside. It was rugged, mountainous and overgrown, with an absence of big cities and prominent communications routes. Tactical targets were hidden among natural features, all very similar. In these circumstances it was impracticable for strike aircraft to seek out targets by themselves.

The need was for slow and manoeuvrable scout aircraft with good cockpit visibility to get into the valleys, find targets and call in strikes. The premium was on good communications with abundant channels, airborne relays, and ground–air coordination. Radio dominated; radar played no role.

T-6 training aircraft were brought in to supply the scouting need; these became known as Mosquitoes. They carried an eight-channel, later twelve-channel VHF radio. Jeeps were similarly fitted to enable air–ground contact.

Strategic Bombing

In July 1950 strategic bombing of North Korea began. Targets were typically explosives, mining and other industrial plants, railways, bridges and military barracks. These were daylight attacks relying either on visual target recognition or, in cloud, use of radar bombing scopes. The latter descended from H_2S equipment of the Second World War.

Heavy cloud cover was typical of the Korean western coast. North Korean topography was far less recognisable than European, and targets had not been extensively studied to identify those features which would be prominent on radar. But radar overcame these problems and sustained an effective strategic campaign.

It began with an attack by 47 B-29s on the Chosen Nitrogen Explosives Factory on the morning of 30 July 1950, in which the leading squadrons bombed by radar and the following squadrons received visual assistance from fires apparent through cloud.

Radio-controlled bombs were used at the end of 1950 and beginning of 1951 to obtain accurate hits on North Korean bridges. These recalled the German Fritz-X; the operator controlled the fins as the bomb descended. The 'Razon' was a 1000-lb bomb, discovered to be too light and replaced by the 12,000-lb 'Tarzon'.

Tactical bombing at close range ahead of the United Nations line – called 'X-ray', later 'Phantom' – began from February 1951. The first idea was for the bombers to position themselves by reference to radar beacons, located near the front, which would show up on the plan position indicators of airborne radar bombing scopes. This was a refinement of the Allied H_2S/H_2X technique in the Second World War. But the beacons proved to be too remote from the targets to be of much help.

The second idea was to vector bombers on to their targets by ground radar. This was in principle a continuation of the last German bombing technique, the Egon system using Freya ground radar and airborne Erstling Identification Friend or Foe. This was successful. The ground controller gave the target approach and bomb release instructions. The ground radar was a later version of the SCR584 gun-laying radar. But while attempts were made to operate with radar beacons airborne on the bombers, in other words closely paralleling the German system, this was found not to work so well as simply using the skin return.

From February 1951 'shoran' was in use. This was an American target-finding system of Oboe type, originating in the Second World War, using simultaneous range measurements. Shoran's accuracy was estimated as a circular error probability of 485 feet, meaning that half the bombs dropped fell within a circle of this radius around the target.[1]

By the time of the Chinese intervention, bombing attacks were concentrated on the relatively narrow territory remaining in North Korean hands. The Yalu crossings and assembly areas became priority targets, though the attacks were restricted to the use of airspace on the Korean side of the Yalu, a severe operational constraint.

Eventually Mig-15s began to contest air superiority over North Korea. They operated from airfields on the Chinese side of the Yalu river, principally Antung in Manchuria. Their aerodynamic technology was good and their performance was high. They had advantages of speed and altitude. For political reasons their bases remained out of bounds to United Nations attack. Correspondingly the Mig-15s did not in general venture south of the 38th parallel. North Korean airspace became a gladiatorial arena between two sanctuaries.

'Mig Alley'

The Mig intervention came slightly ahead of the Chinese ground intervention in October 1950, at the low point of North Korean fortunes. It caused something of a crisis for the United States air force, for all American aircraft were outclassed with the exception of the F-86 and it was necessary to reinforce as heavily with F-86s as possible. All the same it was never possible to match the numbers of Migs.

Despite this, and mainly thanks to an ample margin of pilot competence, F-86 Sabres maintained a measure of daytime air superiority. Patrolling 'Mig Alley' along the Yalu, they attempted to shield the daytime fighter-bombers attacking targets further south. From now on however United Nations aircraft were vulnerable over North Korea, even though the Migs paid heavily for the losses they inflicted. As in the daytime air fighting of the Second World War, this was a visual battle, not dependent on electronics; it continued throughout the war.

The Migs demonstrated again what had been discovered in the Second World War: the daylight vulnerability of bombers. The position gradually deteriorated. This was highlighted by the decision taken on 28 October 1951 to switch bombing to night-time operation.

Strategic bombing now relied heavily on Shoran. The main problem was that maps of North Korea were considerably less precise than Shoran. However it was effective. B-29 Superfortress bombers approached their targets over 'Shoran arcs', analogous to the arcs followed by Oboe-equipped bombers attacking targets in the Ruhr.

By November 1951 the Korean air defence system had developed on an area basis, rather as in the Second World War, with north and south sectors. Sub-sectors could pass on the tracks of intruding aircraft from one to the other, and interceptors were scrambled against 'bogies'.

At the same time, it might be said that 'stealth' entered the Korean War, in the form of 'Bedcheck Charlies', small low- and slow-flying piston-engined Po-2 aircraft which had earlier been an all-but-insoluble problem for the German air force on the Eastern Front in the Second World War. 'Stealth', the concept of minimising observability, particularly to radar, did not find its way into the popular vocabulary until the 1980s. But the Po-2 demonstrated the principle.

These aircraft were difficult to detect, on account of their small size and construction materials which gave a small radar cross-section. This, combined with their manner of flight, made them difficult to shoot down. They sometimes harassed airfields at night by dropping a few small bombs. They were sometimes plotted by radar and successfully intercepted.

From May 1952 ground controlled interception radar was introduced by the Chinese. By day or night it could bring the fighter within a few miles of a target. In daytime it enabled an effective tactic whereby the Migs dropped through cloud cover on to their victims.

The Mig-15s patrolled at night but lacked airborne interception radar. The communists therefore attempted to defend point targets, such as the Yalu crossings, with radar-laid or sound-directed searchlights, illuminating the bombers for attack by fighters. This was a revival of the Second World War's illuminated night fighting. Alternatively flak was laid by radar, especially since bomber raids took advantage of both night and cloud.

By June 1952 the communist powers had immense potential air superiority, in numbers at least, with a total of some 7000 aircraft at Chinese and Soviet bases. But the approximate 5000 Soviet aircraft were not actively deployed and the communist powers indicated that their intentions were limited to defence, including defence of North Korea.

Night Combat

At Kwaksan on 10 June 1952 four B-29 bombers attacking a railway bridge at night were suddenly illuminated by some 24 searchlights while flying on a Shoran arc. Twelve jet fighters, under control from another aircraft, attacked them. Two were lost and a third, badly damaged, made an emergency landing at Kimpo near Seoul. From this time on a new phase in the air war began and jamming of ground radar became indispensable.

For this purpose refurbished Second World War equipment proved adequate. Window was also used. As in the Second World War, electronic countermeasures were applied by special aircraft. Low-level defence suppression attacks were made while the B-29s were bombing from high altitude.

American night fighters stalked night-flying communist aircraft, but the Migs do not seem to have been as vulnerable as other, slower communist aircraft. An F3D-2 Skynight shot down a Yak-15 on 3 November 1952 in the first night jet-versus-jet kill. The first all-radar kill was made by an F-94 Starfire on 30 January 1953. The victim was an La-9, not seen until it burst into flames.

Air fighting in the Korean War was in many ways a microcosm of that in the Second World War. The loss of 16 B-29 bombers to fighters and four to flak was low by comparison with typical Second World War statistics, but the B-29s were at risk for only a small fraction of the time that bombers were when penetrating German skies. No doubt the figure would have been higher but for communist lack of airborne interception radar. Electronic counter measures, in the form of jamming and defence suppression attacks, contributed to holding them down.

B-29s, even though the largest bombers, were a small minority of the aircraft employed. Much of the bombing fell to fighter-bombers, such as the F-105. A more comprehensive picture is seen in the loss of 1041 aircraft of all types to communist action, including 147 to air-to-air combat, 78 to unkown combat action, and 816 to ground fire. By comparison, United Nations forces claimed to have destroyed 976 communist aircraft.

Ground fire emerged in the Korean War as a more formidable cause of loss than fighters – a significant difference to the Second World War.

The Korean War showed that the day superiority fighter by itself was inadequate. It needed to be complemented by its electronically-equipped counterpart the night fighter. The war distantly foreshadowed the merging of these classes. At the time, in the air forces of the west, the day fighter was still a distinct breed from the night fighter, as in the days of the piston-engined fighters of the Second World War. But the term all-weather fighter was arriving, in recognition of the fact that the visual limitations of cloud and night amounted to much the same thing.

In the jet fighter era, the day fighter was recognisable by its unobstructed nose intake, which gave extra performance. The all-weather fighter put its radar radome in the nose and its jet intakes further back. This gave secondary priority to performance. The all-weather fighter was the type destined to endure; the term itself eventually disappeared, but all modern interceptors are on the all-weather pattern.

Soviet achievement in producing an airframe and engine comparable with Western examples was not matched by progress in avionics, otherwise a night or all-weather fighter would have been deployed over Korea. It would have been the proper complement to the Mig-15.

Subsequently a variant of the Mig-15 with airborne radar was produced, but the Soviets no doubt discovered, as did Western designers, that day fighters could not be satisfactorily adapted in this way to night or all-weather operation. Adequate provision for radar could not be made. By the end of the decade all fighters integrated airborne radar into their design and the old duality had disappeared.

A Contrast in Achievement

It is of limited military value to drive bombers from the daylight sky if they cannot be contested in the night sky as well. An effective airborne interception radar would have increased the threat to the B-29s. Although the communist powers vastly improved on Germany's day fighting performace, they did not match the standard of German night fighting, and this reflected weakness in electronics.

The failure in airborne radar is in contrast to the Soviet achievement in ground radar. Why did it occur? Possibly not so much on account of technical difficulties, as though failure to appreciate all the air-fighting lessons of the Second World War.

The aviation progress which, with the help of electronics, created a new generation of fighters, also created a new generation of bombers. The bomber is no less dependent on electronics. The change in bombers after the Korean War witnessed a bigger agony of struggle than the change in fighters did.

It was a progress from the piston-engined era, via the United States' amazing giant hybrid long-range strategic bomber, the B-36, with six piston and four jet engines, to the all-jet B-47 and B-52. These last were destined to survive through decades. The B-52, first flown in 1952, is still in service, perhaps the most remarkable veteran of military aviation's history.

It demonstrated that airframe and engine technology had reached a stable level, providing platforms for continuously advancing electronics equipment, which was the real factor preserving the aircraft's military viability. When at last the B-52 began to reach obsolescence, it was electronics which dictated this more than aeronautical engineering. In the outward shape of its successors, the US's B-1B and B-2 bombers, electronics is seen as the principal design consideration, supplanting aerodynamic performance. The task of aeronautical engineering has become to provide what the requirements of electronic warfare demand.

The Korean War precipitated the final stage of the transformation that, starting slowly after 1945, was complete by 1960. It spurred a vast increase in military budgets, which over the rest of the decade effected a spectacular advance in military technology across the board, including electronics.

In this sense the main significance of the Korean War came after it had finished. It lay in the fact that the war fundamentally changed the West's perception of the Sino-Soviet Bloc, equally with the Sino-Soviet Bloc's perception of the West.

For this reason the war also spurred several new defence agreements. These included alliances made in the mid-1950s between the United States and South Korea and the United States and Japan, and the formation of the South East Asia Treaty Organisation and the Central Treaty Organisation (in the Middle East). The North Atlantic Treaty Organisation, formed in 1949, was joined in 1955 by the Federal Republic of Germany. At this time an eastern counterpart to NATO appeared, the Warsaw Pact.

In short the period from the end of the Second World War to 1960 saw not only the emergence of a second Superpower, but the formation of a new global military-political landscape destined to dominate the world for a long time to come, accompanied by a new generation of military technology.

Military Electronics Exalted

The West had drawn a cordon around the Sino-Soviet Bloc. It had put massive investment into new weaponry. In this process military electronics was exalted as never before. While other technologies advanced, nuclear weapons, aviation, submarines, ballistic missiles, all became increasingly dependent on electronics as the means of control. Like the night bombers and fighters of the Second World War, what they could do was only what electronics allowed them to do. Electronics became the most vital support to the military power of both sides.

It is in the latter part of the 1945–60 period that the Soviet drive for parity in military electronics began to be seen as the key politico-military issue which it has since remained. Ultimately it became the dominant issue in the military balance.

The West has always tended to see the advance of electronics as a strategic tide flowing in its favour. But while nuclear weapons and aviation are, within limits, easy to compare, electronics is less obvious. It has always been much harder to judge the Soviet position. There are more aspects and variables to take into account.

Electronics in the modern Western world, including Japan, has a prominent consumer facet, which until recently has been largely absent from the Soviet Union. This is deceptive. Consumer electronics is a far from adequate guide to military electronics. All that can be said is that it broadly reflects the same sequence of fundamental discoveries. But military electronics is a strong and independent force in pushing development forward.

Insofar as the West's investment meant new technology, it was matched as well as it could be in the communist world. Insofar as it meant mass production, it was often exceeded in the communist world.

There is another special aspect to the period 1945 to 1960 to which electronic warfare made a distinctive contribution.

The Inpact of the Cold War

Even before the Second World War had ended, the long-standing cultural differences between the Western world and Communism were re-emerging. Warm public sentiment about the wartime alliance began to chill. After the war, it chilled ever more quickly as Communism consolidated itself in Eastern Europe and China, as the independence of West Berlin was narrowly sustained by the airlift of 1948. But the principal powers kept their differences under diplomatic control.

For this reason the phrase 'Cold War' became current. Cold War was not only a convenient phrase, but a deliberate policy subscribed to by both sides. It was indeed a strategy, based on the mutual conviction that the other side's position would eventually crumble if the pressure was kept up.

The Korean War was truly a paradox, a hot war between powers engaged in Cold War. Throughout it, the over-riding strategic importance to both sides was to preserve 'coldness'.

This was shown by their scrupulous observation of formalities in their own diplomatic relations, regardless of the killing and brainwashing which went on elsewhere.

In these circumstances electronic warfare acquired a special role. A role that might be called electronics in cold warfare. It was not a simple role.

Firstly, electronics sustained the efforts of both sides to maintain surveillance of each other. It had become by far the most effective technology of espionage.

Secondly, electronic espionage became the subject of a special contest for technical supremacy. It reflected the wartime contest in signals interception and cryptanalysis. This contest could be recognised as a specific trial of electronic strength – or sometimes more appropriately, daring.

Thirdly, electronic espionage became permanently what the Korean War was only briefly – a hot battleground in the midst of Cold War.

It became this because it did not risk rupturing the diplomatic controls preserving mankind from the worst horrors. Nevertheless it began to provoke some of the most strained incidents short of rupture.

Toleration

Espionage was already a diplomatically tolerated battleground; electronic espionage required even more diplomatic toleration. Electronics became espionage's huge extension. This factor put a premium on electronics capabilities, enlarged in turn by the remarkable advance of electronics itself. Electronics intelligence became the active arm of Cold Warfare.

In electronics the new confrontation began, like the Cold War itself, before the old one had ended. The communications interception and cryptanalytic capabilities built up in Britain and the United States were already applied against Soviet communications while the war was in progress, more so in the United States than in Britain. As soon as the war was over, the Soviet Union became the primary target. The interception stations and cryptographic centres were not demobilised but maintained, expanded, sometimes relocated.

The wartime intelligence alliance of the United States and Britain, forged by the secret BRUSA agreement, was reconfirmed in the secret UKUSA agreement of 1947, to which other English-speaking countries adhered, Canada, Australia and New Zealand. This enabled a global signals intelligence network to form, collecting radio and cable traffic everywhere around the world outside the borders of the communist bloc.

A large volume of intercepted Soviet communications was assembled on record under the code name 'Venona', dating back to the early years of war. The earlier material was mostly collected by the United States. Britain became an important collector in 1945. Many low-grade Soviet wartime ciphers presented little difficulty to cryptanalysis, and revealed nothing of value. No progress could be made on Venona's high-grade ciphers until after the war.

Soviet cryptography had begun to use one-time pads for top-security traffic since the 1930s. One-time pads are one-off codes, used for a single message and never repeated. They offer no loophole to cryptography, providing the rule of once-only use is observed. During the war a weakness developed in that the Soviets began to make duplicate use of one-time pads. This was counter to the laws of cryptography, but the Soviets were not the only ones to err in this way. In the Soviet Union the practice is said to have started as a result of wartime pressures, but it continued afterwards.

That the dangers were not realised is hardly surprising. At the time the idea that encrypted messages might be preserved for many years to be attacked by a superior generation of cryptanalytic technology, and that the results of decrypting them would still be of consequence, could hardly have occurred.

By 1948 or 1949, a small proportion of high-grade Venona material had yielded to decipherment. The result was to expose wartime Soviet espionage in the United States, in particular against nuclear weapons development. A number of persons were identified as having given vital information away. The most notorious was Klaus Fuchs, who by himself had largely revealed all the vital atomic secrets.

The uncovering of Fuchs came in late 1949, at the same time as it became obvious, from a Soviet weapons test, that the atomic bomb was no longer an American monopoly. Fuchs, convicted in Britain, was more fortunate than the Rosenbergs, sentenced in the United States to execution a couple of years later. Signals intelligence had contributed to a further chilling of public sentiment.

The Consequences of Compromise

The role of signals intelligence in revealing the atomic spies was not publicly disclosed. It was regarded as a matter of the tightest security. The Soviet Union was left to guess what had happened. It was thirty years before the story came out in the West. But it did not take that long for the Soviet Union to realise that its wartime cryptography had been compromised.

There were numerous Soviet agents in British intelligence. Some at least, such as Philby, were aware of the work being done in America on Venona. Already, from 1948, the Soviets ceased making duplicate use of one-time pads. They had been caught by similar techniques as the Germans up to 1945, but managed to draw some eventual profit from the experience. The principles of technology transfer operated.

Although Venona was to the Soviets what Ultra had been to the Germans, the time-lag between collection and decipherment was greater: several years. Such a time-lag would have rendered Ultra useless.

It needs to be remembered that the Ultra breakthrough came because rules were not properly followed; probably, rules never will be properly followed. But the cryptanalytic technology used against Venona was more advanced by several years than the technology developed in Britain for use against Enigma and other German encryption equipment.

In the late 1940s the Soviets faced the problems of bringing their cryptography and cryptanalysis up to date. The proficiency of the Soviet espionage apparatus was destined to become notorious – but immediately after the war it lacked the technology that had been developed in the west.

Competition in Computing

The Soviets knew something of the war-time work done in Britain, from their agents at Bletchley, and they had acquired German cipher machines. Certainly they would have put all this together – along with the bitter experience of the uncovering of the atomic spy network. They would have realised they needed an operation similar to what was being done under UKUSA.

By itself this would have dictated sooner or later a Soviet interest in electronic computing. The beginnings of electronic computing are now dated to the equipment at Bletchley, kept secret so long it was all but forgotten, but after the war the subject began to blossom independently of cryptanalytic origins, with academic and commercial prototypes reported openly in Western technical literature. It must be presumed that there were other, classified developments as well.

By this time Soviet interest had undoubtedly started, therefore to this time dates the second major aspect of the electronics competition between the United States and the Soviet Union: the competition in computing.

The first aspect, as already described, was the competition in basic electronics technology. Its existence was openly realised in the late 1940s, with debates on Soviet progress in ground and airborne radar. The existence of the second aspect was not openly realised so quickly – but there must have been those who did realise it. They would have been those who worked on classified computer projects in the United States in the late 1940s or early 1950s, plus those privy to the world of cryptanalysis.

Eventually it became an open topic. But this took a long time. It only came after the importance of computing began to grip the public imagination in the West during the 1970s.

This was when the solid-state revolution had swept into the art with an explosive effect. In the 1940s and 1950s computing was based on the switching function of the electron tube. Solid-state electronics first compressed the role of the single tube into the transistor, then compressed transistors by the thousand into single integrated circuits, with results that became obvious to every buyer of a home computer.

At this time, the West congratulated itself on being a long way ahead of the Soviet Union in computers and their applications. In commercial, industrial and consumer spheres this was true.[2] But, specifically, in military computing, or military information technology, the position was less obvious.

Reprojection

Western confidence in the superiority of its military electronic technology waned by the early 1970s but from this time was reprojected in the form of a belief in the superiority of its military computing technology. This became a key issue of electronic warfare in the late 1970s and 1980s, returned to in Chapter 14.

The need to introduce electronic computing into cryptanalysis could not have been missed by the Soviets. Without it their capabilities would have languished. In fact Soviet cryptology is highly rated and this reputation would not be deserved without a foundation in computer technology.[3]

It would not however have been the only way in which they put electronics at the service of surveillance and espionage. They, like the West, had many other espionage requirements. Their espionage task was by no means a mirror image of the West's. In some respects it was easier because it was directed against a relatively open society. On the other hand, they had more to learn and needed to gather more information. Methods of gathering it were basically the same.

The Cold War meant that by the late 1940s, there was a profusion of embassies, consulates, trade missions, United Nations offices and other diplomatic centres across the world embedded in highly suspicious host communities. Even before the war such diplomatic entities had been the target for orthodox forms of signals intelligence, through the interception of radio or cable communications. Great issues had already hung on such interceptions. Now, in the late 1940s, the electronic attack on the embassies was joined by the younger but comparable technique of bugging.

Bugging counts as signals intelligence. It is particularly directed to interception of individual conversations under the most varied circumstances.

Initially it was confined to telephone conversations. It was done by tapping lines or junction boxes in telephone networks. In other words it relied on standard telephone engineering. But electronics advances changed this.

Microwaves multiplied the possibilities for bugging. From the 1940s on this dimension of electronic espionage grew rapidly. Later, microelectronics multiplied the possibilities still further, but microelectronics only came in long after microwaves.

Of course, bugging is still entirely possible using simple telephone technology. Nor need this depend on ordinary phone calls. For example, one method is to adapt an ordinary telephone handset so that it transmits down the line at all times, even when still on the hook. Conversations within range of the telephone handset are automatically signalled at all times to whomever has set up the facility. This is usually the host country's security service acting with the co-operation of the host country's telecommunications authority.

Alternatively wires can be concealed in buildings, connected to concealed microphones. This requires preparations in advance, sometimes years in advance, such as when the building is under construction, conversion or maintenance.

The Magic of Microwaves

The most imaginative contribution of the immediate post-war years owed everything to microwaves. It was a device needing no connections and containing no electronics at all.

Such a device both resonates in response to acoustic vibrations, like a diaphragm, and reflects radiowaves, like a radar target. In some fashion most small metallic objects, from ashtrays to filing cabinets, will do these things.

To be usable as a bug however, the object must resonate sufficiently well to modulate radiowaves beamed upon it. It will then transmit whatever conversation is in progress in the room where it is present. The reflected radiation can be received, regardless of ordinary brick walls, at some distance away, using a directional antenna.

Ideally this technique would be usable with such ordinary objects as are present in offices or homes. In that case there would be no necessity to arrange for the introduction of a special object. But ordinary objects are not efficient enough.

The game is therefore to make an efficient device and incorporate it in an innocuous exterior, not likely to excite suspicion. If for some reason it is suspected and examined, the game is up, but in practice lack of wires means that detection may be escaped for a long time. It is activated simply by beaming at it microwaves on the appropriate frequency.

The most celebrated example turned up in the eagle of the Great Seal presented to the American embassy in Moscow. This was disclosed to the world at a United Nations' Security Council debate following the U-2 affair, described later.

The presence of the device was realised because the voices of American diplomats were sometimes mysteriously picked up by radio receivers which happened to be tuned to the working frequency. This is an obvious disadvantage of any bug which relies on broadcasting the information it acquires, rather than transmitting it over wires. Once the technique is realised, such devices are given away by the need to 'bathe' them with a microwave beam.

Later, microelectronics made it possible to make miniaturised radio transmitters which provided an alternative way of transmitting conversations over a sufficient range. This had the advantage of not needing a fairly strong beam of microwaves to be directed at the location being bugged. Of course, every bugging technique is fundamentally capable of being detected, but diplomatic staffs, being human, often fail to be sufficiently vigilant.

From the 1940s on, this dimension of electronic espionage became increasingly important. Techniques have undoubtedly developed. Microwave radiation directed at embassies became commonplace. Every now and again, the United States and the Soviet Union direct bursts of diplomatic recrimination at each other about embassy bugging. In between they each believe they are getting the best of the game. In practice it is necessary for embassies to screen themselves against microwave radiation, or at least set up screened internal areas.

This was another aspect of electronic warfare which came to prominence between 1945 and 1960 and was destined to remain as a crucial issue to the present day.

Still another special aspect was the role played by electronics in the advent of missiles, or as they were then called guided missiles, in distinction from the unguided rocket projectiles which then, as now, are sometimes employed as aircraft armament.

Into the Missile Age

Germany saw the possibilities of missiles before her defeat in 1945, developing not only the V-2 ballistic missile but the 'Wasserfall' and 'Rheintochter' ground-launched anti-aircraft missiles referred to in Chapter 10. But the technology was premature.

Ten years later, it was moving rapidly ahead. The span of application was enormous. At one end the V-2 type weapon was being enlarged, equipped with a nuclear warhead, and turned first into the intermediate range and then into the intercontinental, ballistic missile. Typical of the first category was the US 'Thor', and of the second, the Soviet 'Sapwood', or SS-6. Electronics was essential to launch control and course guidance.

At the other end, small air-launched missiles promised an answer to the increasingly difficult problem of destroying enemy aircraft. Combat speeds were climbing from the subsonic range typical of the Korean War to the Mach 2 range typical of the early 1960s. From now on, aimed fire by machine guns or canon would only be effective against easy targets.

Rocket propulsion and aerodynamic control of missiles were well understood, but the hurdle to be jumped was electronics able to track the target aircraft and generate the control signals, all packaged within severely confined space. This problem was solved in two alternative types of guidance head. One used radar, miniaturised thanks to higher frequencies. The other leapt to another part of the electromagnetic spectrum altogether – the infra-red.

The Debut of Infra-Red

This was infra-red's real debut on the battlefield. Many previous attempts had been made, dating back to the Second World War and before it, to use infra-red for military purposes. Night vision devices had appeared for driving in darkness for example. Germany was the most active pioneer. But it would not have made much difference to the Second World War if infra-red had not existed. By the early 1960s however infra-red had found a place. It had entered the military inventory as one of the most reliable technologies for target-finding.

From now on the jet fighter was armed with radar or infra-red homing missiles or both and the classic western examples date from this era – 'Sparrow' and 'Sidewinder', both still in use today.

The radar homing missile generally relied on the radar carried by the fighter to continue to illuminate the target. It detected the radiation reflected by the target and homed on to it. This technique, used by Sparrow, is called semi-active guidance.

The infra-red homing missile detects and homes on to the main source of infra-red radiation, the heat emitted by the aircraft's engines. This technique, used by Sidewinder, is passive homing.

It has become common for a single fighter to carry a mix of radar and infra-red types. Infra-red missiles give excellent results, but are ideally used against short-range visually-identified targets. In practice these are the commonest type of target. Cloud is a barrier for infra-red. Radar guided missiles are unaffected by cloud.[4] Experience suggests that for interceptors to launch missiles at targets which cannot be visually identified is a risky proceeding. For this reason the aerial battlefield is largely within the grasp of infra-red.

Compact Warheads

The air-to-ground guided missile was yet another weapon pioneered by Germany, but before its time. After the Korean War it rapidly acquired strategic importance, for thanks to the progress made in nuclear weapons, atomic and thermonuclear warheads shrank in size and missiles of great destructive power could be built for bombers to carry.

Already by the early 1960s the B-52 was equipped with the 'Hound Dog', a strategic 'stand-off' nuclear missile. This meant it could be released hundreds of kilometres away from the target and would complete a programme flight, thus avoiding the need for the bomber to penetrate all the way. High precision was not necessary. A corresponding Soviet combination was the Bear with the 'Kipper' missile. Tactical missiles of this kind, for use against point targets such as ships, brought the revival of the German television guidance concept to provide the higher accuracy required.

But of all the types of missile which entered service in the late 1950s, none had more immediate significance than the ground-to-air type, dedicated to point or area defence. It was destined to play an increasing role in defence against air attack.

Target Tracking and Missile Combat

By comparison with the air-to-air missile, the target had to be acquired at considerable range, often frontally as it approached. Surveillance radar did this. The missile required high initial acceleration to gain altitude and speed. At any defended point, several missiles had to be ready on launchers. Controlling the missile on its way to the target had to be the job of a different kind of radar. One ground-based target track and control radar could handle a sequence of missile launchings.

The most celebrated ground-to-air missile was the Soviet 'Guideline', or SA-2 – really a system comprising a launch site (typically with six missile launchers) and a central control radar, with the code-name 'Fansong'. Originating about the mid-1950s, Guideline was destined to become familiar to the West.

Conventional ground-based surveillance radar was normally used to detect the target aircraft and pass on target coordinates to the SA-2 site. The Fansong radar would then look for the target itself, and follow it constantly. It was an example of a fire-control or target-tracking radar. As already mentioned in Chapter 8, this type of radar differs from the conventional surveillance radar in the way it operates, and it is appropriate to enlarge on the earlier reference.

Conventional surveillance radar completes regular scans around the compass. For example, if rotating once in six seconds, it registers the position of an aircraft at six-second intervals. Of course, it can track the aircraft this way; in fact it can simultaneously track many aircraft. This is 'track-while-scan'.

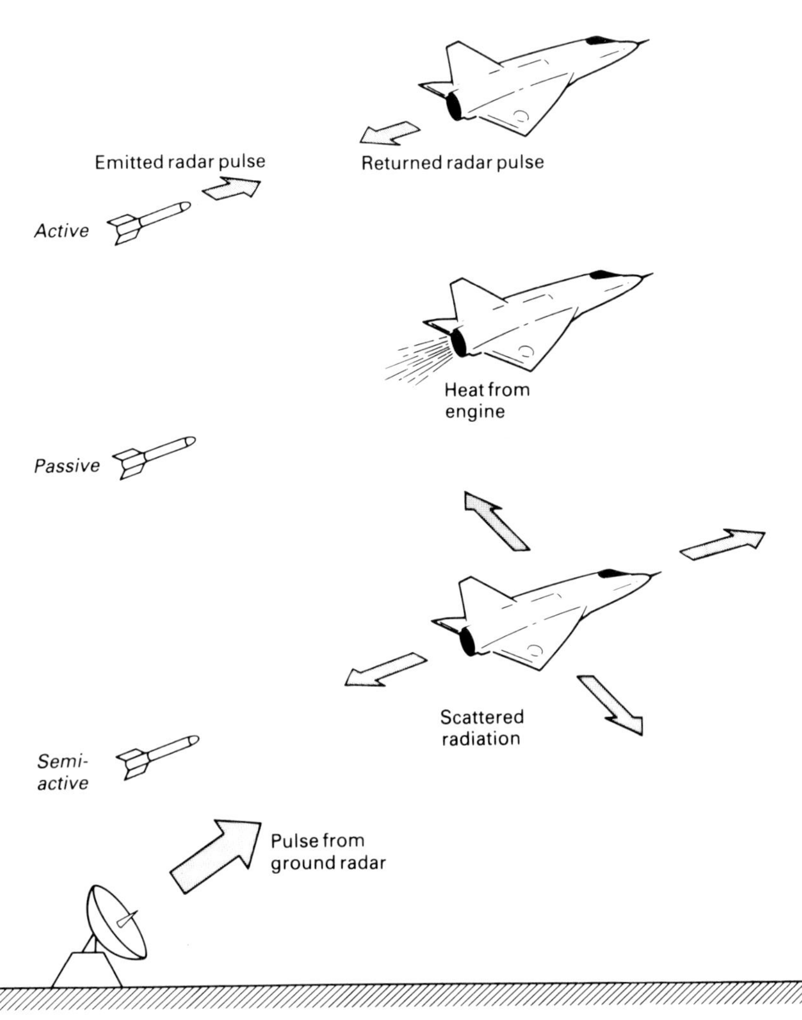

Fig. 12.1 **Active, Passive and Semi-Active Homing** The top illustration shows active radar homing – the missile emits radar pulses and homes on to the reflected signal. Passive homing (middle) is typical of the infra-red guided missile, homing on to the heat emitted by aircraft engines. In semi-active homing (bottom) the target is illuminated by radar, for example on the ground or in an attacking aircraft, and the missile homes on to the scattered radiation.

But if it is necessary to engage an aircraft by firing a missile or flak at it, positions up-dated at six-second intervals are inadequate. The radar has to keep the aircraft under constant observation, to register whatever sudden manoeuvres it may make. This is the job of fire-control radar. There are various ways it can work. Obviously it is necessary for the radar to be aimed constantly at a limited sector of the sky.

Conical Scanning

Special scanning systems for target tracking radars were foreshadowed by the German Wurzburg, which used conical scanning to enable it to keep an aircraft centred in the beam. But their importance increased with the advent of missiles.

Wurzburg's conical scanning was vulnerable to countermeasures. In conical scanning the actual beam rotates in a cone around the axis along which the radar is looking. If the aircraft is not on the axis, the echo will be stronger in one position. The radar repositions its axis so that the echo becomes of constant strength regardless of where the actual beam is around the cone. But an aircraft targeted by a conical scanning radar may mimic the radar transmission, introducing an artificial variation of signal strength. Instead of correctly recognising when it has the aircraft centred up, the radar will look to one side.

Monopulse Scanning

To defeat this, monopulse scanning grew out of conical scanning. The radar transmits a pulse in the direction in which its axis is pointing. Separate receive-only antennas are positioned in two pairs, for azimuth and elevation, above and below and to either side of the transmitting antenna.

The aircraft's position is obtained by comparing the strength of the echoes received in each of the antennas. This is a simultaneous comparison which can be made in principle off a single transmitted pulse. It offers far less scope to countermeasures. There is no scanning transmission to be detected and exploited.

Scan On Receive Only

Fansong exemplified another technique. It aimed at an area of sky about 10 degrees square. It had two fan-shaped beams, one of which swept vertically and the other horizontally. Between the two, the target aircraft was located. Like monopulse tracking, Fansong was workable with the scanning function performed only in receiving mode – 'Scan On Receive Only'.

The missile itself carried a radar beacon, separately registered by the radar.

Thus the radar provided the position and speed of the aircraft and corresponding information about the missile, and the command system had the task of vectoring the missile on to the aircraft through radio instructions. The missile could be detonated by radio or by proximity fuse, as well as impact which was probably unlikely.

The Guideline missile was about two tons in weight and flew at approximately Mach 3.5. It had endurance out to about 40 kilometres range. The Fansong radar worked in the SHF band – near either 3 or 5 gigahertz. The system could handle targets up to high altitude. Up to a point, the higher the better: the radar worked under the most favourable conditions and the interception trajectory would be most easily achieved.

The Ground-to-Air Missile Threat

Ground-to-air missiles posed a severe threat to aircraft. They became indispensable to ground defences. In the United States inventory, 'Hawk' was the counterpart to Guideline. France and the United Kingdom also produced such missiles. Mobile types, in which all the equipment could be carried on gound vehicles, now appeared. Mobility made counter measures more difficult.

Ship-borne versions became, in theory at least, indispensable for naval defence. The theory was not tested in practice until the Falklands conflict of 1982. But the pattern of global tensions at the time of ground-to-air missiles' arrival was such that the Soviet types were destined to see the most service.

The Air Defence Requirement Reviewed

During the mid-1950s the increase of tension and the Soviet acquisition of nuclear weapons recreated for the countries of the West the air defence requirement which, after the defeat of Germany, had temporarily become the sole problem of the Soviet Union. The air invasion threat familiar to Europe in the Second World War came for the first time to the United States.

The Americans created a defensive radar system which was an evolutionary step beyond the British Chain Home system and the German Kammhuber Line. The system took account of the fact that for air defence the United States and Canada were a geographic unity. It was based on three radar lines, the Pinetree, the Mid-Canada, and the Distant Early Warning, the latter being in the far north of Canada and Greenland. On its flanks, the system included offshore radar platforms – 'Texas towers'.

SAGE and NORAD

The communications linking of such a vast network and its executive coordination with interceptors and other means of anti-air defence was a task far more massive than the one Britain had faced in linking Chain Home radar sites to filter rooms and fighter control headquarters. It was set up under the acronym SAGE – Semi-Automatic Ground Environment. In 1957 an integrated command was formed covering both the United States and Canada – NORAD, North American Air Defence.

Chain Home Revived

In Britain, the orginal homeland of strategic radar defence, the renewed threat was met by reviving the Chain Home radar stations much as they had existed at the end of 1945. Only the Chain Home sites survived to permit resurrection; the rest of Britain's war-time radar had gone. Mobile radars were planned to supplement Chain Home. These were projects VAST and ROTOR (1956).[5]

UKADGE and NADGE

But Chain Home was technically obsolete even during the Second World War and it was quickly realised that new radar was needed. A massive and powerful centimetric radar was developed, the Type 80.

The NATO countries began to create a radar chain from the north of Europe to the south. Eventual British and NATO counterparts to SAGE were United Kingdom Air Defence Ground Environment and NATO Air Defence Ground Environment (UKADGE and NADGE).

At this time, the Soviet Union was undoubtedly strengthening early warning radar along her periphery, although with such an enormous boundary a continuous peripheral radar ring was not possible. Defence needed to concentrate on key inner areas, of which Moscow was only one. Moscow was defended by the SA-1 ground-to-air missile system. A crucial issue for United States military planning became the technical characteristics and locations of all the Soviet radar defences. It was necessary to plan counter measures to support a strategic bombing attack.

'The Ace in the Hole'

At this time the 'ace in the hole' theory of electronic warfare went into the ascendant. The outcome of a nuclear war would depend on the first hours or minutes. Swift nuclear strikes became the successor to *blitzkrieg* as the means of reaching a decision. This policy in turn depended on the strategic bomber force's ability to penetrate and reach its targets. Long range missiles could unquestionably reach their targets but in the mid-1950s the main deliverer of nuclear warheads was still overwhelmingly the bomber force.

The chief factor in determining its ability to penetrate was electronic warfare, rendering the defending electronics useless. In sudden emergency, American electronics had to seize supremacy and hold it for a matter of hours, theoretically until all was over. Everything depended on preparations. Superior systems had to be ready for surprise deployment. Electronic warfare had to show itself the trump up the sleeve, the ace in the hole.

This was the logical development from the surprise use of window in the Second World War. With window however the consequences were not final and the other side had time to find a response. From now on, it was intended that this time would be lacking. The final military solution would be, it was thought, the final political solution.

Although the 'ace in the hole' role was a new one, born of the nuclear threat, it was applicable to conventional war. Electronic warfare showed itself as the ace in the hole in the Arab-Israeli wars described in Chapter 13. It contributed to spectacular outcomes, but there were no final political solutions, and therefore the military solutions could not be final either.

ELINT and COMINT

In the circumstances of the mid-1950s, it became vital to maintain an accurate assessment of Soviet radar, to understand the way its technology was developing and to know every position of deployment. This was attempted in many ways. Recording information about radar deployments and emissions is an aspect of 'electronic intelligence' often call ELINT.

Electronic intelligence is not confined to radar. It relates to gathering information about all the opponent's electronic resources, including communications by radio and cable. Much of this falls into signals intelligence. There is yet another term in use, 'communications intelligence'. COMINT. In practice these terms owe more to tradition than to logic and it is profitless to try and distinguish accurately between them.[6]

Signals intelligence tends to relate to radio and cable communications, while electronic intelligence is used more comprehensively, or with specific reference to radar. Inevitably there is an overlap. The concept of the 'electronic order of battle' is very broad, and cannot be confined to radar; it means all the electronic resources which are ready to be employed in conflict, and their modes of use, whether on a local, tactical or a strategic scale.

The aim of electronic intelligence may be stated as discovering information about the other side's electronic order of battle. Signals intelligence, on the other hand, was a military institution long before electronics intelligence was recognised.

In retrospect, British efforts early in the Second World War to discover the nature of German bombing systems were electronic intelligence, though they were not understood as such at the time and no deliberate policy of seeking electronic intelligence had been formulated. It was spontaneous and often the result of one person's intellectual enterprise.[7] Britain's pre-war lack of electronic intelligence exacted a high price; the British war effort never fully recovered from it.

Much of Britain's electronic intelligence came through signals intelligence, in the form of decoded German references to radar or bombing systems.

Sky Spies

Gathering electronic intelligence falls very often to 'ferret' aircraft, which are sent to fly wherever they may perform their tasks. Soviet radar emissions could be recorded from outside the Soviet frontiers. But normal radar emissions do not tell the whole story. They do not reveal the full radar 'order of battle'. The defending country does not show its hand any more than it has to. It is more revealing to record what happens when an aircraft intrudes into vital airspace. Ferrets generally perform by flying in legitimate air space, but from time to time richer hauls are made by over-the-border incursions.

As with signals intelligence, this electronic espionage became the hot battleground in the midst of cold war. During the 1950s incidents began to mount in which American aircraft were attacked and in some cases shot down near the borders of the Soviet Union or other communist countries, generally over sea but sometimes over land. The Baltic was one area of concentration for such incidents, but they occurred to an even greater extent in the Far East.[8] In each of the years 1953 and 1954 there were at least three such incidents, in 1958 four.

In the latter year, for example, on 27 June a C-118 aircraft was shot down by Migs over Armenia, one of the constituent Soviet republics; nine crew members were returned. On 2 September a C-130 was shot down over the same republic; six dead crewmen were returned but 11 were missing and their fate has remained a mystery. This incident was not disclosed until eleven days later. On 17 November there were incidents over the Baltic Sea and the Sea of

Japan, in each case an RB-47 being attacked by Migs without damage or casualties.

It is not necessary to believe that in every case the aircraft was engaged in electronics reconnaissance. It is unlikely that a planeload of seventeen people would be needed for such a purpose; the suggestion has been made that the 11 missing from the incident of 2 September 1953 over Armenia were in fact parachuted down before the aircraft was attacked to establish contact with Armenian nationalists. But the conventional assumption is that in the majority of cases electronic reconnaissance provided the motive for whatever incursion occurred.

The U-2 Story

While this tide of incidents was mounting, the United States embarked on a programme to produce a reconnaissance aircraft that could fly over the Soviet Union or China at heights at which it would be invulnerable. The Lockheed U-2 was the result, history's most famous spy plane. A programme of reconnaissance overflights over the Soviet Union was commenced in 1956. The U-2 was equipped for both photographic and electronic reconnaissance.

As an espionage aircraft, the U-2 could not escape observation by radar. The Soviets knew when it was intruding. This provocative aspect was helpful to its function, for it could record not only the emissions of ground surveillance radars, but the emissions of airborne interception and ground-to-air missile radars when attempts were made, as they most surely would be, to shoot it down.

The inevitable happened. In May 1960 a U-2 attempted an ambitious traverse of the Soviet Union, crossing from Pakistan to Norway. Deep inside the country, near Sverdlovsk, it was brought down by a Guideline missile.

Other incidents in the hot battle of electronic intelligence had precipitated diplomatic clashes of a kind. But for a number of reasons the U-2 incident transcended everything. The aircraft was brought down, not over coastal waters or border regions, but 2,500 kilometres inside the frontier.

Moreover it happened just days before a major summit conference was due to open in Paris between the President of the United States and the Soviet Union's First Secretary. The British Prime Minister and the French President were to participate. It was intended to halt mounting tensions. How well it did so can be imagined.

The United States had not known how deep inside the Soviet Union the U-2 had been lost, nor what had happened to its pilot. The assumption was made, for reasons good or bad, that the pilot could no longer be alive.

The American State Department was put in the position of issuing statements to the effect that the intrusion was accidental and that there had never been any intention to violate the Soviet Union's borders. These rebounded when it was revealed that the pilot, Francis Gary Powers, had been captured alive.

The planned summit collapsed before it had begun. The hot battleground in the midst of the Cold War threatened to rupture its diplomatic constraints.

13

New Frontiers

THE IMMEDIATE effect of the U-2 incident was the conversion of a summit planned with hope of improved relations into a confrontation. Out of it the Soviets got the minimal satisfaction of an American promise not to attempt further incursions.

The promise cost nothing, even though incredulity was expressed that an aircraft flying as high as the U-2 could be brought down by a ground-launched missile. Truly, the event was unprecedented.

But the general fact to be recognised was that electronics and rocket propulsion technology had advanced to a degree which made all aircraft vulnerable in some measure to ground-launched missiles. High altitude was no longer sufficient protection. The point was not contested. Both as a technological achievement and as a landmark in the progress of electronics in warfare, Guideline, no less than the U-2, had gone into history.

The political outcome of the affair was unfortunate in the light of all the ominous developments of the 1950s. If ever the stage had been set for Armageddon, it was now. The world had polarised while entering a new era of fearful military technology. If ever a constructive summit conference could have been hoped for, this was the occasion.

Into Space

Yet the hope was not well-founded. Sooner or later crisis had to come. A build-up of Soviet strategic ballistic missiles obviously threatened. Reconnaissance of Soviet territory was all but indispensable to American security. Fortunately the U-2 incident came at a time when an alternative to reconnaissance aircraft was becoming feasible. By banishing them from Soviet skies, the U-2 incident ensured that the military frontier would move out into space. Reconnaissance satellites had to go where aircraft could no longer go.

Theoretically satellites were not invulnerable, but the day when they could be intercepted was distant. Moreover the right of satellites to overfly all areas of the globe had been implicitly asserted by the Soviet Union in orbiting the world's first satellite. It could not be disavowed, even though it had become of more immediate advantage to the United States. To satellites would fall the future functions of both photographic and electronic reconnaissance.

Much is argued about extending warfare into space. In practice, warfare reached this stage with the deployment of the V-2 in 1944. Space had become an additional ocean across which weapons could travel.

What happened subsequently was, in essence, only the revival of the technology, with the re-introduction of ballistic missiles in the middle 1950s. After that came its elaboration into the military exploitation of satellites from the early 1960s.

It can be argued that ballistic missiles increased international tension by cutting down warning times as compared with the days when nuclear warheads could only be delivered by aircraft. But otherwise the advance into space decreased tension, by providing a means whereby each side could observe the military preparations of the other. Such a means was the only foundation for any sense of security and any confidence in reaching arms limitation agreements.

New Peaks for Electronics

For military electronics, space was an enormous addition to its realm, unquestionably the biggest enlargement in its entire record. Satellite technology was almost all-electronic.

Typically, satellites comprised a core of electronic circuitry, with instruments or sensors to acquire information, solar panels or nuclear devices to supply power, and antennas to receive commands and transmit the data gathered. Communications satellites received transmissions from the ground, amplified and retransmitted them. With all satellites, small thrusters and fuel supplies for maintaining orientation and orbital postioning were under electronic control.

Meeting the Challenges of a Harsh Environment

A new branch of electronics construction arose to ensure high reliability over long periods in the harsh environment of space. This was demanding in many ways, for example the repeated sudden transitions from direct heating in the sun's rays to the cold of complete darkness as the satellite passed into and out of the earth's shadow.

Moreover, miniaturisation and low power consumption were at a premium, for weight was costly and the power-producing solar panels, although large, were limited in size. Fortunately solid-state electronics had arrived; without it the challenge could hardly have been met.

But by itself, one new breed of electronics was not enough. Matching the new electronics in orbit was the new generation of ground-based electronics required for tracking and communications.

Satellite tracking primarily depended on radio. Signals were emitted by the satellite, either spontaneously or in reponse to interrogation from the ground. Radio could determine the satellite's position in time and space, as well as pass commands for operation and receive information which the satellite had collected. Obviously, the frequencies in use had to be those which would not be imprisoned under the ionosphere.

VHF, UHF and SHF would all pass through the ionosphere, following line-of-sight paths. The main premium however was on SHF. With its large bandwidth it had a high information-carrying capacity. Highly directional beams could be transmitted and received with small antennas, which were convenient for spacecraft.

On the other hand in some applications it was an advantage if the signal had a tendency to travel within the ionosphere. Satellites in low earth orbit are within the ionosphere and HF gave extended periods of radio contact.

Another effect became important: the ionosphere could rotate the plane of polarisation. Antennas not restricted by polarisation to receiving in a particular plane were necessary.

But space did not only need radio tracking. It was receiving other visitors, more transitory than satellites: the warheads of ballistic missiles. Means of tracking these were needed for the sake of early warning systems and anti-ballistic-missile defences.

Tracking Warheads

Unlike satellites, warheads were not co-operative. Radio could not track them. The challenge they posed was addressed to radar. It was an unprecedented challenge: to work at enormous ranges and against tiny targets. It would only be solved by a new generation of radar technology.

Ballistic missile early warning radar aimed to see rockets climbing after launch, as soon as sufficient height had been reached to bring them above the horizon. Some factors helped.

The rocket body alone was generally comparable in size with typical airborne targets, while the long plume of incandescent exhaust gases greatly increased the radar echo. Incandescent gas is highly conductive, reflecting rather like a sheet of metal. Moreover the target was not concealed in clutter; there was nothing near it to reflect the pulse with a similar delay in return.

These helpful factors were offset by the operational range of thousands of miles, compared with the two or three hundred miles which was radar's previous maximum. Increase of range reduces the strength of the radar return by the fourth power law, so if the range becomes ten times greater, the echo is reduced by a factor of ten multiplied by itself four times. That is, in the drastic proportion of ten thousand to one.

Consequently the first need was for installations of enormous antenna size and power output. These alone could detect distant ascending missiles and work out their launch trajectories. In this way real attacks could be distinguished from harmless test launches. Impact areas could be predicted. Twenty or thirty minutes warning could be given.

In Computer Alliance

Size and power were still not enough. There was a compelling need to produce results fast under desperate circumstances. This highlighted another facet of the new radar generation: its alliance with the computer. Only computer processing of the radar return could discriminate real from false alarms and predict impact areas, providing maximum warning time, little enough as it would be. But the computer's contribution to radar was not related solely to the missile threat. It was more widely based.

It is appropriate to recall that the first military alliance of computer technology was with radio in the Second World War. As is now known, it was the need to apply rapid methods to the decrypting of intercepted radio signals that forced the pioneer development of electronic computers. However, this development in signals intelligence remained secret while, after the war, computer technology began to develop overtly, for academic, commercial, industrial and military purposes. This process led to the appearance of the mainframe computer.

A Dramatic Increase in Capability

The second military alliance of computer technology came between the mainframe computer and radar in the late 1950s and early 1960s. The mainframe computer brought a dramatic increase to radar's capability, equalling that which the prototype electronic computers of the 1940s had contributed to the collection of signals intelligence from radio.

From now onwards, information could be extracted from the radar return in ways which were impossible when, as in the Second World

War, it was directly displayed on the screen of a cathode ray tube for inspection by a human operator. As the mainframe computer was succeeded by the minicomputer, compact enough to be harnessed individually to ground-based surveillance radars, the significance of this change spread.

Radar had developed using either of two technical approaches: pulses or continuous waves. Pulsed radar was chiefly important, enabling the target's range to be found, and it dominated radar history. Continuous wave radar, using Doppler effect to find the target's velocity in towards or away from the radar, was of subsidiary importance.

But these two approaches could be blended into pulse-Doppler radar, capable of finding both range and velocity. This development began with Germany's efforts to overcome chaff in 1943. It led to moving target indication, a powerful means of discriminating the real target amidst clutter.

Synthetic Displays

With the advent of the computer, pulse-Doppler radar incorporating moving target indication truly came of age. The task of recognising targets and separating them from window and clutter was taken from the human operator and given to the computer. Radar began to evolve towards purely synthetic displays, generated by the computer itself. The display mimicked the plan position indicator, but presented only the targets and eliminated the interference which formerly could make the display difficult or impossible for the eye to interpret.

At the same time, map outlines could be superimposed, out of the computer's memory, so that the position of the target over sea or land or in relation to military objectives could be instantly seen. If needed, small areas could be enlarged to occupy the whole display, the equivalent of switching from a small-scale map to a large-scale one.

Still more significant, the input from secondary radar could be written against the target traces, in alphanumeric symbols, labelling them according to the information being provided through a recognised system of codes.

The operator's task was made easier and more effective. A single operator might be able to control tens of different interceptions, whereas in the days of the Second World War, the operator of ground-controlled interception radar would probably handle no more than two simultaneous interceptions of targets by fighters.

The computer facilitated other techniques, designed to make radar more effective and less vulnerable to countermeasures. For example, by 'compressing' and 'coding' the pulse, so that only the genuine echo would be recognised and accepted while bogus echoes would be rejected. These developments came gradually through the late 1950s, the 1960s and 1970s. They began to arrive in time to help meet the severe though specialised demands of ballistic missile radar.

Anti-Ballistic Missile Radar

In additon to ballistic missile early warning radar, anti-ballistic missile radar was developed, with a different task. It has to find the warhead on its own, after separation from the launch rocket, either when it was already beginning to re-enter the atmosphere, or as long before it re-entered as possible, in order to provide data for the launch of an interceptor missile.

The warhead at this time is a much smaller target that the launch rocket. However, anti-ballistic missile radar defends a specific point or area and only engages warheads approaching it. For this reason the range is shorter, from tens up to a couple of hundred miles, comparable with air defence radars.

Decoys

The target is at high elevation in the sky. High elevation is favourable to radar; sources of confusion or clutter are fewer. Aircraft may be at high elevation, but they are only at short range compared to ballistic warheads. This separates the returns. The only likely clutter is decoys, lightweight inflatable imitation warheads with the same radar reflection characteristics. Separating from the launch rocket at the same time as the warhead, these fly just as well as the heavier warhead in the vacuum of space. They make discrimination impossible until the atmosphere begins to retard them and a difference of velocity appears. They are then detectable by the Doppler effect of a frequency change to the reflected signal.

During re-entry the heavy warhead creates a sheath of incandescent air which, like rocket exhaust, strongly reflects the radar pulse. By this time it has parted company from the decoys.

Detection

The radars developed for rocket launch and warhead detection can also detect satellites in low earth orbit. But satellites, unlike warheads and missiles, may go well out of radar range. In geostationary orbit, at 40,000 kilometres above the earth's surface, a satellite may be impossible to detect by radar, because of the fourth-power law. Only the satellite's 'owner', knowing the exact frequencies to use and the orientation of the antennas, can track and communicate with it by radio. Deep space is a good hiding place.

While ground-based radio and radar were responding to the challenge of warheads and satellites, satellites turned their attention to ground-based radio and radar. They became ideal 'ferrets' to spot the locations and record the characteristics of military radio and radar installations.

Not only could they perform the typical tactical function of gathering information in swift passes at low altitude; they could, from the much higher altitude of geostationary orbit, steadily acquire signals intelligence from specific geographical areas.

Intelligence Gathering

The development of these satellite intelligence-gathering capabilities became a major theme of electronic warfare from the early 1960s and continues without interruption to the present day. Satellite intrusions are not of themselves provocative, but aircraft intrusions coordinated with ferret satellite passes can still provoke defensive electronic reactions for the ferrets to record.

Long-Range Communications

Satellites did still more. They brought a major change to ground-to-ground radio. The relay satellite at last offered an alternative to HF for long-range point-to-point military communications.

No longer was it necessary to rely on the ionosphere to reflect radiowaves down to earth at places far beyond the horizon. A relay satellite sufficiently high to be visible from both the transmitting and receiving locations could link them instead.

The quality of transmission was higher. SHF was the ideal frquency band, offering greatest bandwidth. The geostationary orbit was generally best, except for communications with places at high latitude, when the satellite appears very low on the horizon, but other types of orbit could counter this problem.

Surveillance

To radar, satellites offered a dramatic new vantage point. Orbital radar is highly specific against surface ships: ships, being large masses of metal, show up well against surrounding water. A small number of orbiting radar stations can record the movements of all ships on the oceans. But radar needs high power, higher in general than can be delivered by solar panels. Radar surveillance from orbit demanded the orbiting of nuclear reactors. This course was followed by the Soviet Union – to its embarrassment when more than one reactor-equipped satellite went out of control.

Virtually all this technology was embryonic, or implicit, by the late 1950s. Only time was needed to bring it into being, on a scale which was destined to stretch from months to ten or fifteen years. Some of it was beginning to appear in operational form even when the U-2 was shot down.

'Nautilus'

Yet another dimension of war was emerging. This was the nuclear-powered submarine. The first nuclear-powered submarine, launched by the United States, the *Nautilus*, was soon followed by a Soviet equivalent in the mid-1950s. From the early 1960s, the nuclear-powered submarine carrying strategic nuclear missiles, capable of being fired submerged, began to enter the navies of the United States and Britain, and later the Soviet Union and France.

This weapon system was a revolution in itself. It was a totally different means of dispersing, concealing and protecting the nuclear deterrent. It quickly became one of the three basic legs of the 'strategic triad', along with nuclear-armed aviation and ground-based nuclear missiles. It put unprecedented responsibility on to navies. It also marked a watershed in the development of anti-submarine warfare and sonar. The possibilities of concealment open to submarines with virtually unlimited underwater endurance and higher submerged speeds than the majority of surface warships gave them a large measure of invulnerability.

They were best stalked, when stalking was possible at all, by other 'hunter-killer' nuclear submarines. Sonar, hitherto the junior partner of radio and radar, acquired equal status, for which it was hardly ready. The improvement of sonar technology became a new challenge to electronics, drawing massive research and investment, cloaked by more intensive security than that applied to any other branch of electronic warfare. The attempt to keep track of hostile nuclear submarines led to the emplacement of passive, listening arrays on the ocean floor – the SOSUS system of the United States.

In general, it remained true that the underwater world was dominated by acoustic signals and excluded electromagnetic waves. But the effort to communicate with submarines submerged for months on end focused attention on the ability of extremely low frequencies, measured in tens or hundreds of hertz, to penetrate seawater to some depth. The drawbacks were considerable: enormous power requirement, enormous antenna size, and extremely slow message transmission. Nevertheless some installations of this type were built.

The Dawn of a New Era

In many different ways the end of the 1950s and beginning of the 1960s was a profoundly significant time. A new and deeper awareness of the role of electronics in warfare emerged.

Understanding grew that what had happened in the past was not a series of haphazardly occurring electronic inventions conveniently applicable to war, but an evolutionary progression of developments with laws that could be formulated. It was realised that these laws were based on physical science and would always govern what was possible. Electronic warfare, it was realised, might be analysable and predictable to a degree unknown in other military spheres.

Symbolic of this realisation was the appearance of what is probably the foundation classic of the subject, *Principles of Electronic Warfare*, by Robert J. Schlesinger, published in the United States in 1961.

'Instruments of Darkness'

While Schlesinger's book was essentially a textbook, concerned with techniques and the underlying physical and mathematical principles, the same awakening attitude to electronic warfare was reflected in a different book, published five years later, in 1966, in Britain.

It was not the first literary treatment of electronic warfare, for this was given by Sir Winston Churchill within his six-volume opus *The Second World War*. But the new book, *Instruments of Darkness*, by Alfred Price, for the first time recognised that the electronics and countermeasures of air warfare from 1939 to 1945 formed a selective aspect of military history demanding attention in its own right, just as for example the history of tank warfare did. The book's title was a Shakespearian quotation epitomising the fact that the role of electronic warfare in the air applied pre-eminently to night-time conflict. Like *Principles of Electronic Warfare*, Price's book became a classic.

A New Boost to Momentum

Possibly, if the planned summit meeting between President Eisenhower and First Secretary Khrushchev in 1960 had been completed successfully, it would have slowed the military momentum of the 1950s, but the U-2 incident ensured the opposite result: the momentum was boosted, and with special orientation towards space and electronics.

The role of electronics grew as other roles declined. The technical capabilities of the Superpowers in making hydrogen bombs and rockets, and aircraft to carry them, became increasingly difficult to distinguish. Sizes, weights and warhead yields might be argued, but without very much comfort.

America's Lead

The one arena where the United States confidently claimed superiority was electronics. Space enlarged this arena many times. Consequently, military advantage in electronics became even more important than it had been in the 1950s. It became the principal support to the United States' economic advantage.

The lines along which American military strength would develop were now determined. Sophisticated weaponry and means of surveillance multiplied, owing almost everything to electronics. Simultaneously, overwhelming preponderance was built up in numbers of nuclear warheads and means to deliver them. The doctrine of massive nuclear retaliation arrived.

The Cuban Crisis

The Soviet Union's economy did not permit an immediate ambition to level the numbers. But an opportunity to achieve something of the same kind offered when Cuba went communist. In October 1962 the Soviet Union stationed numerous ballistic missiles on the island. Smaller and far less costly than intercontinental ballistic missiles, they nevertheless brought targets throughout the United States under threat of attack at much shorter range and with much reduced warning time.

This implied a sudden tilt in the balance of power and deterrence. It was rejected by the United States. The result was the Cuba Missile Crisis of October 1962, two years and four months after the U-2 incident.

Crises were only to be expected in the world situation passed down by the 1950s, but while the U-2 incident was of a kind to resolve itself into nothing more disagreeable than increased mutual ill-will, no such hopeful outlook was obvious when President Kennedy told the Soviet Union to take its rockets out of Cuba.

Humanity could have been arriving at the end of the road. But the President had little choice.

The ostensible purpose of the Soviet installations was to deter an American invasion of Cuba aimed at destroying the communist regime. In fact they provoked an immediate threat of invasion to destroy the missiles.

This outcome highlighted what is always the weakness of nuclear deterrence. The purpose of military strength is to give confidence, particularly in the hour of need, but nuclear strength becomes less and less comforting as the crunch draws near. The premium on first strike grows. The premium on restraint goes negative. This is true for both sides. Each side's confidence in its own strength drains away at the time when it is most necessary.

A Quid Pro Quo

Confronted by the United States' naval superiority, the Soviet Union was sufficiently wise to agree to remove the missiles. The diplomatic *quid pro quo* was a guarantee that if they were voluntarily removed Cuba would not be invaded. In return for humiliation, the Soviet Union obtained something to claim as useful.

Electronic warfare was never a crucial issue during the crisis, even though the Guideline ground-to-air missile system confirmed its ability to shoot down U-2s by claiming another victim.

The Soviet Union Turns to the Sea

However just as the U-2 incident obliged the United States to embark on the new ocean of space, so the Cuban confrontation obliged the Soviet Union to embark on the old ocean of water, remedying its weakness with the most sustained build-up of surface naval power in Russian history.

This build-up thrust an undoubted challenge at the Soviet electronics industry, for the modern surface warship is the most intense point concentration of electronics combat equipment that exists.

It is hardly surprising that one man, Admiral Gorshkov, is associated both with the transformation of the Soviet navy into one of the world's most powerful surface fleets, and with the most famous aphorism of electronic warfare: 'the next war will be won by the side that controls the electromagnetic spectrum'.

The appearance of the Soviet surface navy gives the strongest visual confirmation of the existence and strength of the Soviet military electronics industry.

The Cuban Missile Crisis passed into history, like the U-2 incident, leaving the world unscathed, though seeded with another direction of arms development. Meanwhile given the unresolved tension it was inevitable that the storm would break out again. It came just two years later.

Vietnam – A Lightning Conductor

This was the war in Vietnam. It became a long contest. While it lasted, it proved to be something of a lightning conductor, drawing the confrontational enthusiasms of the Superpowers into an arena where political doctrines and conventional weaponry were tested without igniting global conflict. When eventually it subsided, the world was relaxing into an era of détente.

Begun in August 1964 and ended by the Paris agreement of January 1973, it was destined to be, amongst other things, a passage of arms in electronic warfare on a scale not witnessed since the Second World War.

The conflict in Vietnam was a legacy from the former French colony of Indo-China, surrendered in the Second World War to Japanese control. Vietnam was one of four nations to emerge on Indo-Chinese territory, the others being Laos, Cambodia, and Thailand. After the war France attempted to reassert authority in Vietnam, but retired following defeat at Dien-Bien-Phu in the north of the partitioned country. Support of the southern part against the militant north eventually fell to the United States. From 1964, American resistance to the Viet Cong, the guerrillas operating in the south, escalated into formal war with North Vietnam as well.

Aviation played a major role. In the south, helicopters gave close support to ground forces engaged against guerrillas. Strategic B-52 bombers heavily bombed areas where high guerrilla concentrations were suspected. Fighter bombers attacked point targets in the north.

Vulnerability of Aircraft

Helicopters were vulnerable to fire from the ground and many were lost. They were also attacked on their air bases in South Vietnam by guerrillas. Many fighter-bombers used against the north were lost to guerrilla action whilst on their bases in the south. The B-52s on the other hand operated with impunity. Their altitude put them above ground fire and they were based on the island of Guam, beyond reach of guerrilla warfare.

In the north the pattern was different. The American fighter-bombers were used against targets such as ammunition storage areas and key junctions on guerrilla supply routes. These operations called for precision low-level attack. The North Vietnamese fought back with Guideline ground-to-air missiles, with fighter aircraft, and above all with flak. This was point defence flak, sometimes put up in barrages, sometimes radar-directed against specific aircraft. These defences were vastly more effective than the opposition offered to American aircraft in the Korean War.

Towards the end of the war, from April 1972, B-52s were used for strikes against the north, in the region of the capital Hanoi and its port Haiphong. At this time American hopes of victory had been abandoned and the purpose of these strikes was to provide leverage in diplomatic negotiations aimed at ending American involvement, which no doubt is why the operations were code-named 'Linebacker'. But sending B-52s to the defended skies of the north exposed these large aircraft for the first time to serious risk.

The main causes of aircraft loss throughout the war were flak and guerrilla attack against bases. Setting aside the latter as being an aspect of ground warfare, flak dominated operational losses of aircraft. Ground-to-air missiles came well behind in second place, and losses to fighters came a minor third. North Vietnam deployed relatively few fighters. Altogether many thousands of American aircraft were destroyed.

Radar Dependency

As the most effective defence, flak was not radar-dependent in the day, but radar-dependent at night. Ground-to-air missiles on the other hand were totally radar-dependent. The fact that they shot down a far smaller number of aircraft is not necessarily a measure of comparative efficiency. Flak was encountered as the point defence system of innumerable minor targets, but only major targets were defended by missile emplacements.

B-52 Versus Guideline

The special interest of the B-52 raids against the north was that only Guideline missiles could threaten them. The battle between B-52s and Guidelines came towards the end of eight years in which technology on both sides advanced through several stages.

The B-52 raids used every standard resource of electronic warfare to protect the heavy bombers, which unlike the fighter-bombers had no reserve of manoeuvrability with which to try and escape.

A fighter-bomber, detecting the launch of a Guideline ahead of it, could go into a steep nose-dive. It took several seconds for the missile's command guidance system to pick up the missile after its near-vertical launch and begin directing it at the plummeting target. The missile had to be swung sharply downwards. When this occurred, opportunity came for the fighter-bomber to pull out of its dive and go into a climb. It was generally impossible for the missile to follow it.

This tactic alone did not answer all requirements. Sometimes cloud prevented observation of the Guideline launch.

'Wild Weasels'

An important measure became the use of 'Wild Weasels', aircraft dedicated to suppressing the defences. Wild Weasels were equipped to detect the radars used for missile guidance. They could employ stand-off jamming or launch a 'Shrike', an anti-radiation missile which would fly down the radar beam and explode at the radar antenna.

The obvious counter was to turn the radar off. Discretion in the use of radar became a feature of electronic war for the first time in Vietnam. Another alternative was to set up spoof transmitters mimicking the emissions of genuine radar sites in the hope that anti-radiation missiles would be uselessly expended upon them.

The B-52 raids were carried out at night and protected by Wild Weasel aircraft. Out of 700 B-52 night sorties against the north, some fifteen bombers were shot down, a lost rate of 2 per cent. Though the number of sorties was low by comparison with figures typical of the massed raids of the Second World War, the loss rate was also low by the same standards.

On the other hand much had changed, in that individual aircraft had become vastly more expensive than their Second World War counterparts. Replacement production no longer ran to thousands of aircraft a month.

The Significance of Electronics in the War

Electronics was as essential over North Vietnam as it was over Germany, both to the attack and the defence. Without it, the defence could not operate. Without electronic countermeasures, on the other hand, it is generally conceded that seventy-five B-52s or more might well have been lost. The judgement is generally made, no doubt reflecting the costliness of B-52s, that such a loss rate would have been insupportable and would have compelled the abandonment of the attack.

A significant factor additional to the bomber costs would have been the extra aircrew falling into North Vietnamese hands as prisoners of war. Many aircrew, shot down in fighter-bombers and helicopters, were already prisoners of war. As it was, their steadily increasing number compromised American resolution. It was one of the issues compelling America to abandon the war.

The significance of electronics in the Vietnam War is part of the broader significance of the air war, just as it was in the Second World War and the Korean War.

Air power did not become finally decisive in any of these conflicts, in the sense of forcing political settlements, but it became progressively more decisive from the Second World War through to Vietnam. In Korea and even more in Vietnam it was the most playable card in the American negotiators' hands.

In Vietnam electronics contributed primarily to the defence against air war. In contrast to Korea this was chiefly ground-based defence. The air attackers' electronic countermeasures were secondary, a response. Electronics was chiefly a restraint on air war in Vietnam, in contrast to its enabling role over Germany and Korea.

The most enduring lesson of the Vietnam War was that, ultimately, political factors are decisive. Technology cannot deliver an outcome counter to basic political realities.

At the same time the war confirmed that the Soviet Union was supplying military electronics able to stay in the ring with American military electronics. The technology gap was questionable. The only way to make a comparison is to calculate what would have happened if Soviet aircraft had been employed in attacking a comparable land area fortified with American missiles. The information to do this does not exist.

The Value of the Overall Mix

The effectiveness of the Soviet-supplied defences of North Vietnam cannot be judged purely by the loss rates inflicted by missiles. What counted was the overall mix of flak, missiles and aircraft; it is a question of the optimum outlay and the way resources were committed as between the three arms.

If there had been more missile emplacements in North Vietnam, the costs of the American bombing would undoubtedly have been higher. Purely in the contest between the missiles and the B-52s, it took about 50 missile launches for every B-52 brought down. The cost ratio was guessably in favour of the missiles.

Airborne interception never became a major defensive tactic. But the Vietnam War was notable for seeing the introduction of infra-red guided air-to-air missiles on North Vietnamese aircraft.

Electronics was far from being confined to the air war in Vietnam. A considerable variety of sensor devices was deployed to aid the ground battle against guerrillas. These were designed to detect human beings and operational movements, through vibrations, chemical effects and so forth. They made no difference to the outcome.

The Arab-Israeli Wars

Friction in South East Asia was paralleled by friction in the Middle East. This was the simmering conflict between Israel and neighbouring Arab states. On two occasions, in 1967 and 1973, the simmering broke out into open warfare. The wars were both of short duration. Because they were of short duration, there was no progressive development of technology during them; each side fought with the weapons it had when war broke out.

The 'Ace in the Hole'

For this reason, the Arab-Israeli wars highlight the 'ace in the hole' theory of electronic warfare. Everything depended on electronics superiority at the given instant when the attack was launched. In 1967 it was launched by the Israelis (the Six-Day War, June 1967), in 1973 it was launched by the Arabs (Yom Kippur War, October 1973). On both occasions the aggressors exploited secret electronic preparations to achieve initial success.

It was a revival of *blitzkrieg* with electronics even more to the fore than in 1939 and 1940. The enemy's radar and radio were surprised by obliterative jamming and deception. The general techniques were well-known, but success at the given moment depended on exact knowledge of the enemy's current order of electronics battle.

The Arab-Israeli wars accomplished nothing conclusive. It was impossible that they should. The 'ace in the hole' style electronic warfare could not therefore accomplish anything permanent either, but it had a sensational element which attracted attention and even admiration, despite the fact that no new principle was revealed.

To be self-justifying 'ace in the hole' techniques need both to overwhelm the other side and lead to an enduring political solution. In the contemporary climate of international relations, this amounts to a contradiction in terms.

The Arab states were armed with Soviet-bloc weapons, the Israelis with variously-sourced equipment, some of it of their own development, most of it from the West. Israel's main supporter was the United States.

In the Arab attack launching the Yom Kippur War of 1973, a remarkable range of new Soviet equipment was deployed. Egypt and Syria had been supplied with a series of new surface-to-air missiles, beyond the long-familiar Guideline. They included the SA-6 which used continuous wave radar, thereby defeating radar countermeasures based upon conventional pulsed radar. Had not the Americans moved swiftly to provide electronic countermeasures pods for Israeli aircraft, losses to the SA-6, already alarming, might well have become catastrophic.

Even more significantly they included the SA-7, a portable missile with infra-red homing, often lethal against low-flying aircraft. This was a major military initiative. It compromised the role of aircraft in close-support operations, led to the search for infra-red countermeasures, and obliged new tactical thinking.

A Proving Ground

Support from the world's centres of military development ensured continual upgrading of weapons even during the six-year intermission between the wars, a period known to the Israelis as the War of Attrition. Thus the Israeli-Arab conflict was constantly used by the Superpowers as a hot proving ground for the latest in electronic warfare, with frequent limited hostilities.

The War at Sea

One of these hostile incidents was the sinking of the Israeli destroyer *Eilat* off Port Said by Soviet-supplied Styx naval surface-to-surface missiles. These were launched by the Egyptians from Soviet-supplied patrol boats. This event, on 21 October 1967, has gone down as the first occasion on which a surface warship was lost in such a way. In this historical sense it had more significance than it did for the Arab-Israeli conflict.

The Styx anti-shipping missile claimed more victims in the Indo-Pakistan conflict of 1971. But it was not until the Falklands War of 1982 between Britain and Argentina that the threat of missiles to warships had to be taken seriously as a potentially decisive issue. Nevertheless at this time, 15 years after the first demonstration, it came as a surprise.

One remarkable but isolated incident of the Six-Day War in 1967 was the savage attack by Israeli aircraft and gunboats on the American electronic espionage ship *Liberty*. This occurred halfway through the six days (8 June 1967, the war having broken out on 5 June), off the Sinai peninsula near the Gaza strip, that is in sensitive waters between the two sides.

There were more than 100 casualties aboard the badly-damaged American vessel, of whom more than thirty were killed. The United States Government accepted compensation and the Israeli explanation that the attack was in error. The ship was said to have been mistaken for an Egyptian destroyer equipped for electronic countermeasures.

But no subsequent investigator has endorsed this. The belief endures that the attack was deliberate against a well-identified target. The conclusion must be that there were some secrets which even Israel's best ally could not be allowed to discover. Or else that the United States was, in reality, concerned that the war should not swing too heavily one way or the other and was electronically undermining the Israeli offensive.

The Pueblo *Affair*

Both the United States and the Soviet Union have used ostensibly peaceful vessels equipped for electronic espionage. This would seem an entirely legitimate and economical means of intelligence collection. The United States however had another unfortunate experience when the *Pueblo* was captured off the coast of North Korea on 23 January 1968. The incident was remarkable for the political embarrassments which resulted, rather than any technical revelations about electronics eavesdropping.

After 1973, détente brough a temporary lessening of tensions in the Middle East. But unlike Indo-China, where the fighting had ended too, no resolution of the fundamental political problem was obtained.

14

Dominance

In the mid-1970s tension between the Superpowers fell slightly. An era of détente arrived. While it lasted, which was not long, rivalry in weapons development and electronic warfare abated. When it collapsed, which was in 1979/80, new rivalry broke out.

This was remarkable as being a rivalry expressed above all in electronics. Hitherto military rivalry had been dominated by nuclear weapons. The public assumption continued to be that nuclear weapons were the mainstay of deterrence.

But while new developments in nuclear weapons were part of the rivalry, nuclear weapons were in changed relationship to electronics. Nuclear weapons had always relied to greater or lesser extent on electronics for their means of delivery. Now electronics bid to be the dominant partner.

Means of delivery increased in number and variety and became more sophisticated. This was reflected in several weapon systems but above all in two mobile types of strategic nuclear missile, namely American cruise missiles and Soviet ballistic SS-20s, both ground-launched and intermediate range.

The new American cruise missiles navigated themselves electronically over varied terrain to strike highly specific targets. They marked no special achievement in nuclear warhead construction, but were only made possible by advances in computers and miniaturisation.

Directed Energy – A Turning Point

These were deployed weapons. In research the new direction of nuclear technology was 'directed energy weapons' – warheads which projected their explosive effects preferentially in a particular direction, rather than equally in all. In other words they were the nuclear equivalent of shaped-charge conventional warheads, such as those used to penetrate armour on tanks by projecting a narrow jet.

Directed-energy nuclear weapons were created to serve the purposes of long-range battle under electronic control, in which a destructive effect generated at one point would be aimed by electronic means at another point thousands of kilometres away

The bridge across which the destructive effect would transit was space. The destructive effect could only be electromagnetic radiation itself, since other effects of a nuclear explosion would expend themselves locally. It would in fact be X-rays concentrated into a beam by the construction of the nuclear warhead. This would mark the first time for electromagnetic radiation to be cast in the destructive role; hitherto its power levels had only ever been adequate for communication. Evolution had reached a new turning point.

The primary target for this technology was ballistic missiles during launch. To this extent the new technology was a defensive technology. It defended with space-crossing weapons against space-crossing weapons. This led to the name 'Strategic Defense Initiative' (SDI), announced by the American President in March 1983, generally paraphrased 'Star Wars'.

This military technology had a surprising aspect, in that it opened the way for nuclear weapons to be completely substituted by electronics, substituted that is even as the source of the destructive energy. Electronics and electromagnetic radiation could at last go into harness on their own for destructive purposes. Electronics could provide not only the targeting but the destruction.

Beaming Destruction

It could do this in various ways. It could create intense laser beams or charged particle beams.

The laser beam, as a beam of electromagnetic radiation, is in principal similar to the intense X-ray beam produced by a directed-energy nuclear explosion. The latter is technically a laser beam, though not lending itself to such accurate focusing as a laser beam at a frequency near visible light. Some focusable laser beams, such as that generated by hydrogen and fluorine in the infra-red, are capable of projecting high destructive energy.

Charged particle beams are produced by the high-energy accelerators used in physics for research into the elementary constituents of matter. The idea of adapting large, cumbersome physical apparatus to military needs is problematic. But in principle this type of beam can be aimed against a remote target with similar destructive effect to a laser. As a beam of mutually repelling particles however, it presents added difficulties of focusing and propagation, particularly through the atmosphere.

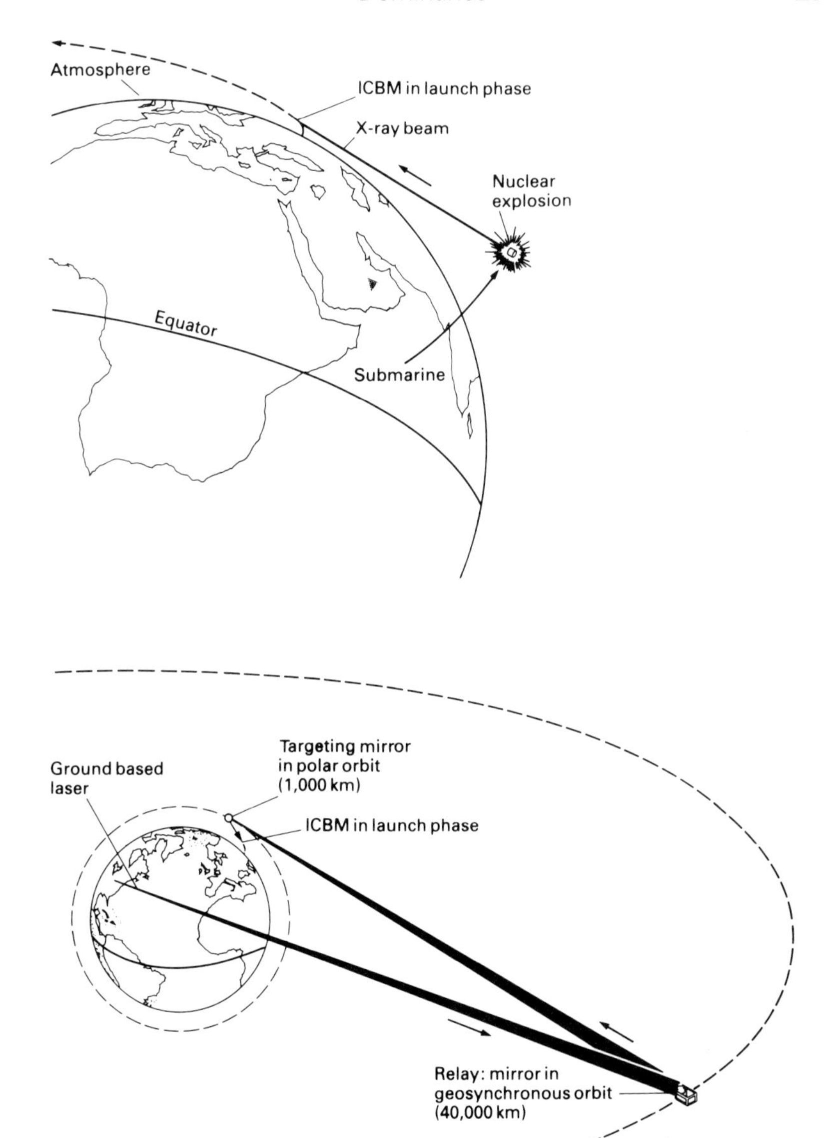

FIG. 14.1 **'Star Wars'** The above illustrations show two of the main concepts of the Strategic Defence Initiative (SDI). Top, a directed energy nuclear explosion: a warhead launched by submarine projects a powerful burst of X-rays at an intercontinental ballistic missile rising from its launch silo. Bottom, a ground-based laser reflected firstly from a mirror in a geosynchronous orbit and secondly from a mirror in polar orbit in order to strike a missile in launch phase.

The problems of aiming and attaining sufficient accuracy, whether with lasers or charged particle beams, over ranges measured in thousands of miles, are obviously high. The infra-red laser needs to be reflected from one giant mirror to another positioned in space and oriented with extreme accuracy.

Even if solutions are notionally within the ability of electronics to provide, dependable military hardware is a challenge of a different order. In any event these weapon systems will not exist except in concept for many years. The momentum towards disarmament may halt their development, but history does not encourage the faith that such a halt would be permanent.

They are the major systems relying on electronics to accomplish destructive effect, but not the only ones. Another line of possibilities is opened up by 'smart rocks' and 'brilliant pebbles'. These terms designate one and the same idea but in different sizes, namely the use of electronic sensors and control to manoeuvre small unarmed interceptor devices into the paths of warheads, or other space hardware. The destructive agency in this case is the kinetic energy of impact.

Collisions in space between approaching objects at high closing speeds release enormous kinetic energy. But objects are not always approaching, and it may sometimes be necessary to boost a projectile to high speed in order to intercept a target. A piece of conceptual space artillery is provided by the 'rail gun', in which electrical acceleration pushes projectiles in space to speeds much higher than can be achieved in the lower atmosphere.

All these techniques of battle are linked to space. The destructive influence, whatever it is, propagates or travels through space. It is directed at targets which even if intercepted at low altitude are space-faring vehicles. Often however it is directed at satellites forming part of the enemy's military inventory – reconnaissance, early warning, and communications satellites, space stations, space-based weapons.

Nevertheless it is clear that if such targets as these can be destroyed at long range, many other targets can also be destroyed, including earth-bound ones. The new technology has its offensive as well as its defensive potential. The new military prospect which electronics conjures up is a prospect of war in space coupled to war on earth.

But this is not the only vision of future warfare owed to electronics. Military planners have turned from wars in space with renewed concern to restrain conflict on earth. They seek to ensure that the chances of escalation from local conventional conflict to nuclear and space conflict are minimised.

One way of doing so is by improving capability to fight conventional wars. This gives hope of retaining control of incipient and minor conflicts. For this purpose, electronics is no less necessary. In fact it is more so, for there is no enthusiasm nowadays to improve conventional defence by increasing personnel numbers in the armed forces.

Power with Restraint

In the circumstances, the need is to improve the efficiency with which smaller numbers of personnel are used. This means improving the effectiveness of non-nuclear weapons; developing 'smart' weapons (i.e. those with terminal guidance); improving surveillance; guaranteeing that organised warfare can be carried on under sensitive political control. To be able to exercise power with restraint, the first essential is to know what is happening and to preserve communications.

In the late 1970s and early 1980s, 'C3I' systems – command, control, communications and intelligence systems – attracted strong attention. They were, in effect, the up-dated equivalent of the radio networks pioneered in war by Germany in the late 1930s. They aimed to ensure all the communications links needed on the battlefield – a much wider range than was necessary in the 1930s.

In the circumstances of modern land battle, a large number of service personnel have to be directly accessible to each other for operational purposes, just as a large number of the civilian population are directly accessible to each other for business purposes through the conventional telephone network. Radio rather than cable has to be the mainstay of battlefield communications, for the sake of both mobility and freedom from physical destruction.

Of course, nodal points of a battlefield network – the equivalents of telephone exchanges – are liable to destruction by air attacks, or sudden enemy penetrations, and the system has to offer a variety of alternative routes for getting communications through from every point to every other point. It must bring these into play automatically.

Moreover it has to incorporate encryption. It has to cope with the prospect of nuclear explosions occurring in the extensive territory over which it is operating. It must also cope with the fact that its subscribers cannot be relied upon to be found in the listed 'directory' location; they may have been obliged to move at short notice without warning.

An important technological advance enabling the rise of C3I systems was digital processing. In the historical competition between analogue and digital signals, the pendulum again swung to the digital side, and for the same reason as in the early days of radio: greater robustness and immunity to distortion. But 80 years after radio's beginning, 'pulse code modulation' as it was called was capable of transmitting information far more rapidly than the old Morse Code, sufficiently rapidly in fact for analogue signals such as the human voice to be reduced to digital form, transmitted without distortion, and then reprocessed into analogue form intelligible to the ear.

Typical of C_3I systems was the British 'Ptarmigan'. As an organised area network of telecommunications, it gave possibilities beyond those of conventional tactical radio. It offered a basis for computer-based systems designed to hold all the information on battle positions, strengths of units, and availability of supplies that field commanders need to take decisions. This information could be displayed on consoles just like business information in an office, but at military headquarters and command posts throughout the battlezone.

At sea the corresponding development was computer-based systems enabling warships to fight with coordination of inputs from radar, sonar, and radio, and corresponding coordinated control of on-board weapon systems. Typical of these was the 'Aegis' system deployed in the United States navy.

These 'action information organisations' displayed all inputs to the captain and other executive officers in a central command room, in a well-protected location inside the ship, lavishly equipped with electronics. This became the nerve-centre during combat, supplanting traditional control from the bridge.

New Dangers and Urgency

This change reflected new dangers and urgency in war at sea. It reflected the crucial importance of electronic warfare in naval operations, and the premium on rapid response for the sake of survival. The warship is a large fighting unit concentrated at a point location, vulnerable to outright loss through just a single failure to detect and intercept an incoming missile or torpedo.

An army company or battalion dispersed over territory is not vulnerable in the same way. The same is even more true of air defence systems of the 'air defence ground environment' type, which are integrated over large areas and have widely dispersed 'assets', such as aircraft and radar stations, amounting in all to considerable defence in depth.

But as the 1980s passed into the 1990s, it became clear that the actual daily threat, the most likely cause of human loss, was not so much war as terrorism, often coupled with local conflicts, guerrilla warfare, or even drug smuggling. Against this both nuclear deterrence and conventional military strength were helpless. Only electronics had ideas to offer.

Beyond terrorism was the threat of proliferation of nuclear weapons into countries and disputes where they would not perform any deterrent or other plausible military function, but only endanger lives and environments. International controls, intelligence, inspection, and reconnaissance, all relying on electronics, offered the only hope of preventing this.

To the whole span of problems confronting ministries and departments of defence, from the possibility of space war to the need for controlling conventional war, preventing terrorism and restraining the spread of nuclear weapons, electronics was the common answer.

Imperceptibly, so imperceptibly that many failed to see it happening, military strategy for dealing with the problems of the late 20th century receded from nuclear deterrence and reformed itself around electronics. It might have been said that the era of electronic deterrence had begun to arrive.

No one used the term. But even without recognising it, politicians and military leaders were compelled to travel along this road. As environmental concern and pressure for disarmament mounted, mutual security through ever more comprehensive surveillance at last seemed a more hopeful philosophy than nuclear deterrence. The demands of surveillance, from the detection of explosives in airline luggage to imagery from orbit, could only be met by increasing investment in electronic systems.

This change happened against a background of political events which broke the Cold War mould that had imposed a pattern on world history since the end of the Second World War.

The starting point for these developments was the balance between the Superpowers at about 1975. Its preservation still rested on nuclear deterrence, in the shape of mutual assured destruction – MAD. This was combined with the doctrine of flexible response, intended to control escalation and give time for common sense to prevail.

Each Superpower accepted that broad parity had been reached in nuclear weapons and the means of delivery: the 'strategic triad' of land-based missiles, submarine-based missiles, and nuclear-armed aviation. There was no inclination to leapfrog, rather an acceptance that leapfrogging held nothing in prospect.

More than ever, any qualitative difference between the United States and the Soviet Union depended on electronics. The question was how far the gap between them had narrowed since 1945, when it was strongly in favour of the United States.

New Twists

What tended to happen to the gap was that it would narrow for a while, then would come some new twist to the technology spiral, and the United States would hope once more to draw ahead. This happened about 1960, when the United States was benefiting from a tide of electronic miniaturisation. In 1975 it was poised to happen again, thanks to the tide of computer development in the West which brought mini computers and eventually micros.

A practical difference was highlighted when, in 1976 an advanced Soviet Mig-25 aircraft was landed in Japan by a defecting Soviet pilot, Victor Belenko. Examination showed that the electronics harked back as far as the age of electron tubes.

Western military electronics had long since been based on solid-state devices in all except critical power or frequency applications. In the Soviet interceptor the electronics equipment was the functional counterpart of Western equipment, but because of dependence on electron tubes, it consumed more power, occupied more space, and admitted of less refinement. To this degree the comparison was flattering to the West.

But there was a downside to this assessment, not so flattering. The electronics was enclosed in a 'Faraday cage', to insulate it from outside electrical interference. It was realised that the Soviets had taken seriously a problem which had not received so much attention in the West, that is, of the continuing functioning of electronic equipment in the conditions of nuclear war.

A nuclear explosion radiates an extremely powerful pulse of electromagnetic radiation. This induces extremely high voltages in electrical conductors. It is capable of damaging electrical and electronic equipment up to many hundreds of miles away.

Solid-state electronics is inherently vulnerable to high voltage overloads. Static electricity off clothing can destroy integrated circuits. It was realised that thanks to the combination of the Faraday cage with electron-tube-based electronics, the Soviet formula was more resistant to the electromagnetic pulse than Western electronics.

Correspondingly, a new direction began in Western military electronics from the late 1970s, putting stronger emphasis on protection against the distant effects of nuclear weapons. In this sense, Belenko's Mig taught the West more about military electronics than the West expected.

This was a new direction necessitated by logical military considerations. But some other new directions, including the actual multiplication of strategic mobile missile systems and the potential emplacement of military systems in space, were the result of crumbling détente. These were forcing the world by the early 1980s to contemplate nuclear war as a realistic possibility.

The ending of détente was speeded by two events. The first was the collapse of the pro-Western regime in Iran, in 1979, and with it the Central Treaty Organisation, a key sector of the Western cordon around the Soviet Union.

Although this was a blow to the United States, it was highly significant that the blow did not originate with the United States' ideological opponents in the Warsaw Pact.

Instead it was an Islamic reaction against Western cultural values which turned into a national revolution. It symbolised the beginnings of a tendency for the world's one-axis political-military polarisation to dissolve, and to be replaced by multi-axial polarisations. Emerging nationalistic and religious forces in the Middle East were independent of both American and Soviet interests. They were in some degree hostile to both.

This was not realised at the time. The Soviet intervention in Afghanistan at the end of 1979 was a reaction to the same ferment, but because it was seen in the light of the old one-axis polarisation it became the second event in quick succession to disturb détente.

East-West Relations Inflamed

It inflamed America's indignation against Iran into intensified suspicion of the Soviet Union. America's Western partners, which had tried to stand aside from the dispute with Iran, joined in hostility to Soviet policy in Afghanistan.

Yet another war came which had no relevance to East-West relations but brought the same message of depolarisation still more obviously. This was the Falklands War between Argentina and Britain, which Argentina began by invading the Falkland Islands at the beginning of April 1982, claiming them as her own under the name of the Malvinas. It had nothing to do with either NATO or the Warsaw Pact and it was fortuitous that one of the parties, Britain, was a NATO member.

The conflict was between nations different culturally and linguistically, but it never acquired any element of ideological confrontation. This was significant. It could have turned to ideological confrontation even if there was no ideological difference to begin with.

Britain was supported by the United States. Argentina, which was inadequately equipped for the war which she had herself started, might have looked for Soviet-bloc weapons. The Soviet bloc and Argentina might have drawn together under the banner of opposition to colonialism.

But this never happened. Argentina coped as well as she could with the problems of acquiring weapons on the arms markets of the world outside the Soviet bloc, despite British efforts to close these to her.

What relevance did these events have in terms of electronic warfare? Ever since the end of the Second World War, the development of electronic warfare had been driven by the world's one-axis military polarisation. Only this drive could have carried electronic warfare on to an apocalyptic scale and out into space. But electronic warfare was now about to be seen on smaller stages.

Purely in itself the Iranian revolution had small relevance to electronic warfare.

Evidently signals intelligence had given the United States little warning of what was to happen in the country, or, alternatively, the signs had been misread or had failed to be acted on at decision-making levels, as had happened before.

The American position in electronic reconnaissance of the Soviet Union was weakened. Surveillance facilities at stations in Iran had to be abandoned.

There was no passage of arms. There was an attempt to rescue American hostages from the former embassy building in the Iranian capital Teheran, which failed for technical reasons connected with aviation not electronics.

The War of the Heat-Seeking Missile

The Afghan War was of greater interest from the standpoint of electronic warfare. At one time, electronic warfare was the hinge on which the war in Afghanistan seemed poised to turn. If there was one single electronics technology on which the war depended and which became a key political issue, it was the heat-seeking missile.

The Afghan War was land-locked, in a mountainous country which offered every assistance to irregular forces. It became a contest between the Soviet-supported government based in the capital Kabul and a variety of tribal opponents collectively termed *mujaheddin* supported chiefly out of Pakistan with American-supplied weapons.

In the war's early stages, Soviet ground-attack aviation, troop-landing helicopters and helicopter gunships proved highly effective in suppressing the *mujaheddin*.

The *mujaheddin* attempted to counter with miscellaneous anti-air weaponry, including the portable Soviet SA-7 heat-seeking missile which since the Yom Kippur War had become the international standard of its kind, readily available on arms markets. With the SA-7, infra-red technology achieved at altitudes up to a few thousand feet and over ranges of a few miles what it did in the Sidewinder at the greater ranges and altitudes typical of air-to-air combat. In both cases the tail pipes of the target aircraft or helicopter provided a good heat source for the missile to home on to.

The SA-7 had already provoked a proliferation of counter-measures in Israel and the West. Among them was the inconvenient emergency measure of lengthening the tail pipes in the hope of limiting damage. On helicopters, relatively slow-moving, non-agile and therefore at particular risk, infra-red beacons ('hot bricks') were sometimes mounted, to project a rotating cone of radiation around the on-coming missile with the aim of confusing its tracing. This reflected the relative crudity of the SA-7's tracking system. But the most successful was the dispensing of copious quantities of heat-emitting flares as decoys. In the Afghan War the Soviet forces proved well supplied with these.

The United States saw the best way of helping the *mujaheddin* as providing a more modern missile than the SA-7, with improved manoeuvrability and a more discriminating heat-seeking head. This was the Stinger.

However, the arrival of Stingers made no measurable difference to the last few years of the war. They posed a more serious threat to aviation, but this had evidently long ceased to be a critical factor in the Soviet-supported government's battle with the *mujaheddin*. When the Soviet Union agreed in 1988 to withdraw its forces from Afghanistan, it did so in pursuit of its own policy of revived détente with the West. The necessity for this new, more friendly attitude was dictated by domestic economic and political considerations, and irritants to the West such as the presence of Soviet forces in Afghanistan were incompatible with it. Perhaps the Soviets also realised that given the nature of Islamic sentiment, the Kabul government would prove stronger without them.

War in the South Atlantic

The Falklands War was the most varied demonstration of electronics in warfare since the end of the Second World War and, because it was largely a maritime conflict, displayed the heightened and more crucial role of electronics which is typical at sea. It included air-to-air combat using missiles, ground defence against air attack using ground-to-air missiles, and ship defence against air attack.

The same comment can be made about the Falklands War as about the revolution in Iran – namely that signals intelligence, or any other intelligence for that matter, had evidently given no warning of the impending event, at least to the British government. Perhaps warnings had not been passed on.

Vulnerable Communications

Fighting in the Falklands was long-range power projection by naval means, with shipborne air and land forces. On the Argentine side, political and operational control were co-located in the Argentine capital Buenos Aires, while the occupation force was for all practical purposes marooned on the islands. This created a communications weakness. Radiocommunications were crucial to the conduct of the war but vulnerable to interception or jamming.

The aim of the British task force was to dominate the sea and air around the Falklands and then land forces to re-occupy the islands. On the British side political control was in London, 12,500 kilometres away from the operational control aboard an aircraft carrier in the South Atlantic.

This gap was bridged by radio communications via satellite. But as the British defence communications satellite Skynet was not stationed where it could support the link, British communications were made through American defence satellites.

The link worked well enough, despite stories to the effect that radars and other electronic warfare equipment on the British warships had to be turned off to allow it to function without interference. This of course would have left warships dangerously exposed to surprise attack.

The only alternative means of long range communication would have been use of the HF band, but it is probable that much larger amounts of information needed to be passed than could have been comfortably handled by HF. Satellite communications channels, using SHF, have much larger bandwidth.

The British practised the standard arts of electronic warfare against the Argentines, particularly signals intelligence against mainland-to-islands communications. Argentine codes were broken. A feature of the war was Argentine failure to coordinate military initiatives between mainland- and island-based forces. This probably reflected the difficulties of the communications link, and the fact that nothing that passed over it was secure.

The Argentines had no countering success with signals intelligence.

Exocet

One of the most successful Argentine initiatives was attacking British ships with Exocet missiles, launched by aircraft from beyond the horizon. These missiles, typical of many anti-surface-ship missiles, homed on to targets using radar. The radar mounted on the missile was fully active: it both transmitted and received. Exocets were one of the few examples of Argentina's use of electronic warfare weapons systems, and although only a few of these missiles were available to her for air-launching, those few had an effect out of proportion to their number.

Following the first British loss to an Exocet, the destroyer *Sheffield*, a crucial aspect of the war became the battle to defeat the Exocet's homing radar.

There were two ways of doing so. One was the use of chaff – small aluminised plastic slivers working on the same principle as window. To defend a warship it was necessary to bloom a cloud of chaff when an Exocet missile approached. The chaff cloud would greatly enlarge the apparent target. The warship would be inside this enlarged target, but providing the cloud was bloomed in such a way that the warship was not at the centre, the Exocet would pass through and continue beyond.

The cloud had to be bloomed with chaff-dispensing mortars or rockets, launched from the warship being defended. The radar was a miniaturised set working on a frequency between 15 and 20 gigahertz; correspondingly, individual chaff lengths were about a centimetre.

The radar did not have the capability to discriminate between the reflections from the chaff and from the warship; this was possible in principle but would have been difficult since, in contrast to aircraft, ships move slowly. The velocity difference between warship and chaff is small, and the frequency difference minute. There are limits to the refinement of a radar carried in a missile warhead.

Ten Seconds

In practice little more than ten seconds warning of an approaching Exocet, travelling at high subsonic speed a few feet above the waves, could be expected. The decoy rockets needed to start dispensing chaff within a second or so of being launched.

Ideally they needed to be launched under computer control, the computer taking account of the missile's direction of approach and the wind direction, and programming a simultaneous manoeuvre by the warship to minimise the profile presented. This degree of sophistication was not reached during the conflict.

But using chaff it was possible to give the smaller warship up to a few thousand tons displacement a good chance of evading Exocet attack. Protecting large warships such as aircraft carriers of 20,000 or more tons was hardly possible this way; the weight of chaff needing to be bloomed in a few seconds would have been too great.

In such cases a decoy helicopter was a more feasible alternative, picking up and returning the radar's pulses and so simulating a target. Exocets travelled at a constant low height above the water. Providing the helicopter was at sufficient altitude the missile passed harmlessly underneath. In this method a helicopter on constant decoy duty was required.

Problems of Target Acquisition

One danger remained when decoying Exocets: that the missile, having missed its first target, would lock on to another nearby vessel. It was in this way that a large supply ship, the *Atlantic Conveyor*, was reputedly lost, with near-disastrous consequences.

The battle with Exocets highlighted the shortcomings of British naval radars. There was no radar which could be relied on to pick an incoming Exocet out of the background clutter caused by waves; the missile was deliberately programmed to take advantage of such clutter.

Indeed, not only Exocets, which presented a tiny frontal area, but aircraft attacking at low altitude were difficult radar targets, given that many additional sources of clutter were present, such as low distant coastlines, rain squalls and storms. Against clutter of all kinds, only radars equipped with moving target indication were effective, and there were not enough of these.

Any war is bound to show up deficiencies of equipment. Surveillance radar aboard British warships was clearly unable to give adequate warning against the constant threat of low-level aircraft or missile attack. In reality however deficiencies of surface radar were a limited part of the problem: fundamentally the correct way of meeting the threat was with airborne early warning radar. From an aircraft equipped with surveillance radar and patrolling at eight to ten thousand metres, incoming attacks could be detected at a range of three or four hundred kilometres. The risk of surprise could be eliminated.

With radar, it does not matter whether range is given by the height of the target or the height of the radar. The two are additive. A low-altitude target comes over the horizon to a high-altitude radar at the same range as a high-altitude target to a ground radar.

The British criticised themselves for their lack of airborne early warning radar. But only the United States among Western nations would have been able to meet the need, having begun to develop airborne early warning aircraft in the early 1970s.

'AWACS'

The Americans had two current types. One was the land-based Boeing AWACS (airborne warning and control system), mounting a surveillance radar in a rotating dome above the fuelage of an adapted Boeing 707 airliner. The other was the Grumman Hawkeye, a smaller two-engined aircraft carrying a similar dome, developed for naval purposes and deployable from land or large aircraft carriers.

AWACS represents a pinnable of electronic warfare. It has an operational crew of 17, including a battle team of eight and a battle commander. It is a flying command post, formed around the basic input provided by an advanced phased-array S-band radar, with all the

PLATE 14.1 **Boeing AWACS** The Boeing Airborne Warning and Command System (AWACS) is the ultimate in the long line of dedicated electronic warfare aircraft stretching back to the Second World War. The radome contains the planar array antenna of a long-range S-band surveillance radar, and is rotated to scan the horizon up to 250 miles away (depending on the aircraft's altitude, typically about 10,000 metres in normal operations). The crew of seventeen includes a battle commander and an air defence team of eight. Vital to the functioning of AWACS are the radio links through which it passes back the stream of information from its radar.

radio communications links necessary to integrate it with ground and naval forces and overall military and political control. Its systems are highly resistant to electronic countermeasures. It is the West's strategic ultimate in the evolution of dedicated electronic warfare aircraft which began in the Second World War. Its only counterpart is the somewhat larger Soviet Mainstay.

After the Falklands, Britain ordered the Boeing AWACS, but neither this nor the smaller Hawkeye would have helped Britain at the time, since Britain had no way of basing and operating them in the battle-zone.

In the circumstances Argentina had more satisfaction with the American-made surveillance radar she had installed on the Falkland Islands. This proved remarkably resistant to all British efforts at destruction using anti-radiation missiles. Probably one of the defensive measures was diverting the missiles with decoy transmitters into anti-radiation missile pits.

Air Combat

For air combat, the British had only about thirty subsonic Harrier short take-off and land interceptor aircraft. These were deployed from aircraft carriers. In spite of their small number they inflicted relatively large losses upon the more numerous and theoretically more formidable Argentine air arm.

The British aircraft operated at short range from their aircraft carrier bases while the Argentine aircraft came from mainland bases some 650 kilometres away. The long range and absence of in-flight refuelling deprived the Argentine aircraft of much opportunity to use their superior performance against British aircraft.

In practice the opportunity, such as it was, was discarded totally; in the brief combat time available to them, Argentine aircraft attempted to press home attacks against British warships rather than engage the defending fighters.

Patrolling British aircraft intercepted incoming Argentine aircraft from the stern, using infra-red heat-seeking Sidewinder missiles. This traditional form of attack proved highly effective; the Argentines lacked warning equipment and the majority of Argentine pilots shot down never realised that they had been at hazard.[1]

In this respect the Argentines were not equipped at all for the electronic battle which accompanies contemporary air fighting. This failure doomed their cause, for air operations were the only means open to the mainland forces to contest British supremacy over the air and water around the Falklands.

Eliminating the Naval Threat

Their navy gave them no ability to do so. This was demonstrated at an early stage by the sinking of the Argentine cruiser *General Belgrano* by a British nuclear submarine.

The approximate location of the *General Belgrano* was obtained by intelligence, the original source of the information almost certainly being the surveillance systems of the United States. The information was passed by radio to the submarine, which succeeded in finding the target and shadowing it. Finally political approval for the sinking was given by radio from London.

This stroke had the instant effect of depriving Argentina of one branch of her armed forces. Every remaining Argentine warship had to be regarded as being at serious hazard to a British weapon system to which there was no counter. The Argentine navy could not put to sea. This was a strategic disaster from which there was little hope of recovery. It happened early in the conflict.

If Argentina had had nuclear hunter-killer submarines, the British attempt to recover the islands would have been imperilled. The Argentine navy did have a small number of modern conventional submarines, but lacked the sources of target intelligence which would have been needed to make effective use of these. Slower moving and range-restricted compared with nuclear submarines, they could not rely exclusively on sonar.

Damages from Air Attack

As it was, relying on air attacks using Exocet missiles and ordinary bombs, Argentina sank six British surface vessels and seriously damaged seven others. Many British warships were struck by conventional bombs which failed to explode; had Argentine bombs exploded more consistently, British losses would have been significantly higher.

British anti-air missile systems, the short-range Sea Wolf and long-range Sea Dart deployed on ships, and the ground-deployed Rapier, did not guarantee the degree of protection against air attack that had been expected. The most serious threat to Argentine aircraft came from the Sidewinder-armed Harriers.

Defending fighters, operating over a wide area, can take the initiative against incoming attackers. Ground- or ship-based point-defence systems on the other hand can only engage attacking aircraft on the final run-in to the target that is being defended. Better scores are likely for the defending fighters.

Since this was the pattern in the Falklands, it casts doubt on the Argentine air strategy, which was to go for ships and disregard aircraft.

It was understandable that the Argentines saw the warships and naval auxiliaries as the crucial targets. If enough were destroyed, Britain would be compelled to call off her attempt to recover the islands. But the force of Harrier aircraft was small and not replenishable. The defensive air shield might have been eliminated if, to begin with, it had received the undivided attention of the more numerous, higher performance Argentine aircraft. This was true even if combat times were limited.

A more serious defensive situation would then have loomed for Britain. Her military task would have been more difficult, for ground- and ship-based missiles were demonstrably incapable of substituting adequately for the Harriers.

Night Vision

Various forms of electro-optical equipment, such as low-light level and thermal imaging systems were used by both sides especially in the ground fighting which formed the terminal phase. Both low-light level and thermal imaging systems operate in dark or near-dark conditions. Much of the ground fighting was at night, a pointer to the advantage which the attacking British probably hoped to obtain from night-fighting equipment. It should be said that the Argentines also proved well equipped in this respect.

During the 1970s and 1980s night vision was offered by an increasing variety of devices. These are based on amplifying low natural levels of light by electronic means, or alternatively utilising the infra-red radiation emitted by all bodies (except those at absolute zero temperature). They generally operate the camera of a closed-circuit television system.

The advantage which they gave to troops properly trained in their use in the Falklands may have been substantial, but was not crucial. The war was strategically lost for the Argentines with their inability to relieve or reinforce their island garrison from the mainland. The morale of their forces could only collapse, sooner or later.

While night-vision systems represent an advance for electronics in land warfare, they do not yet amount to the transformation which radio and radar brought to night air warfare. They fall far short. They have surveillance value, but they have not yet captured such an important military function as infra-red target-seeking against aircraft. This remains infra-red's main and vital contribution to military technology. Aircraft use thermal imaging as FLIR, forward looking infra red.

Lebanon 1982

The Falklands War lasted a few months. Before it was over, war broke out again in the Middle East, beginning with an Israeli attack on the south of Lebanon, at the beginning of June 1982. This was an attempt to eliminate bases of Palestinian resistance organisations. It brought about a conflict with Syria in and over the heavily defended Bekaa Valley, fought out between hundreds of tanks and aircraft on each side.

This had been foreseen by the Israelis and once again they sprang electronic warfare as the ace in the hole. Intensive jamming was based on up-to-the-minute knowledge of frequencies employed by the many Soviet ground-to-air missile systems which defended the Bekaa. To obtain this intelligence, Israel made use of drones, or remotely-piloted vehicles.

Having negated the ground defences, the Israelis used airborne early warning aircraft for control of the air fighting – Hawkeyes acquired from America. The Israeli air force utterly outclassed the Syrians in air-to-air combat. The Syrian air force had Soviet aircraft which were not equipped electronically to the same standard as Israeli aircraft. Israeli preparations to take the initiative had been based on electronic warfare.

In the short term Israel achieved its military objectives, humiliating the Syrians and embarrassing their Soviet arms suppliers in the process, but no stable political outcome resulted.

On the contrary the fighting in the Lebanon stirred a complex cauldron of political and military tendencies in the Islamic world which it was beyond the capability of the Israelis, or of the United States, or of the United Nations, to control. America was seen as the Israeli's principal backer, and generalised Islamic resentment at events in the Lebanon turned into intensified anti-American terrorism during the rest of the 1980s.

The War Against Terrorism

This was not the only source of terrorism in the world, but it was among the most powerful. Moreover, terrorists linked up.

Whether there can ever be a political solution to terrorism seems questionable when new political problems are constantly coming into being. However energetically political problems are tackled, there is a limit to what can be achieved before a new stratum of tensions is laid over the most recent one.

Terrorism by itself does nothing to solve the problems which produce it. For a long time to come, the only practical measure against it will be the attempt to prevent tragic human consequences, primarily by security measures using all the resources of electronics.

Nevertheless the Americans tried a formal military counterstrike, early in 1986, against Libya, long suspected as a focus of Islamic terrorism.

The raid was aimed at two groups of targets, one at Tripoli, the other at Benghazi, both on the coast.

The western targets near Tripoli were attached by FB-111 fighter-bombers flown from bases in Britain. Taking into account that the aircraft were refused permission to overfly by various European countries and had to skirt the Iberian peninsula, this was the longest-range air strike ever mounted, exceeding the range of the Guam-based strikes by American B-52 bombers against North Vietnam. As the fighter-bombers lacked the range of B-52s, multiple in-flight refuelling was necessary.

The eastern targets near Benghazi were attacked by aircraft flown off American carriers in the Mediterranean.

Precision Bombing

The raid was carried out at night. This probably reflected the Libyan air force's inability to offer resistance at this time. Little effort was apparently either expected or made at air interception. The main defences were the surface-to-air missile sites on the Libyan coast. Specialist electronic warfare aircraft were used to suppress these with jamming and anti-radiation missiles.

The raid attempted pinpoint bombing, apparently in an attempt to kill the Libyan leader.Each attacking aircraft was equipped with 'Pave Tack' or 'TRAM', systems enabling it to designate its target by pointing a laser beam. With these systems the laser beam is automatically held on the designated target regardless of the aircraft's manoeuvres, while reflection of the laser illumination provides the homing signal for self-guiding bombs. In theory they should have demonstrated that the problem of precision bombing by electronic means, one of electronic warfare's most classic themes, had at last been brilliantly solved; but most commentators concluded otherwise.

War in the Gulf

Another aspect of the turmoil of the Middle East at this time was war between Iraq and Iran. Various countries were drawn into an attempt to ensure the freedom of shipping in the Persian Gulf, by minesweeping and provision of naval escorts. Considerable naval deployments, of which the largest came from the United States, produced some illuminating sidelights on electronic warfare.

Naval Vulnerability

An Exocet missile hit on the US warship *Stark*, accidental but with disastrous results, reiterated the lesson of naval vulnerability demonstrated in the Falklands. Subsequently the US cruiser *Vincennes*, equipped with the Aegis battle control system, accidentally shot down an Iranian airliner that was wrongly identified as an Iranian warplane threatening the ship.

This incident demonstrated naval vulnerability from the opposite viewpoint. In other words, the command tensions which it causes, and the consequent tendency for a commander at sea to make the worst-case assumption in an effort to ensure survival. On the evidence of both the *Stark* and *Vincennes* incidents, the ability of naval forces to control limited conflict is questionable. In such operations naval instability can have adverse consequences. The *Vincennes* incident fanned the flames of anti-American Islamic terrorism, and is probably to be regarded as responsible for the subsequent destruction by terrorist bomb of an American airliner over the Scottish town of Lockerbie a few months later.

It seems probable that larger scale naval engagements would also reflect the same vulnerability and instability.

Further Advances in Electronic Warfare

One way of measuring the advance of electronic warfare is through the progress that is occurring in extending the use of the electromagnetic spectrum. After the advance to SHF, or centimetric waves, which happened in the Second World War, the next major advance was the leapfrog to infra-red, which had never become an effective military technology in that war, despite German attempts to use it.

This left the next logical stage as the infilling of the gap between the centimetric region and infra-red – millimetric waves, the frequencies from 30 gigahertz to 300 gigahertz. The chief opportunity these offer is for millimetric radar. It has the advantage of needing only small, compact apparatus. It offers high resolution, and is highly sensitive to Doppler effect. Conceptually, it can be used in missiles designed to find small targets, such as tanks.

But millimetric waves differ from all the longer radio waves in one important respect. For the latter, the atmosphere is transparent. True, rain and other atmospheric precipitations are detectable in UHF and SHF and this affects radar operation, but it does not prevent it. With millimetric radar, atmospheric absorption is greater, even without atmospheric precipitation, and it is so marked as to limit operation to relatively short ranges.

This is not necessarily a drawback. In some cases it is an advantage, providing short range is all that is required. A radar working on such a frequency cannot be detected at distances much beyond its operational range. This is extremely valuable from the point of view of evading countermeasures.

The Limits to the Advance Up the Frequency Spectrum

These characteristics shown by millimetre waves are even more evident in the next division of the frequency spectrum, submillimetre waves, from 300 gigahertz to 3000 gigahertz. Here radio waves begin to merge into infra-red.

In additional to the limitations imposed by range and sensitivity to precipitation, millimetre and submillimetre waves are as yet difficult to generate at the power levels that might be necessary. For these reasons, electronic warfare's advance up the frequency spectrum remains, in general, halted at SHF, or at least, only a little beyond the top end of the SHF band at 30 gigahertz.

Infra-Red

From this point it leaps to the infra-red. Remembering that bandwidths are defined over a 1:10 interval of frequencies, infra-red occupies rather more than two such intervals of the frequency spectrum, from 3000 gigahertz to where visible light begins at a frequency of about 400,000 gigahertz. Of course there is no sharp transition point between any of the radio bands, which merge gradually into each other, but the transition to visible light is, relatively speaking, sharply marked.

With applications in heat-seeking missiles, thermal imaging, and target-designation lasers, infra-red remains the upper limit for electronic warfare, save only to the extent to which visible light contributes.

Visible Light

For visible light to qualify in electronic warfare, it needs to be used in an electronic rather than a purely optical system. Television is the prime example, applied for instance to the remote control of missiles by monitoring the picture provided by a television camera mounted in the missile's nose.

In such an example as this, the electromagnetic spectrum is being used for 'seeing' function, analogous to the use which the eye makes of it. A picture is produced, and information is derived from the picture. In other words, the incoming signal is simultaneously analysed for different directions and different intensities as well as different frequency components.

Radio and radar are 'hearing' functions. Information is obtained by 'listening' for the signal, analysing it and observing how it varies over periods of time, which of course may be very short. Admittedly directionality is obtained by scanning, and a picture, such as the picture provided by a plan position indicator, is built up. Yet this is short of the mapping of the visual world made possible by light.

There is nothing to say that this is a rigid functional division. Light is well suited to create a picture because of its high resolving power, but the top practical end of the radar frequency range, SHF, has resolving power adequate for many purposes, and a logical development would be the appearance of a 'microwave camera', able to produce a picture of the environment as seen by microwaves. This would increase the resources of military electronics against countermeasures. It would make it more comparable to the human eye, which we do not believe is easily fooled.

The resources of the eye against optical countermeasures are strong, though there are examples of the latter such as smokescreens and camouflage. Nevertheless the ultimate optical countermeasure, the invisible soldier, is a long way from reality, and there are good reasons founded in physics to suppose it to be impossible.

Low Observables

The equivalent of the invisible soldier in electronic warfare is 'stealth'. mentioned in earlier chapters. Another way of describing stealth is as 'low observables', which indicates that what is important for military purposes is a general reduction of visibleness. That is, not only to radar, but such as can be achieved by camouflage against optical recognition and reduction of all emissions capable of giving the target's presence away. These include electromagnetic emission, sound emissions, and chemical emissions (for example, exhaust fumes).

Two Aspects

Stealth is a long-existing concept on which increased emphasis fell during the 1980s, particularly on two of its aspects.

The first and perhaps most important, though least realised, is increased acoustic stealth applied to submarines. Many technologies have contributed to the silencing of submarines, particularly improved propeller design, and above all cladding with acoustically absorbent tiles. In the latter, the Soviet submarine fleet appears to have led. At all events by the late 1980s, Soviet underwater stealth was putting stress on the long-range detection capability of the West's passive sonar systems. Victory in a contest of this kind is registered by compelling increasing recourse to active systems, a process which was well under way in Western navies.

The second, much more notorious aspect is the reduction of visibility to radar. This reflects the tremendous importance which radar has acquired as the universal military watchdog of skies, seas, space and terrain.

The concept of reducing the radar cross-section of a target, that is its tendency to reflect radar waves, is certainly as old as the Second World War. Germany made energetic efforts to protect her submarines by applying radar absorbent materials to superstructures and schnorkels.

Subsequently the manufacture of radar absorbent materials (RAMS) became increasingly important to radar itself. It is impossible to obtain the best performance from a radar mounted for example on a warship, unless reflections from nearby metal structures are eliminated by cladding them with absorbent materials. Otherwise targets may be reflected from false directions. For this purpose highly specific, 'narrow band' absorption at the radar's frequency is adequate.

In due course this technology began to be applied to objects of radar surveillance such as fighter bombers and missiles, which need to penetrate as far as possible before radar recognition triggers defensive response. For this, 'broad band' absorption materials are required, since defensive radar frequencies vary widely. However, the perceived value of doing this was always kept in check by the consideration that a reduction in radar cross section produces a much smaller relative reduction in the range at which the target is likely to be detected.

For example, if the radar cross section of a fighter-bomber is reduced by ten times, it does not mean that the fighter-bomber can get ten times nearer its target before being detected. If the detection range against a particular defending radar is initially 100 kilometres, it comes down not to 10 kilometres, but only to about 56 kilometres. In view of the added weight and enlarged contours from cladding with radar absorbent material, this may be worth nothing, indeed be a disadvantageous exchange.

Nevertheless the incentive to reduce radar cross section grew steadily during the 1970s, finally reaching a turning point at the end of the decade. What was different about stealth in the 1980s was that it symbolised a new order of design priorities.

Before, aircraft and ships had been designed according to various criteria, not including stealth, and measures were afterwards taken, if expedient, to reduce the extent to which they reflected electromagnetic radiation. What can be achieved in such circumstances is limited by the basic structure. In the 1980s stealth became a factor in design from the start, if not the chief factor. This was reflected above all in the stealth fighters and bombers of the United States.

Eliminating Right Angles

Designed-in stealth aims to reduce radar reflectivity by combining the use of radar absorbent materials (RAMs) with favourable structural features. It is necessary to eliminate metallic surfaces at right angles to each other and right-angled metallic panels. Obtuse and acute angles are preferable. The vertical tail fin is usually a strong source of reflections. So are jet engine intakes and tail pipes. It is desirable to shield engines from direct observation by radar, and also to shield the jet efflux, itself a reflector. Smooth contours help.

Normally when a target such as an aircraft is tested for radar reflectivity from all directions, large variations are seen. This is because of the different areas and different structural profiles presented, head-on as compared with broadside for example. Stealth attempts to minimise such radar scintillations.

High performance is not compatible with designed-in stealth. When it is partly or wholly abandoned for the sake of stealth, this indicates that the premium on stealth for the particular mission for which the aircraft is designed is greater than that of performance. This became true for the succession of bombers designed in the United States to succeed the 30-year veteran B-52, namely the B-1, the B-1B, and the B-2.

Warships were long left out of the drive for a low radar cross section, but the events of the Falklands War with numerous missile attacks on ships hastened a change in this attitude. A warship, being hundreds or thousands of tons of metal, cannot be hidden from radar, but its reflectivity can be reduced, and this is valuable, because it helps with the task of creating decoy targets with radar cross sections greater than that of the warship. For both warships and aircraft, a difference of seconds in time of discovery may make all the difference between disaster and survival, or between a successful mission and an unsuccessful one.

Radar manufacturers during the 1980s were far from passive observers of a trend which menaced the military technology they offered. Radar technology burgeoned in many ways, partly as a reaction against stealth, partly in response to other military challenges.

The reaction against stealth led to radars capable of detecting smaller and smaller targets at ever-greater ranges. The typical S-band ground-based surveillance radar, with an operational range out to about 500 kilometres, remained hard to beat. The maximum range is against targets at high altitude, where there is generally little clutter in which the target may be lost.

At low altitude the horizon limits range to tens of kilometres. The warning time is less, but this has always been so and is due to factors

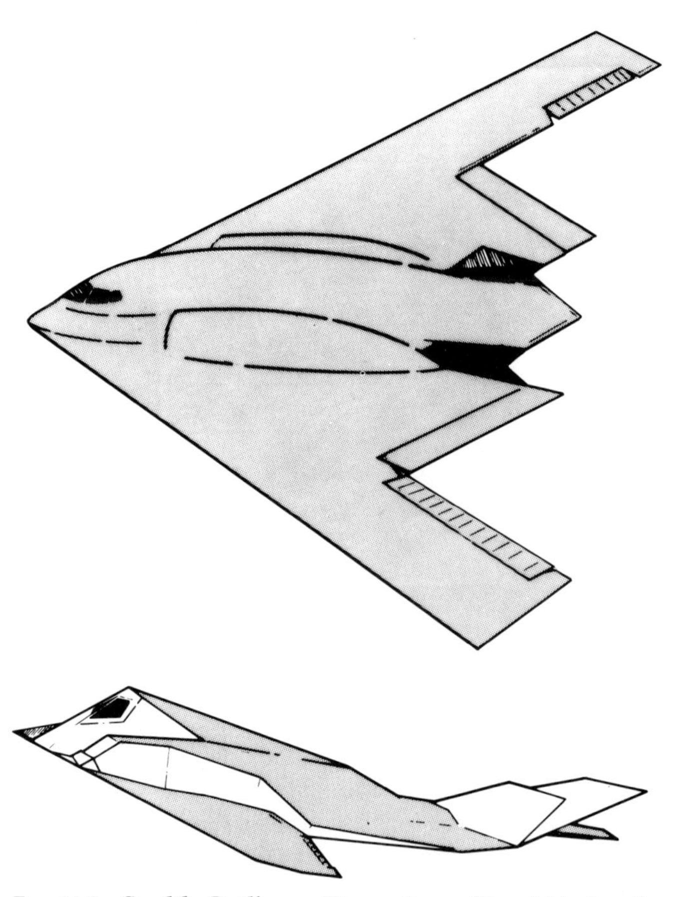

Fig. 14.2 **Stealth Outlines** The outlines of 'stealth' aircraft, most notably the United States' F-117A (top) and B-2 (bottom) depart radically from aerodynamic tradition in the interest of reducing radar cross-section. Avoidance of right angles in favour of obtuse or acute angles leads to lozenge-like shapes. Contours are otherwise smooth and covered with radar-absorbent materials. Jet intakes and effluxes are minimised or dispersed and shielded. With these design priorities, aerodynamic performance takes second place. Stealth becomes the over-riding factor in mission accomplishment. Radar's response is in the direction of increased networking of stations and broad bandwidth.

other than stealth. When the aircraft comes above the horizon the range is already so short that it is favourable to radar. But at low altitudes sources of clutter are more abundant and the value of stealth is that it enables an aircraft to take full advantage of them.

Nevertheless radar cross section is not the same at all frequencies. As the radar frequency goes down it becomes progressively more difficult to reduce radar cross section, either by absorbent materials or by structural methods. For this reason, renewed emphasis began to fall on radars working in the middle and lower part of the UHF band, or with a wide simultaneous selection of frequencies. The latter is termed ultra wide bandwidth radar.

A New Shield

In the 1980s radar was called upon for a new air defence shield around the United States. For this the frequency fell back to HF, where radar defence chains had started, in Britain's Chain Home.

Now however the technology was Over-the-Horizon (OTH) radar. It utilised HF's unique ability to reflect down from the ionosphere in order to achieve ranges up to three thousand or more kilometres, coverage not beginning until a range of about seven hundred kilometres was reached. This was bistatic radar – the transmitting and receiving sites were no longer co-located, but separated by 100 or more kilometres. Antennas were on an even more massive scale than with Chain Home – kilometres wide.

The Americans deployed such sites inland, so that the effective coverage of the radar began at the coast and reached out over thousands of kilometres of ocean to east, west and south. It promised to be specially valuable against drug-smuggling aircraft and boats from South America.

One problem with such radar is the variability of the ionosphere for HF propagation. In practice, monitoring the ionosphere is a basic part of the operational routine of over-the-horizon radar, so that the frequencies chosen will be those which give the desired results. It cannot be assumed that the full range of HF up to 30 megahertz is always available.

On the other hand there is an important advantage in the reduction of frequency. Stealth technology is most successful in the middle of the SHF band. It is increasingly discounted as the radar frequency drops through UHF and VHF bands. Radar absorbent materials and coverings become increasingly heavy, thick and impracticable. It is totally discounted at HF.

Over-the-horizon radar is primarily a means of ocean surveillance; interpretation of the return signal from a large land mass with many sources of HF interference is a far more complex matter.

As already mentioned, another means of ocean surveillance has been provided by satellite-based radar. Satellite and airborne radar can use a technique known as sideways-looking-radar (SLR), or synthetic

PLATE 14.2 **Over-the-Horizon Backscatter Radar** This photograph shows the transmitting antenna of an Over-the-Horizon (OTH) Backscatter radar located in the United States. The antenna is 3,630 feet long and up to 135 feet high. OTH radar is an example of bistatic radar – i.e. the receiving antenna may be located a hundred or more miles away from the transmitter. It operates in the HF band and utilises the bending of the radiowaves back down from the ionosphere to achieve surveillance out to more than two thousand miles. (*Photo: By courtesy of General Electric [US]*)

PLATE 14.3 **A Surface Ship Command System** Among the most recent naval electronic command systems is the Surface Ship Command System (SSCS) produced in Britain for the Type 23 frigate. Located in a well-protected operations room, it integrates sensor inputs (e.g. radar and sonar) with data links and navigation inputs (e.g. from satellites). It makes available stored information (e.g. charts, data on weapons systems which may be encountered). It enables command decisions to be taken, communicated and executed, including the use of missiles, torpedoes, guns. It may be compared with traditional naval command from the bridge, relying on visual battle assessment, optical signalling, communications by runner, mechanical repeaters and speaking tubes. SSCS uses up to twelve consoles, two of which are illustrated in this photograph. The consoles use advanced colour, high-definition cathode ray tube displays combining plan position indicators with alphanumeric labelling and information tables. The PPI on the left shows a radar tactical situation display, computer-generated from the 'raw' radar return, and that on the right a computer-processed sonar 'waterfall' display. 'Waterfall' means renewed from the top downwards; it contrasts with the radar PPI which is generated by radial sweep. The sonar display is in three sections, progressively narrower from left to right. SSCS hardware is manufactured by Racal and the software is provided by Dowty-Sema. (*Photo: By courtesy of Racal*)

aperture radar. The radar looks out to the side, perpendicularly to the forward motion of its platform, and the scans are combined electronically to create a strip-form picture.

Until recently the need for high power and consequently a nuclear reactor was a drawback to satellite radar. But with the launch in 1989 of the secret Lacrosse espionage satellite which uses solar panels, the United States demonstrated an attempt to overcome this problem. It marked a step forward in the use of radar from satellites for military surveillance and intelligence purposes, an area in which radar has hitherto lagged behind radio. Further radar-imaging satellites have followed from both America and the Soviet Union.

At present, the forward thrust of conventional electronic warfare comes most strongly from radar. Radio has become stable. In the climate of electronic deterrence, radar has a special role. It is the guardian of national airspace, boundaries, coasts, and off-shore waters. The unsettling implications of its apparent failure are sometimes demonstrated by incidents such as the arrival of a German civilian pilot in a small single-seater aircraft to land unannounced in Moscow's Red Square.

The stealth direction of contemporary electronic warfare seeks to undercut radar's capability to act as national watchdog. Of course, radar is progressing itself, and there is no present indication that the contest between radar and stealth is about to collapse in stealth's favour. The renewed vigour of radar development has been seen with horror by the protagonists of stealth aircraft, as undercutting prototype weapon systems created at enormous cost.

Nevertheless, stealth is potentially destabilising, just as Star-Wars development of electronics' destructive capability is potentially destabilising. As with nuclear weapons, there is no guarantee that further development of electronic warfare will increase security; it may erode security for both sides.

The aim of contemporary political-military strategy is demonstrated in the Intermediate Nuclear Force Treaty signed between the United States and the Soviet Union in 1988: the attempt to arrest the destabilising effect of unrestricted nuclear weapons deployments and to liquidate the most destabilising of the deployments so far made. There is no reason for electronic warfare to be exempt from the same process, indeed precedents exist in the limitation of anti-ballistic-missile defence radars established by the ABM Treaty of 1972 and its protocol of 1974.

One of the next steps in arms agreements between the Superpowers should be a comprehensive treaty governing the development and deployment of electronic warfare. It would be in the interests of global stability, and give the new era of electronic deterrence the hope of a more lasting and less terrifying state of peace than nuclear deterrence provided.

Nuclear deterrence began to be phased out by the deliberate decision of the Superpowers when they realised the mutual risks they were running from the weapon systems they were creating. They began to prefer reliance on mutual surveillance, with electronic intelligence gathering as its principal means. Beyond electronic deterrence no other deterrent formula is in sight, yet the human animal remains imperfect.

Bibliography

The following bibliography includes only books which have been actively consulted by the writer. It does not attempt to be a complete bibliography of the subject.

Airborne Electronic Warfare, Martin Streetly. Jane's Publishing Company, UK 1988.

Airships in Peace and War, Robert Jackson, Cassell, London 1971.

The Army Air Forces in World War II, Editors W F Craven and J L Cate. University of Chicago Press. Volume 1: *Plans and Early Operations, January 1939 to August 1942*. US 1948. Volume 2: *Europe: Torch to Pointblank, August 1942 to December 1943*. US 1949. Volume 4: *The Pacific: Guadalcanal to Saipan, August 1942 to July 1944*. US 1950.

Battle for Space, Curtis Peebles. Blandford Press, UK 1983.

Blitzkrieg, Len Deighton. Jonathan Cape, London 1979.

Bomber Command, Max Hastings. Michael Joseph, UK 1979.

British Intelligence in the Second World War, Hinsley, Thomas, Ransom, Knight. Three volumes. HM Stationery Office, London 1979–85.

The Codebreakers, David Kahn. Weidenfeld & Nicolson, London 1973.

The Defence of the United Kingdom, Basil Collier. HM Stationery Office, London 1957.

The Defence of the Reich, Werner Held and Holger Nauroth. Arms & Armour Press, London 1982.

Electronic Warfare, Mario de Arcangelis. Blandford Press, UK 1985.

Full Circle, Air Vice Marshal J E Johnson. Chatto & Windus, London 1964.

GCHQ. The Secret Wireless War 1900–1986, Nigel West. Hodder & Stoughton, UK 1987.

Giants in the Sky: A History of the Rigid Airship. Douglas H Robinson. Foulis & Co, UK 1973.

The Gotha Summer: The German Daytime Air Raids on England, May–August 1917, C M White. Robert Hale, UK 1986.

The History of Electric Wires and Cables, R M Black. Peter Peregrinus Ltd, London 1983.

History of the German Night Fighter Force 1917–1945, Gebhard Aders. Jane's Publishing Company, London 1979.

A History of the Marconi Company, W J Baker, Methuen, London 1970.

A History of the United States Army Air Force 1907–1957, Editor Alfred Goldberg. D Van Nostrand Company, US 1957.

History of US Naval Operations in World War II, Samuel Eliot Morison. Little, Brown and Company, Boston. Vol I: *Battle of the Atlantic, 1939–1943*. US 1960. Vol. IV: *Coral Sea, Midway and Submarine Actions, May 1942–August 1942*. US 1953. Vol. X: *The Atlantic Battle Won, May 1943–May 1945*. US 1962.
Hitler's Spies, David Hahn. Hodder & Stoughton, UK 1978.
Hitler's War on Russia, Paul Carell. George G Harrap, UK 1964.
The Hut Six Story, Gordon Welchman. McGraw-Hill, USA 1982.
Implementing the Lessons of the Falklands Campaign. HMSO, London 1987.
Instruments of Darkness. Alfred Price. Macdonald and Jane's Publishers Limited, London 1977.
International Countermeasures Handbook 1986. EW Communications Inc, US.
Introduction to Radar Systems, Merrill I Skolnik. McGraw-Hill International 1980.
Inventor and Entrepreneur, Recollections of Werner von Siemens. Lund Humphries, London 1966.
Mayday, Michael R Beschloss. Faber & Faber, London and New York 1986.
Modern Naval Combat, David Miller and Chris Miller. Salamander Books, UK 1986.
Naval Radar, Norman Friedman. Conway Maritime Press, UK 1981.
Operation Overflight, Francis Gary Powers. Hodder & Stoughton, UK 1970.
Phantom over Vietnam, John Trotti. US Presidio Press, UK Airlife Publishing 1984.
Power of Speech. A History of Standard Telephones and Cables 1883–1983. Peter Young. Allen & Unwin, London 1983.
Principles of Electronic Warfare, Robert J Schlesinger. Prentice-Hall International Inc, US 1961.
The Rise and Fall of the Luftwaffe, David Irving. Weidenfeld & Nicolson, London 1973.
The Royal Corps of Signals, Major General R F M Nalder. Royal Signals Institution, London 1958.
The Schellenberg Memoirs, Walter Schellenberg. Andre Deutsch, London 1956
The Second World War, Winston S Churchill. Cassell & Co., London. Six volumes, 1948–54.
The Secret War, Brian Johnson, BBC, London 1978.
Seek and Strike: Sonar, anti-submarine war and the Royal Navy 1914–54, Willem Hackmann. HMSO, London 1984.
Spycatcher, Peter Wright. William Heinemann, Australia 1987.
Spy-Tech, Graham Yost. Yarrap, UK 1985.
Stealth Aircraft, Bill Sweetman. Airlife Publishing Limited, UK 1986.
The Strategic Air Offensive Against Germany 1939–1945, Sir Charles Webster and Noble Frankland. HMSO, London 1961.
The Strategy of Electromagnetic Conflict, Editor: Lieutenant Colonel Richard E Fitts. Peninsula Publishing, US 1980.
Studies of War, P M S Blackett. Oliver & Boyd, Edinburgh 1962.
Synthetic Aperture Radar Systems, Robert O Harger. Academic Press, London and New York 1970.
Technical History of the Beginnings of Radar, S S Swords. Peter Peregrinus, London 1986.
Telephony and Telegraphy A, Sydney F Smith. Oxford University Press, UK 1974.
Three Steps to Victory, Sir Robert Watson-Watt. Odhams Press, UK 1957.
Tsushima, A Novikoff-Priboi. Translated by Eden and Cedar Paul. George Allen & Unwin, London 1936.
Ultra at Sea, John Winton. Leo Cooper Ltd, London 1988.

Ultra Goes to War, Ronald Lewin. Hutchinson, UK 1978.
The Ultra Secret, F W Winterbotham. Weidenfeld & Nicolson, UK 1974.
Understanding Computers, Dr Richard Stevens. Oxford University Press 1986.
The Underwater War 1939–1945, Richard Compton-Hall. Blandford Press, UK 1972.
The United States Air Force in Korea 1950–1953, R F Futrell. Duell, Sloane & Pearce, New York 1961.
Vietnam Air Wars, Rene J Francillon. Temple Press, UK 1987.
The World Crisis 1911-1918, Winston S Churchill. New English Library, UK 1960.
Zeppelin Adventures, Rolf Marben. Greenhill Books, Lionel Leventhal, UK 1986.
Zeppelins over England, Kenneth Poolman. Evans Brothers, UK 1960.

Chapter Notes

Introduction

1. Quoted from *The Second World War*, Volume II, Chapter XIX.

Chapter 1: Historical Questions

1. The standards which Churchill set in writing about the Second World War have not yet been re-approached, rather there has been a falling away from them. Despite the difficulties of achieving impartiality, which he could not entirely overcome, given the atmosphere of the immediate post-war world, he wrote with a sense of European and world history generally lacking in subsequent authors.
2. This phenomenon may have been known much earlier. It was only at this time that knowledge of Greek was returning to Western Europe, and provided a word for it.
3. The following quotation is taken from *A History of Electric Telegraphy to the Year 1837*, by J J Fahie, published in London in 1884, by E & F N Spon: 'Schilling's first application of electricity was to warlike ends. We learn from Hamel that the war impending between France and Russia, in 1812, made him anxious to devise a conducting wire which could be laid, not only through moist earth, but through long stretches of water; and which should serve for telegraphic correspondence between fortified places and the field, as well as for exploding powder mines.

   'So diligently did he work at this task that before the autumn of the same year he had "contrived a subaqueous galvanic conducting cord" (a copper wire insulated with a solution of india-rubber and varnish), and an arrangement of charcoal points, by means of which he was able to explode powder mines across the Neva, near St Petersburg. At Paris, during the occupation of the allied troops, in 1814, he also frequently ignited gunpowder across the Seine with this *electric exploder*, to the great astonishment of the *gamins*.'

   The reference to Hamel is to *A Historical Account of the Introduction of the Galvanic and Electromagnetic Telegraph into England*, by Dr Hamel, London 1859 (a reprint by Cooke of an earlier original).
4. In early times, the Leyden jar was used to hold an accumulation of electrostatic charge. That electricity would flow from such an accumulation along a suitable conductor was known since at least 1730. In that year, in London, Stephen Gray found that electricity would flow over a damp hemp cord, suspended on silk threads,

for several hundred feet. He thus demonstrated conduction, through the damp hemp, and insulation, by the silk. Metallic wire improved the range of conduction up to several miles.

In 1795, use of electricity to transmit information was suggested in Barcelona by Don Francisco Salva. Twenty-two wires, one for each letter of the (Spanish) alphabet, were to be individually insulated with paper, coated with pitch, bound together, laid in underground tubes, and coated with resin. Eventually a 26-mile long telegraph was laid between Madrid and Aranjuez, worked with electrostatic charges.

Detecting electrostatic charge by attractive/repulsive effects was a difficulty. Ronalds' proposal to the British Admiralty incorporated pith balls on the ends of the wires. These would swing apart when charged. It is hardly surprising the Admiralty turned him down.

From 1800 the steady current available from the chemical battery was a competitor to electrostatic charge. The current could be detected at the receiving end by its chemical action in decomposing acidulated water with the evolution of bubbles. This was still too slow for an efficient telegraph. Baron Schilling made a telegraph on this principle in 1809, but it needed 35 separate wires for the letters of the alphabet and numerals. The battery, or voltaic pile, was connected to one wire at a time. The wires were separately insulated and laid up together.

5. The New York harbour cable was rubber insulated and laid in a lead pipe. Although the first submarine cable linking England and France was laid in 1850, it was not until the following year that a second cable established reliable communication. Other cables followed between England and the Continent and England and Ireland. Attempts were made in 1857 and again in 1858 to span the Atlantic by submarine cable, but despite a short-lived connection in the latter year, reliable transatlantic cable communications were not established until 1866.

Chapter 2: Battleground

1. This is necessarily a very summary reference to Hertz's work. He used many different types of spark apparatus. An interesting series of articles appeared in the UK journal *Electronics and Wireless World* during 1988, the centenary year of Hertz's discovery.
2. With such long cables as transatlantic submarine cables, a problem existed in getting the signal through. But telegraphic messages could be successfully transmitted if the electrical characteristics of the cable were right. This was appreciated after earlier failures in which the signals injected at the transmitting end were not recognisable at the receiving end.
3. Usually coupled with the name of the French scientist Branly.

Chapter 3: The Passing of the Spark

1. Although the word 'electronics' was in occasional use from 1910, radio engineering was the established term. Electronic engineering became a popular term after the Second World War and gradually replaced radio engineering.
2. There was also electrical engineering, dealing with power applications of electricity.

Radio engineering, electromechanical engineering and electrical engineering were practical divisions of the same technology based on electrons. The modern tendency is to dissolve these distinctions. See for example the article on electronics in the Macropaedia Section of the *Encyclopedia Britannica*.

3. Conflict between these branches of electrical technology has not been a theme special to electronic warfare, but has long been a feature of peace-time competition in telecommunications. Electronic engineering has gradually driven out electro-mechanical, but the process has taken a long time.

Chapter 4: The Coming of HF

1. Although tuning was understood and a patent for controlling frequency existed (the Marconi 'four sevens'), it was difficult to be certain of the frequency actually being generated.
2. Satellites brought the possibility of long-range communication using the higher frequency bands. These bands pass through the ionosphere and can be received and relayed back to earth from satellites. But this development did not come until the 1960s.

Chapter 5: Radio Revolution

1. The advent of the steam-driven ironclad warship also made Tsushima different from Trafalgar.
2. Briefly, experiments were tried with a 'sub-cloud car', lowered about 800 metres below the Zeppelin from cloud into clear air. Instructions were transmitted by telephone. The system evidently did not prove workable.
3. Stories that German agents in London operated a radio beacon to guide Zeppelins until discovered by the British police cannot be substantiated and having regard to the state of technology at the time seem highly unlikely.
4. The concept of the heavy bomber originated in Russia before the outbreak of the First World War, with Sikorsky's 'Ilya Muromets', a type which subsequently carried out numerous raids on German targets, but the Eastern Front does not seem to have produced any advances in airborne radio.
5. Quoted from Eden and Cedar Paul's translation of Novikov-Priboi's *Tsushima*, published by Allen and Unwin in London, 1936.
6. Deliberate jamming is said to have occurred in civilian practice before its military use, as for example during the Admirals Cup races in the United States in 1901. But jamming would always happen with a number of early spark transmitters in close proximity, regardless of intent, unless a division of time bands had been worked out and agreed beforehand.
7. Rozhestvensky's thirty ships were blocked by a larger number of Japanese, under the command of Admiral Togo. There were more large warships and guns on the Russian side, but the largest Japanese warships were bigger and more heavily armour-protected than their Russian counterparts. The Japanese flagship *Mikasa*, for example, was 15,321 tonnes against the 13,717 tonnes of the Russian flagship *Suvorov*, both having four 12-inch guns as primary armament. The Japanese had

three other ships comparable to *Mikasa* and the Russians had four other ships comparable to *Suvorov*.

But the Japanese were faster and undoubtedly better handled by their fresh crews. It was the first great naval battle unconstrained by wind and sail. Togo headed off Russian attempts to continue northwards or disengage. One by one, the major Russian ships were sunk, including the *Ural*. The battle continued through the night with attacks from Japanese torpedo boats. The following day the Russian admiral Nyebogatov, who had succeeded to the injured Rozhestvensky's command, surrended. Seventeen of the thirty Russian ships had been sunk and four captured. Three smaller vessels, a light cruiser and two mine-layers, escaped to Vladivostok, the rest to internment in neutral ports. The Japanese lost only three torpedo boats.

8. See *Spycatcher*, by Peter Wright, Heinemann, 1987, Chapter 2.
9. There were 64 capital ships at sea out of a total of some 250 between the two sides. Displacements were up to 24,000 tons.

Chapter 6: Revolution upon Revolution

1. With, of course, the outstanding exception of the Assistant Director of Intelligence, R V Jones (later Professor R V Jones).
2. It should be mentioned that in 1941, in Germany, an electromechanical computer was devised, using about 2,000 relays, the control devices characteristic of electromechanical engineering. This was the Z3 of Konrad Zuse. It was programme-controlled from holes punched on 35 mm film. It and subsequent Zuse computers were used for what would now be called computer-aided design and industrial process control. In 1941 Zuse and a colleague pointed to the possibility of using an electron-tube-based computer, working about 1000 times faster than a relay-based computer, for decoding radio messages. Nothing came of this. See *Understanding Computers*, by Dr Richard Stevens, Oxford University Press, 1986.
3. The British took extreme precautions to protect the secrecy of their cryptographic operation against Enigma. During the war the intelligence produced was distributed under strictest supervision. After the war the operation remained completely unknown to the public until the appearance of *The Ultra Secret* by F W Winterbotham in 1974. Circumstances leading to the publication of the book are controversial, but its ultimate importance was that the revelation of Ultra prompted the British government to commission 'British Intelligence in the Second World War' by Hinsley, Thomas, Ransom and Knight. This cast new sidelights on almost the entire history of the war. By implication it required thorough-going new analysis and assessment, a process which is still far from complete.

   This is only part of the legacy of Ultra. Another is numerous unresolved questions. What happened after the war, for example when the British were supposedly dismantling their Bletchley equipment yet setting up GCHQ, and at the same time allegedly selling Enigma machines to people they thought they might like to spy on, allowing it to be understood that the encryption was totally secure? At what time did American skills and equipment in this area leapfrog British? The Americans were given British assistance for aspects of their cipher-breaking against the Japanese, over which they still maintain secrecy.

4. This viewpoint was expressed by the Russian scientist Piotr Kapitsa in Moscow in February 1944, in an address entitled 'The Role of Science in the Patriotic War', reprinted in the Russian journal *Nauka i Zhizn*, Issue 5 for 1985.

Chapter 7: The Challenge of Radar

1. This underlies the celebrated fourth power law of radar. On a one-way trip, as with radio, the strength of the signal decreases in proportion to the square of the distance. When the signal goes and comes back, the effect is compounded. The strength of the signal returned to the radar has decreased in proportion to the fourth power of the target range.
2. The cavity magnetron's discoverers were Randall and Boot, working at Birmingham University in 1939/40.

Chapter 8: Radio versus Radar

1. The relevant part of the Oslo Report was section 8, as follows:
   Air Raid Warning Equipment. At the time of the attack by English airmen on Wilhelmshaven at the beginning of September the English aircraft were already sighted 120 km from the German coast. Along the whole length of the German coast are short-wave transmitters of 20 kW power which send out quite short pulses of 10^{-5} seconds duration. These pulses are reflected by aircraft. Near to each transmitter there is a receiver, tuned to the same wavelength. After an interval the reflected pulse from the aircraft reaches the receiver and is recorded on a cathode ray tube. From the interval . . . the distance of the plane can be computed. [Quoted from translation of the Oslo Report given in *British Intelligence in the Second World War*, Hinsley *et al.*, HMSO, Volume 1.]
2. This observation is not intended as a criticism direct or indirect of the decision to drop the atomic bombs. Examination of moral issues cannot be part of the purpose of this book.
3. The Germans knew that their airborne transmissions were being monitored. But as the Battle of Britain progressed they could not manage without airborne radio, and used it increasingly despite rules enjoining radio silence. They knew they were giving something away, but did not know how much, and were anyway aware that the British had radar, which they probably regarded as the main source of information on the movements of their aircraft. And to the majority of people in the British defensive effort also, the radar contribution was more obvious. No assessment was made at the time of the balance between sigint and radar. What the Germans understandably could not realise was that, because of the limitations of British radar, the information they were giving away through their airborne radio transmissions was far more vital than it would have been otherwise. But even if they had realised this, they would probably still have been unable to dispense with airborne radio.
4. Probably two flights were made to spy on British radar: a 44 hour 51 minute flight on 12–14 July 1939, along the East Coast of England, and a 48 hour flight on 2–4 August, during which the airship was seen inland over Scotland. RAF Spitfires were sent to intercept. The airship was LZ 130, a new 'Graf Zeppelin', first flown on 14 September 1938. The earlier and famous Graf Zeppelin had by this time been

grounded. See *Giants in the Sky: a History of the Rigid Airship*, Douglas H Robinson, G T Foulis & Co Ltd, UK 1973.

Chapter 9: Reversal of Roles

1. At the same time as Gee was devised in Britain, a similar system called Loran was devised in the United States, operating in MF. This was intended purely for navigation and became permanently established in this role.

Chapter 10: Climax

1. See the paper presented by A E Hoffmann-Heyden at the IEE seminar on radar development to 1945 held in London 10–12 June 1985. Wurzlauss was succeeded by Tastlauss and Windlauss.

Chapter 11: Sonar versus Radar and Radio

1. There were other regional conflicts, the battle of South East Asia between Japan and China with her allies, and the battle of North East Asia between Japan and Russia. But these were not decisive.
2. See *Seek and Strike*, Willem Hackmann, London, HMSO 1984.
3. The use of cathode ray tube direction finding sets was not confined to the Battle of the Atlantic. First use came with rapid commissioning on the eve of the Munich Conference in 1938, as with the five Chain Home radar stations. At one time or another cathode ray tube direction finding sets were used in connection with control of fighter aircraft; raids on Germany; transatlantic bomber ferrying; locating ditched aircraft; and countering the German meacons deployed against British navigational beacons. The equipment was produced by the British Plessey Company.

Chapter 12: Transformation

1. This figure is given in *The United States Air Force in Korea 1950–53*, by R F Futrell, in relation to the period 1 June to 30 September 1950.
2. By the late 1980s, neglect of microelectronics was one of the charges laid by Soviet President Mikhail Gorbachev against preceding administrations. For the euphoria surrounding computer technology in the late 1970s, and its role as a capitalist scourge of communism, see *The Mighty Micro*, by Christopher Evans, UK 1979.
3. See *The Codebreakers*, David Kahn, 1968.
4. For a practical account of the use of infra-red and radar homing missiles, see *Phantom over Vietnam*, by John Trotti, 1984 (US Presidio Press, UK Airlife Publishing).
5. There were two parts to the British radar project, VAST and ROTOR. VAST was for several hundred mobile radars mounted on prime movers, i.e. self-mobile, and ROTOR was for some fifty static radars and control centres in this country. Behind the sudden gestation of this plan and its subsequent abandonment an as-yet untold story lies.

6. Various attempts are made to define these terms. See for example *The Strategy of Electromagnetic Conflict*, Peninsula Publishing, 1980, Chapter 4. There is no agreement on formal definitions.
7. The reference is to R V Jones.
8. See the list provided by *The Strategy of Electromagnetic Conflict*, Chapter 4. Any such list is inevitably incomplete.

Chapter 14: Dominance

1. See the admirable survey contributed by Alfred Price to *International Countermeasures Handbook 1986*, EW Communications Inc, US.

Glossary

AEW	Airborne early warning
AI	Air interception
AM	Amplitude modulation
ASV	Anti-surface vessel radar
AWACS	Airborne warning and control system
BMEWS	Ballistic missile early warning system
COMINT	Communications intelligence
CRT	Cathode ray tube
CW	Continuous wave
DF	Direction finding
ECCM	Electronic counter-countermeasures
ECM	Electronic countermeasures
ELINT	Electronic intelligence
EMP	Electromagnetic pulse
ESM	Electronic support measures (Passive electronic warfare equipment designed to detect and analyse hostile radio and radar emissions, with the aim of providing information on the enemy's use of electronic equipment and any threats that the enemy may be making. For example, radar warning receivers)
FM	Frequency modulation
GCI	Ground controlled interception
HF DF	'Huff-duff'. High frequency radio direction finding
IFF	Identification Friend or Foe
MTI	Moving target indication
OTH	Over the horizon
PCM	Pulse code modulation
PPI	Plan position indicator
PRF	Pulse repetition frequency
RAM	Radar absorbent material
R/T	Radio telephony
RHAW	Radar homing and warning
SAM	Surface-to-air missile
SHORAN	Short-range navigation system

SIGINT	Signals intelligence. The intelligence obtained from observing and recording the electronic signals of third parties, and, if appropriate and possible, decrypting them
SLR	Side-looking radar
TA	Traffic analysis, that aspect of signals intelligence concerned with recognising the operational procedures and locations of a third party's communications networks
TINA	Technique of identifying individual radio operators by the characteristics of morse transmissions
W/T	Wireless telegraphy
Y Service	Tactical signals intelligence, concerned usually with low-grade codes and ciphers, intercepted near a battle zone.

Appendix

Correspondence with Sir Edward Fennessy

Sir Edward Fennessy was concerned with British area-defence radar from the initial setting-up of the Chain Home system before the Second World War to the revival of the radar chain in the mid 1950s when Chain Home was initially refurbished then replaced with Type 80 radar. In the following correspondence he replies to the author's questions concerning the first activation of Chain Home radar during the Munich Crisis of September 1938, the operational capabilities of Chain Home, and its eventual replacement.

From author's letter to Sir Edward Fennessy:

Which were the five stations operational at the time of the Munich Crisis? I would imagine that the location of the five stations of 1938 reflected the directions German bombers might strike from. The German coast between Holland and Denmark? Or did we think, even at the time of Munich, that they would fly through the airspace of the Low Countries or Northern France?

I think this was what might perhaps be called the 'East coast Phase' of CH. Of course, what we did not foresee was that our defensive flank would be turned by the fall of France. Then began the 'South Coast Phase'. CH coverage had to be expanded urgently. The September 1939 positions did not go far enough. It was the South Coast stations that the Germans attacked once the Battle of Britain had started.

I am interested in your comment that 'there was a weakness in the use of a remote filter room'. Evidently the filter room was necessary to interpret the information the individual CH stations provided. But, did some potentially useful information get lost in sending the results on from the local filter room to the centre? Or did the other information available at the centre help in clarifying the individual station inputs, in a way not possible locally?

I am also interested in your comment on radar's 'not inconsiderable limitations'. It prompts me to ask, how far did we in Britain understand the strengths and weaknesses of the strategic radar shield that we had created? We began by regarding it as crucially important, but after the middle of 1941, when Germany turned against Russia, we no longer saw it in the same light. Instead we got into centimetric radar, but this was more tactical.

As a result, when anxieties similar to those of 1938 began to loom again, after the Korean War, in the mid-1950s, our rather amazing reaction was to restore the CH stations. Yet it is possible to argue that, even by 1942, they were understood as representing an already obsolete technology. They had already played their historical role.

Reply from Sir Edward Fennessy:

The five 'Munich' CH stations were Dover, Canewdon (near Southend) and Bawdsey, and to the best of my recollection Dunkirk (near Canterbury) and Great Bromley (between Canewdon and Bawdsey). These five stations were all that were then built and operational of the twenty recommended in 1935 by the Research Committee of the Committee of Imperial Defence covering the Tyne to Southampton, Thus, as you will see, plans had been laid to prevent the flank being turned and all twenty were operational by September 1939.

I cannot agree with you that the September 1939 coverage was inadequate for the Battle of Britain. For several operational reasons, including the limitations of German fighter range as escort cover from Northern France, the main attacks were between Ventnor and the Thames, where our cover was good. We also had in reserve mobiles that we used to plug the gaps created by the bombing of Ventnor and Poling. In 1941, when night raids to targets other than London came, we built the West Coast Chain.

With regard to filter rooms. The problems of obtaining accurate bearing and height information from CH called for very skilled interpretation of the raw radar data. This could most effectively be done at a central point (Fighter Command) where all relevant information could be used by highly skilled personnel. This was particularly so in early 1940 when we had a lot of problems in maintaining the stability of CH calibration.

Regarding the issue of the limitations of CH radar. The answer is we fully understood its limitations. The great merit of CH, and here Watson-Watt and Wilkins had shown great wisdom, was that an effective CH system could be built between 1935–1939 since it employed state-of-the-art equipment. Had they gone at the start for centimetric equipment we would not have had a working system with which we could have fought and won the Battle of Britain. The CH Chain was crucial to fighting and defeating a massive air onslaught on a broad front by daylight, this it did.

By 1942 the potential of the magnetron enabled us to plan and build centimetric radars for a wide range of operational applications. But even then, had we had to face the 1940 threat once again we would have had to turn to CH.

It was not until the mid-1950s, when under my Managing Directorship of Decca Radar we developed Type 80, a very high power centimetric station with a massive aerial, that the RAF had a wide area, long range, coastal defence system to replace CH. Pending the Type 80 development and installation, CH was refurbished as the only available system. True, as you say, its historical role was over but it would have been all we had, pending the arrival of Type 80, had a major air offensive been mounted against the United Kingdom.

Index